Project-Based Inquiry Science™

AIR QUALITY

Janet L. Kolodner

Joseph S. Krajcik

Daniel C. Edelson

Brian J. Reiser

Mary L. Starr

IT'S ABOUT TIME®

AUTHENTIC AND SUSTAINABLE STEM™

333 North Bedford Road, Mount Kisco, NY 10549
Phone (914) 273-2233   Fax (914) 206-6444
www.iat.com

Program Components

Student Edition	**Durable Equipment Kit**
Teacher's Planning Guide	**Consumable Equipment Kit**
	Multimedia
	— **NetLogo software**
	— **PBIS Content DVD**

Printed and bound in the United States of America.

ISBN 978-1-60720-801-3

4th Printing

4 5 6 7   20 19 18 17

This project was supported, in part, by the ***National Science Foundation*** under grant nos. 0137807, 0527341, and 0639978.
Opinions expressed are those of the authors and not necessarily those of the National Science Foundation.

PBIS Authors

Janet L. Kolodner is a Regents' Professor in the School of Interactive Computing in the Georgia Institute of Technology's College of Computing. Since 1978, her research has focused on learning from experience, both in computers and in people. She pioneered the Artificial Intelligence method called *case-based reasoning*, providing a way for computers to solve new problems based on their past experiences. Her book, *Case-Based Reasoning*, synthesizes work across the case-based reasoning research community from its inception to 1993.

Since 1994, Dr. Kolodner has focused on the applications and implications of case-based reasoning for education. In her approach to science education, called Learning by Design™ (LBD), students learn science while pursuing design challenges. Dr. Kolodner has investigated how to create a culture of collaboration and rigorous science talk in classrooms, how to use a project challenge to promote focus on science content, and how students learn and develop when classrooms function as learning communities. Currently, Dr. Kolodner is investigating how to help young people come to think of themselves as scientific reasoners. Dr. Kolodner's research results have been widely published, including in *Cognitive Science, Design Studies,* and the *Journal of the Learning Sciences.*

Dr. Kolodner was founding Director of Georgia Tech's EduTech Institute, served as coordinator of Georgia Tech's Cognitive Science program for many years, and is founding Editor in Chief of the *Journal of the Learning Sciences*. She is a founder of the International Society for the Learning Sciences, and she served as its first Executive Officer. She is a fellow of the American Association of Artificial Intelligence.

Joseph S. Krajcik serves as director of the CREATE for STEM Institute and is the Lappan-Phillips Professor of Science Education at Michigan State University. CREATE for STEM (Collaborative Research for Education, Assessment and Teaching Environments for Science, Technology, Engineering and Mathematics) is a joint institute between the College of Natural Science and the College of Education that seeks to improve the teaching and learning of science and mathematics kindergarten through college through innovation and research. During his career, Joe has focused on working with science teachers to reform science teaching practices to promote students' engagement in and learning of science. Joe served as lead writer for developing Physical Science Standards for the *Next Generation Science Standards* and the lead writer for the Physical Science Design team for the *Framework for K – 12 Science Education*. He has authored and co-authored curriculum materials, books, software, and over 100 manuscripts. Joe served as president of the National Association for Research in Science Teaching from which he received the Distinguished Contributions to Science Education Through Research Award in 2010. Joe also received the 2014 George G. Mallinson Award from the Michigan Science Teachers' Association for overall excellence of contributions to science education over a significant period of time. The University of Michigan, where Joe was a faculty member for 21 years before join MSU, recognized him for his commitment to graduate student education by presenting him with the Faculty Award for Distinguished Graduate Mentoring. Joe received his Ph.D. in Science Education from the University of Iowa. Prior to receiving his Ph.D., Joe taught high school chemistry and physical science in Milwaukee, Wisconsin for eight years.

Daniel C. Edelson is an educational researcher and developer. He is the Executive Director of the Biological Sciences Curriculum Study (BSCS). He came to BSCS from the National Geographic Society, where he served as Vice President for Education from 2007-2014. Prior to that, he was on the faculty of the School of Education and Social Policy at Northwestern University for 14 years, where he founded and led the Geographic Data in Education (GEODE) Initiative. Dr. Edelson has authored a number of middle and high school science programs, including the high school environmental science text, *Investigations in Environmental Science: A Case-Based Approach to the Study of Environmental Systems*. His research on instructional materials design, teacher professional development, educational technology, learning, and motivation has been published in a wide range of publications including the *Journal of the Learning Sciences*, the *Journal of Research on Science Teaching, Science Educator,* and *The Science Teacher*.

Brian J. Reiser is professor of learning sciences at Northwestern University. Dr. Reiser's research examines how to make the scientific practices of argumentation, explanation, and modeling meaningful and effective for classroom teachers and students. Dr. Reiser is a member of the National Research Council's (NRC) Board on Science Education. He has served on the NRC committees authoring the reports *Taking Science to School, A Framework for K-12 Science Education* (which guided the development of the *Next Generation Science Standards*), *Developing Assessments for the Next Generation Science Standards,* and *Guide to Implementing the Next Generation Science Standards*. Dr. Reiser has also worked with Achieve to provide feedback on the design of the *Next Generation Science Standards (NGSS)*, and on the tools to help states implement *NGSS*. Dr. Reiser is currently collaborating with several state initiatives to design and provide professional development for K-12 teachers to support them in realizing the reforms in *NGSS* in their classrooms.

Mary L. Starr is the Executive Director of the Michigan Mathematics and Science Centers Network. She works with each of the 33 Mathematics and Science Centers in Michigan. She is supporting the transition of Michigan science teachers and teacher leaders to 21st century science teaching. She also works independently with school districts throughout the country as they work to understand and implement the *Next Generation Science Standards* and integrate their science teaching for all students. She has served as a consultant and co-PI on several NSF grants to increase knowledge of best practices in science teaching and technology integration.

Acknowledgements

Three research teams contributed to the development of *Project-Based Inquiry Science (PBIS)*: a team at the Georgia Institute of Technology headed by Janet L. Kolodner, a team at Northwestern University headed by Daniel Edelson and Brian Reiser, and a team at the University of Michigan headed by Joseph Krajcik and Ron Marx. Each of the PBIS units was originally developed by one of these teams and then later revised and edited to be a part of the full three-year middle-school curriculum that became PBIS.

PBIS has its roots in two educational approaches, Project-Based Science and Learning by Design™. Project-Based Science suggests that students should learn science through engaging in the same kinds of inquiry practices scientists use, in the context of scientific problems relevant to their lives and using tools authentic to science. Project-Based Science was originally conceived in the hi-ce Center at the University of Michigan, with funding from the National Science Foundation. Learning by Design™ derives from Problem-Based Learning and suggests sequencing, social practices, and reflective activities for promoting learning. It engages students in design practices, including the use of iteration and deliberate reflection. LBD was conceived at the Georgia Institute of Technology, with funding from the National Science Foundation, DARPA, and the McDonnell Foundation.

The development of the integrated *PBIS* curriculum was supported by the National Science Foundation under grant nos. 0137807, 0527341, and 0639978. Any opinions, findings and conclusions, or recommendations expressed in this material are those of the authors and do not necessarily reflect the views of the National Science Foundation.

PBIS Team

Principal Investigator
Janet L. Kolodner

Co-Principal Investigators
Daniel C. Edelson
Joseph S. Krajcik
Brian J. Reiser

NSF Program Officer
Gerhard Salinger

Curriculum Developers
Michael T. Ryan
Mary L. Starr

Teacher's Planning Guide Developers
Rebecca M. Schneider
Mary L. Starr

Literacy Specialist
LeeAnn M. Sutherland

NSF Program Reviewer
Arthur Eisenkraft

Project Coordinator
Juliana Lancaster

External Evaluators
The Learning Partnership
Steven M. McGee
Jennifer Witers

The Georgia Institute of Technology Team

Project Director:
Janet L. Kolodner

Development of PBIS units at the Georgia Institute of Technology was conducted in conjunction with the Learning by Design™ Research group (LBD), Janet L. Kolodner, PI.

Lead Developers, Physical Science:
David Crismond
Michael T. Ryan

Lead Developer, Earth Science:
Paul J. Camp

Lead Ethnographer:
Barbara Fasse

Assessment and Evaluation:
Jackie Gray
Daniel Hickey
Jennifer Holbrook
Laura Vandewiele

Project Pioneers:
JoAnne Collins
David Crismond
Joanna Fox
Alice Gertzman
Mark Guzdial
Cindy Hmelo-Silver
Douglas Holton
Roland Hubscher
N. Hari Narayanan
Wendy Newstetter
Valery Petrushin
Kathy Politis
Sadhana Puntambekar
David Rector
Janice Young

The Northwestern University Team

Project Directors:
Daniel Edelson
Brian Reiser

Lead Developer, Biology:
David Kanter

Lead Developers, Earth Science:
Jennifer Mundt Leimberer
Darlene Slusher

Development of PBIS units at Northwestern was conducted in conjunction with:

The Center for Learning Technologies in Urban Schools (LeTUS) at Northwestern, and the Chicago Public Schools
Clifton Burgess, PI
for Chicago Public Schools;
Louis Gomez, PI.

The BioQ Collaborative
David Kanter, PI.

The Biology Guided Inquiry Learning Environments (BGuILE) Project
Brian Reiser, PI.

The Geographic Data in Education (GEODE) Initiative
Daniel Edelson, Director

The Center for Curriculum Materials in Science at Northwestern
Daniel Edelson,
Brian Reiser,
Bruce Sherin, PIs.

The University of Michigan Team

Project Directors:
Joseph Krajcik
Ron Marx

Literacy Specialist:
LeeAnn M. Sutherland

Project Coordinator:
Mary L. Starr

Development of PBIS units at the University of Michigan was conducted in conjunction with:

The Center for Learning Technologies in Urban Schools (LeTUS)
Phyllis Blumenfeld,
Barry Fishman,
Joseph Krajcik,
Ron Marx,
Elliot Soloway, PIs.

The Detroit Public Schools
Juanita Clay-Chambers
Deborah Peek-Brown

The Center for Highly Interactive Computing in Education (hi-ce)
Phyllis Blumenfeld,
Barry Fishman,
Joseph Krajcik,
Ron Marx,
Elizabeth Moje,
Elliot Soloway,
LeeAnn Sutherland, PIs.

Field-Test Teachers

National Field Test
Tamica Andrew
Leslie Baker
Jeanne Bayer
Gretchen Bryant
Boris Consuegra
Daun D'Aversa
Candi DiMauro
Kristie L. Divinski
Donna M. Dowd
Jason Fiorito
Lara Fish
Christine Gleason
Christine Hallerman
Terri L. Hart-Parker
Jennifer Hunn
Rhonda K. Hunter
Jessica Jones
Dawn Kuppersmith
Anthony F. Lawrence
Ann Novak
Rise Orsini
Tracy E. Parham
Cheryl Sgro-Ellis
Debra Tenenbaum
Sarah B. Topper
Becky Watts
Debra A. Williams
Ingrid M. Woolfolk
Ping-Jade Yang

**New York City
Field Test**
*Several sequences of PBIS
units have been field-tested
in New York City under
the leadership of Whitney
Lukens, Staff Developer for
Region 9, and Greg Borman,
Science Instructional
Specialist, New York City
Department of Education*

6th Grade
Norman Agard
Tazinmudin Ali
Heather
  Guthartz Aniba
Asher Arzonane
Asli Aydin
Shareese Blakely
John J. Blaylock
Joshua Blum
Tsedey Bogale

Filomena Borrero
Zachary Brachio
Thelma Brown
Alicia Browne-Jones
Scott Bullis
Maximo Cabral
Lionel Callender
Matthew Carpenter
Ana Maria Castro
Diane Castro
Anne Chan
Ligia Chiorean
Boris Consuegra
Careen Halton Cooper
Cinnamon Czarnecki
Kristin Decker
Nancy Dejean
Gina DiCicco
Donna Dowd
Lizanne Espina
Joan Ferrato
Matt Finnerty
Jacqueline Flicker
Helen Fludd
Leigh Summers Frey
Helene Friedman-Hager
Diana Gering
Matthew Giles
Lucy Gill
Steven Gladden
Greg Grambo
Carrie Grodin-Vehling
Stephan Joanides
Kathryn Kadei
Paraskevi Karangunis
Cynthia Kerns
Martine Lalanne
Erin Lalor
Jennifer Lerman
Sara Lugert
Whitney Lukens
Dana Martorella
Christine Mazurek
Janine McGeown
Chevelle McKeever
Kevin Meyer
Jennifer Miller
Nicholas Miller
Diana Neligan
Caitlin Van Ness
Marlyn Orque
Eloisa Gelo Ortiz
Gina Papadopoulos
Tim Perez
Albertha Petrochilos
Christopher Poli

Kristina Rodriguez
Nadiesta Sanchez
Annette Schavez
Hilary Sedgwitch
Elissa Seto
Laura Shectman
Audrey Shmuel
Katherine Silva
Ragini Singhal
C. Nicole Smith
Gitangali Sohit
Justin Stein
Thomas Tapia
Eilish Walsh-Lennon
Lisa Wong
Brian Yanek
Cesar Yarleque
David Zaretsky
Colleen Zarinsky

7th Grade
Mayra Amaro
Emmanuel Anastasiou
Cheryl Barnhill
Bryce Cahn
Ligia Chiorean
Ben Colella
Boris Consuegra
Careen Halton Cooper
Elizabeth Derse
Urmilla Dhanraj
Gina DiCicco
Lydia Doubleday
Lizanne Espina
Matt Finnerty
Steven Gladden
Stephanie Goldberg
Nicholas Graham
Robert Hunter
Charlene Joseph
Ketlynne Joseph
Kimberly Kavazanjian
Christine Kennedy
Bakwah Kotung
Lisa Kraker
Anthony Lett
Herb Lippe
Jennifer Lopez
Jill Mastromarino
Kerry McKie
Christie Morgado
Patrick O'Connor
Agnes Ochiagha
Tim Perez
Nadia Piltser
Chris Poli

Carmelo Ruiz
Kim Sanders
Leslie Schiavone
Ileana Solla
Jacqueline Taylor
Purvi Vora
Ester Wiltz
Carla Yuille
Marcy Sexauer Zacchea
Lidan Zhou

8th Grade
Emmanuel Anastasio
Jennifer Applebaum
Marsha Armstrong
Jenine Barunas
Vito Cipolla
Kathy Critharis
Patrecia Davis
Alison Earle
Lizanne Espina
Matt Finnerty
Ursula Fokine
Kirsis Genao
Steven Gladden
Stephanie Goldberg
Peter Gooding
Matthew Herschfeld
Mike Horowitz
Charlene Jenkins
Ruben Jimenez
Ketlynne Joseph
Kimberly Kavazanjian
Lisa Kraker
Dora Kravitz
Anthony Lett
Emilie Lubis
George McCarthy
David Mckinney
Michael McMahon
Paul Melhado
Jen Miller
Christie Morgado
Maria Jenny Pineda
Anastasia Plaunova
Carmelo Ruiz
Riza Sanchez
Kim Sanders
Maureen Stefanides
Dave Thompson
Matthew Ulmann
Maria Verosa
Tony Yaskulski

AIR QUALITY

Air Quality

Air Quality is based on *What Affects the Quality of Air in my Community?*, a unit developed by the University of Michigan Center for Highly Interactive Classrooms, Curricula & Computing in Education (hi-ce) and The Center for Learning Technologies in Urban Schools (LeTUS).

Air Quality
Lead Developers
Mary L. Starr
Janet L. Kolodner

Contributing Field-test Teachers
Asher Arzonane
Matthew Carpenter
Anne Chan
Lizanne Espina
Steven Gladden
Stephan Joanides
Christopher Poli
Caitlin Van Ness
Cesar Yarleque

What Affects the Quality of Air in My Community?
Principal Investigator
Joseph Krajcik

Research Associate
Elena S. Takaki

Literacy Expert
LeeAnn M. Sutherland

Lead Developers
Amy Wefel
William J. Bobrowsky
Barbara Hug
Jonathon Singer

Contributors
Tali Tal
Hsin-kai Wu
Ron Marx

Contributing Field-test Teachers
Karen Amati
Barbara Case
Denise Hafner
Alycia Meriweather
Deborah Peek-Brown
Evelyn Whitner

Detroit Public Schools Urban Systemic Initiative
Juanita Clay Chambers, Chief, Office of Curriculum—Detroit Public Schools

The development of *Air Quality* (*PBIS* Edition) was supported by the National Science Foundation under grant nos. 0137807, 0527341, and 0639978. The development of *What Affects the Quality of Air in my Community?* (University of Michigan edition) was been supported by the National Science Foundation under grant no. 9720383. Any opinions, findings, and conclusions or recommendations expressed in this material are those of the authors and do not necessarily reflect the views of the National Science Foundation.

Table of Contents

Learning Set 4

Science Concepts: *Fossil fuel, acid, neutral, base, salt, acid rain, ion, ionic bond, pH scale, metal, nonmetal, food chain, greenhouse effect, global warming, global climate change, neutralization, buffering capacity, working with maps, analyzing data, modeling, making observations, making inferences, using scientific tools, making predictions, comparing and contrasting data, sharing data, working with graphs, using evidence to explain.*

Learning Set 5

Science Concepts: *Air-pollution legislation, Clean Air Act, The Environmental Protection Agency, catalyst, catalytic converter, electrostatic precipitator, wet scrubber, National Ambient Air Quality Standards, physical separation of mixtures, chemical separation of mixtures, biofuel, biomass, nonrenewable energy, renewable energy, alternative energy, Smog Alert, indoor air pollution, using visualization tools, making observations and inferences, analyzing observational and experimental data, reading and analyzing data, organizing data, comparing and contrasting data, sharing data, using evidence to explain.*

Answer the Big Question

Introducing PBIS

What Do Scientists Do?

1) Scientists...address big challenges and big questions.

You will find many different kinds of *Big Challenges* and *Questions* in *PBIS* Units. Some ask you to think about why something is a certain way. Some ask you to think about what causes something to change. Some challenge you to design a solution to a problem. Most of them are about things that can and do happen in the real world.

Understand the Big Challenge or Question

As you get started with each Unit, you will do activities that help you understand the *Big Question* or *Challenge* for that Unit. You will think about what you already know that might help you, and you will identify some of the new things you will need to learn.

Project Board

The *Project Board* helps you keep track of your learning. For each challenge or question, you will use a *Project Board* to keep track of what you know, what you need to learn, and what you are learning. As you learn and gather evidence, you will record that on the *Project Board*. After you have answered each small question or challenge, you will return to the *Project Board* to record how what you've learned helps you answer the *Big Question* or *Challenge*.

Learning Sets

Each Unit is composed of a group of *Learning Sets*, one for each of the smaller questions that need to be answered to address the *Big Question* or *Challenge*. In each *Learning Set*, you will investigate and read to find answers to the *Learning Set's* question. You will also have a chance to share the results of your investigations with your classmates and work together to make sense of what you are learning. As you come to understand answers to the questions on the *Project Board*, you will record those answers and the evidence you've collected. At the end of each *Learning Set*, you will apply your knowledge to the *Big Question* or *Challenge*.

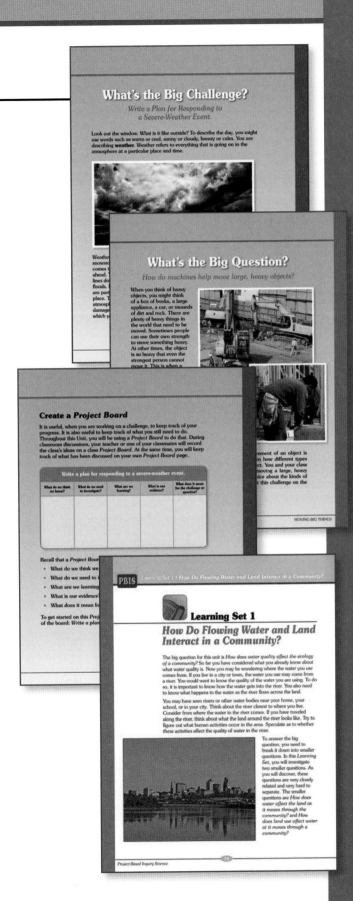

AIR QUALITY

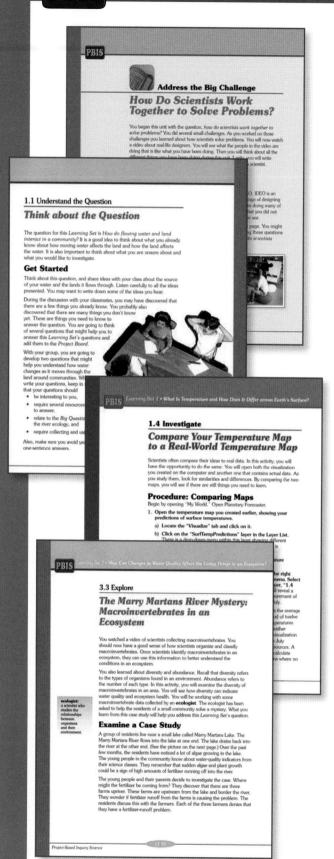

Answer the Big Question / Address the Big Challenge

At the end of each Unit, you will put everything you have learned together to tackle the *Big Question or Challenge*.

2) Scientists...address smaller questions and challenges.

What You Do in a Learning Set

Understanding the Question or Challenge

At the start of each *Learning Set*, you will usually do activities that will help you understand the *Learning Set's* question or challenge and recognize what you already know that can help you answer the question or achieve the challenge. Usually, you will visit the *Project Board* after these activities and record on it the even smaller questions that you need to investigate to answer a *Learning Set's* question.

Investigate/Explore

There are many different kinds of investigations you might do to find answers to questions. In the *Learning Sets,* you might

- design and run experiments;
- design and run simulations;
- design and build models;
- examine large sets of data.

Don't worry if you haven't done these things before. The text will provide you with lots of help in designing your investigations and in analyzing your data.

Read

Like scientists, you will also read about the science you are learning. You'll read a little bit before you investigate, but most of the reading you do will be to help you understand what you've experienced or seen in an investigation. Each time you read, the text will include *Stop and Think* questions after the reading. These questions will help you gauge how well you understand what you have read. Usually, the class will discuss the answers to *Stop and Think* questions before going on so that everybody has a chance to make sense of the reading.

Design and Build

When the *Big Challenge* for a Unit asks you to design something, the challenge in a *Learning Set* might also ask you to design something and make it work. Often, you will design a part of the thing you will design and build for the *Big Challenge*. When a *Learning Set* challenges you to design and build something, you will do several things:

- identify what questions you need to answer to be successful
- investigate to find answers to those questions
- use those answers to plan a good design solution
- build and test your design.

Because designs don't always work the way you want them to, you will usually do a design challenge more than once. Each time through, you will test your design. If your design doesn't work as well as you'd like, you will determine why it is not working and identify other things you need to investigate to make it work better. Then, you will learn those things and try again.

Explain and Recommend

A big part of what scientists do is explain, or try to make sense of why things happen the way they do. An explanation describes why something is the way it is or behaves the way it does. An explanation is a statement you make built from claims (what you think you know), evidence (from an investigation) that supports the claim, and science knowledge. As they learn, scientists get better at explaining. You'll see that you get better, too, as you work through the *Learning Sets*.

A recommendation is a special kind of claim—one where you advise somebody about what to do. You will make recommendations and support them with evidence, science knowledge, and explanations.

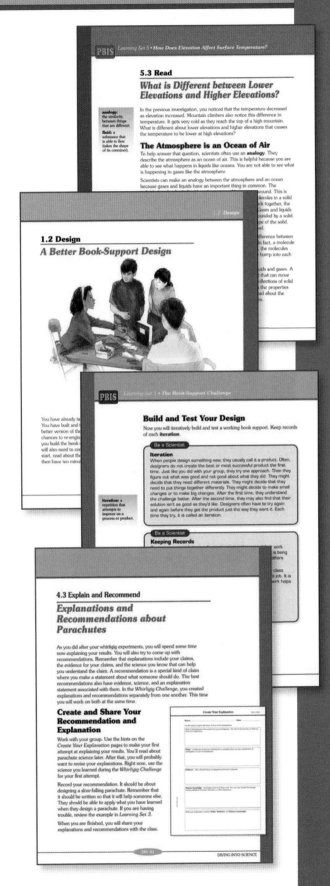

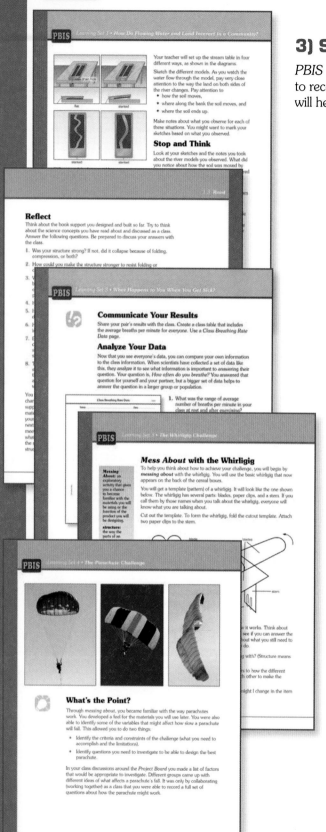

3) Scientists...reflect in many different ways.

PBIS provides guidance to help you think about what you are doing and to recognize what you are learning. Doing this often as you are working will help you be a successful student scientist.

Tools for Making Sense

Stop and Think

Stop and Think sections help you make sense of what you've been doing in the section you are working on. *Stop and Think* sections include a set of questions to help you understand what you've just read or done. Sometimes the questions will remind you of something you need to pay more attention to. Sometimes they will help you connect what you've just read to things you already know. When there is a *Stop and Think* in the text, you will work individually or with a partner to answer the questions, and then the whole class will discuss the answers.

Reflect

Reflect sections help you connect what you've just done with other things you've read or done earlier in the Unit (or in another Unit). When there is a *Reflect* in the text, you will work individually, with a partner or your small group to answer the questions. Then, the whole class will discuss the answers. You may be asked to answer *Reflect* questions for homework.

Analyze Your Data

Whenever you have to analyze data, the text will provide hints about how to do that and what to look for.

Mess About

"Messing about" is a term that comes from design. It means exploring the materials you will be using for designing or building something or examining something that works like what you will be designing. Messing about helps you discover new ideas—and it can be a lot of fun. The text will usually give you ideas about things to notice as you are messing about.

What's the Point?

At the end of each *Learning Set*, you will find a summary, called *What's the Point?*, of the important information from the *Learning Set*. These summaries can help you remember how what you did and learned is connected to the *Big Question or Challenge* you are working on.

4) Scientists...collaborate.

Scientists never do all their work alone. They work with other scientists (collaborate) and share their knowledge. *PBIS* helps you be a student scientist by giving you lots of opportunities for sharing your findings, ideas, and discoveries with others (the way scientists do). You will work together in small groups to investigate, design, explain, and do other things. Sometimes you will work in pairs to figure out things together. You will also have lots of opportunities to share your findings with the rest of your classmates and make sense together of what you are learning.

Investigation Expo

In an *Investigation Expo*, small groups report to the class about an investigation they've done. For each *Investigation Expo*, you will make a poster detailing what you were trying to learn from your investigation, what you did, your data, and your interpretation of your data. The text gives you hints about what to present and what to look for in other groups' presentations. *Investigation Expos* are always followed by discussions about the investigations and about how to do science well. You may also be asked to write a lab report following an investigation.

Plan Briefing/Solution Briefing/Idea Briefing

Briefings are presentations of work in progress. They give you a chance to get advice from your classmates that can help you move forward. During a *Plan Briefing*, you present your plan to the class. It might be a plan for an experiment or a plan for solving a problem or achieving a challenge. During a *Solution Briefing*, you present your solution in progress and ask the class to help you make your solution better. During an *Idea Briefing*, you present your ideas. You get the best advice from your classmates when you present evidence in support of your plan, solution, or idea. Often, you will prepare a poster to help you make your presentation. Briefings are almost always followed by discussions of your investigations and how you will move forward.

Solution Showcase

Solution Showcases usually appear near the end of a Unit. During a *Solution Showcase*, you show your classmates your finished product—either your answer to a question or your solution to a challenge. You also tell the class why you think it is a good answer or solution, what evidence and science you used to get to your solution, and what you tried along the way before getting to your answer or solution. Sometimes a *Solution Showcase* is followed by a competition. It is almost always followed by a discussion comparing and contrasting the different answers and solutions groups have come up with. You may be asked to write a report or paper following a *Solution Showcase*.

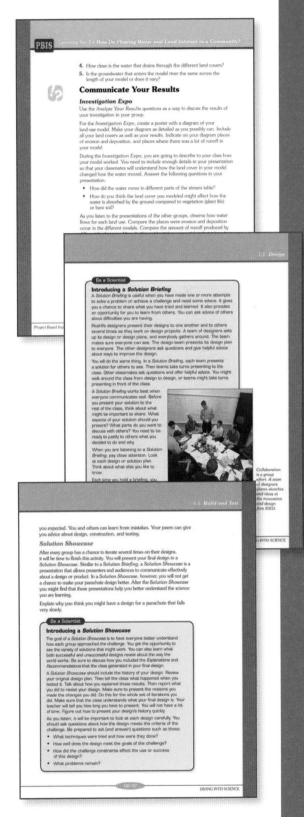

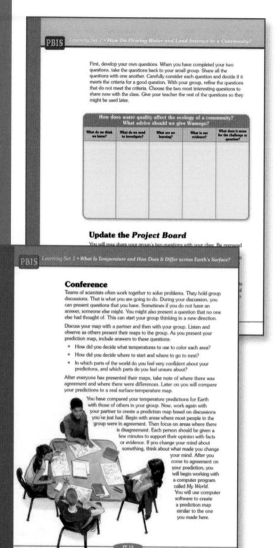

Update the Project Board

Remember that the *Project Board* is designed to help the class keep track of what they are learning and their progress towards a Unit's *Big Question* or *Challenge*. At the beginning of each Unit, the class creates a *Project Board*, and together you record what you think you know about answering the *Big Question* or addressing the *Big Challenge* and what you think you need to investigate further. Near the beginning of each *Learning Set*, the class revisits the *Project Board* and adds new questions and things they think they know. At the end of each *Learning Set*, the class again revisits the *Project Board*. This time you record what you have learned, the evidence you've collected, and recommendations you can make about answering the *Big Question* or achieving the *Big Challenge*.

Conference

A *Conference* is a short discussion between a small group of students before a more formal whole-class discussion. Students might discuss predictions and observations, they might try to explain together, they might consult on what they think they know, and so on. Usually, a *Conference* is followed by a discussion around the *Project Board*. In these small group discussions, everybody gets a chance to participate.

 What's the Point?
Review what you have learned in each *Learning Set*.

 Stop and Think
Answer questions that help you understand what you've done in a section.

 Communicate
Share your ideas and results with your classmates.

 Record
Record your data as you gather it.

AIR QUALITY

As a student scientist, you will...

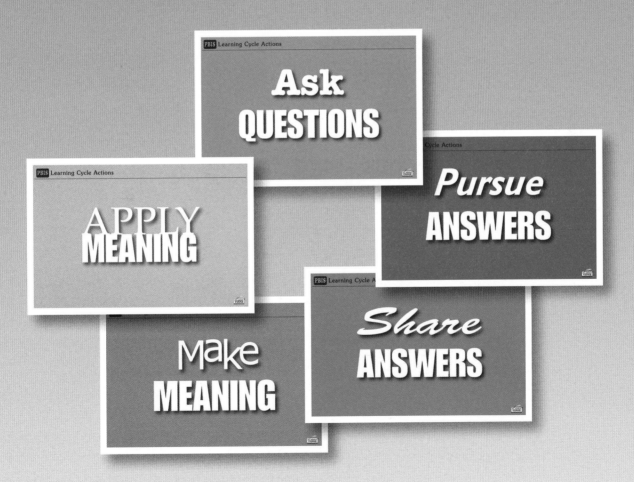

What's the Big Question?

How Can You Improve Air Quality in Your Community?

The Air You Breathe

Once there was a peaceful land named Malaire. Malaire was a small country with mountains on three sides and a blue sea gently bathing the fourth side. The snow-capped mountains reached to the sky and cradled the land like a protective hand. The sea provided white sandy beaches for the happy children to run on and to splash in the water.

From the foothills of the mountains, one could see a lovely view of fields below. The checkered pattern of farmland was a mixture of greens and browns and yellows. Malaire was a country of farmers. Every farmhouse was surrounded by trees—shade trees, flowering trees, and fruit trees of every kind. And the flowers, such beautiful flowers you have never seen. Small wildflowers filled the shady places around the trees, and bold wildflowers captured the sunny meadows. The people of Malaire were happy, very happy, in their beautiful little country.

But one day, a young man from Malaire went on a journey over the mountains to explore the lands beyond. It was many weeks before he returned, and when he did return, it was clear from his strange clothes that he was a changed person. "What a dull, backward country we have," he lamented to the people of Malaire. "All we do is farm. We have nothing to buy, nothing to sell. We don't use money. Everyone is the same, and we don't make anything."

"We make our own clothes and our shoes. We make butter and cheese. We make wonderful pies and cakes and soups. We even make our own houses," his parents said.

"No, no! That's not what I mean. We need cities and factories like in the other lands."

"But we are happy," the people told him. "Everyone is healthy and strong."

"Well, I'm not happy!" retorted the young man. "And if you had seen all that I have seen—electricity and cars and cities—in the lands across the mountains, I don't think you would be happy either." With that, he stomped off and went back across the mountains, leaving Malaire forever.

But people were no longer as happy now. "Perhaps he is right. Perhaps we need factories and cities," they said to each other. So they sent a delegation through the mountains to the neighboring lands to find out about cities and factories. The delegation brought back experts, who immediately started making changes.

The experts took most of the farmers from their fields and set them to work building a city along the beach. House after house was built, then factory after factory. A few men still farmed, but now they farmed much larger fields. At the bidding of the experts, they cut down trees to make bigger fields to grow more crops.

Trees were also cut down and burned in the factories and homes for heat. Smoke began to fill the sky. The factories started turning out shoes by the thousands and dumping leftover leather and chemical wastes into a river that flowed to the sea. Soon there were no fish. Other factories started making paper from trees, and thereafter, the air always had a bad smell.

Newly trained salesmen took the shoes and paper through the mountains and sold them. They brought back automobiles, and soon every family in Malaire had an automobile. Every Sunday, each family got in its car and drove, bumper to bumper, up into the mountains over a new road, to get some fresh air.

Eventually, all the large trees were gone, and there was no wood to burn. "We need coal," said the experts, and they began looking for coal. They found it in the foothills. They brought in huge machines that tore up the earth and took out the coal. They took the coal into the city, and as coal burned in all the factories and homes, the air quality got worse and worse.

"Let's start using electricity," said the experts. So a power plant was built, and power lines were stretched everywhere in the city, using coal to generate electricity for the homes and businesses. The air got worse and worse.

Then, for a full week, the wind blew in from the sea. The hazy air hung over the city. People wheezed and coughed, and their eyes watered. The smelly air was thick with grimy particles from the coal and wood burning. Birds began to die. Old people and children became sick, too. No one knew why. No one tried to find out why.

Finally, the wind shifted. The wind took the bad air out to sea. Everyone breathed deeply again and smiled. More houses were built, and more factories, too. The power plant had to expand. Trains and tracks were built to cross the mountains, and an airport was built so they could start using jets. Both the trains and the jets burned fuel. They burned more and more fuel as the people of Malaire took more trips.

Again, the wind blew in from the sea, this time for ten days. The people coughed and wheezed, and their eyes watered. More birds died, and the few remaining trees began to lose their leaves. No one knew why. The air hung like a gloomy blanket, touching everything. Trees and flowers died, even weeds, and finally everyone was very sick, every single person in Malaire.

Then the wind changed, blowing the haze away. But now people were leaving Malaire. Malaire was no longer a happy place to live. No one could remember exactly when Malaire changed from being a happy place to being a sad place. No one could remember who was responsible. And so, the people packed up their children and their dogs and their cats and drove out onto the wide highways. They pointed their cars toward the hills and sped away, searching for a better place to live than Malaire.

As the last bit of exhaust from the last car disappeared into the air, the country sat there—silent. The factories had stopped. The homes were silent. Nothing moved.

Reflect

1. The story of Malaire is a parable. A parable is a short story that teaches some truth or lesson. What truth or lesson does the parable of Malaire teach?

2. How does your community compare to Malaire? Do you think the air quality in your community could get as bad as the air in Malaire?

3. How do you think you could keep the air in your community from becoming as bad as the air in Malaire?

4. How could the air in Malaire be improved? How do you think you could use what you read about Malaire to improve the air in your community?

polluted: containing substances that can cause harm to people, plants, animals, and structures; unclean or impure.

pollutant: a substance that can make air, soil, or water harmful to organisms and structures.

air quality: the condition of air in terms of the amount of pollutants it contains.

On a moment-to-moment basis, air is the most important thing in your life. You inhale and exhale air constantly. Parts of air keep you alive. And yet, you can't see it. You can't usually smell it or taste it. What exactly is air? In this Unit, you are going to explore the composition and characteristics of air—what it is and what is in it. You will look at what air is in its very basic components. You will learn how air becomes **polluted**, or comes to contain substances that can cause harm to organisms and structures. You will explore how the quality of air can affect the plants, animals, and humans in a community. This will all help you to improve your answers to the *Reflect* questions.

Polluted air contains substances that can cause harm to organisms and structures. These substances are known as **pollutants**. A measurement that describes air in terms of the amount of pollutants it contains is **air quality**. Good air quality describes a lower amount of pollutants, whereas poor air quality describes a larger amount of pollutants.

Air quality affects everyone. Unlike other substances you take into your body, such as food, you cannot choose the type of air you breathe. You must take in the air that surrounds you. In this Unit, you will learn that air quality is not an individual concern. Air quality is a concern for entire communities, regions, and nations. You will explore case studies involving two different regions of the United States. Each region has different issues regarding air quality. You will also learn about legislation, such as the Clean Air Act, that has been passed in an effort to improve air quality. In the end, you will discover how people affect air quality and create global climate change.

The *Big Question* for this Unit is a very important one: *How can you improve air quality in your community?* To know if the air you breathe in your own community is good, you need to know what good and poor air quality are. You also need to know where your air comes from and how air can become polluted. You will read about **air pollution** in California and in New York State, what is being done to improve the air in those places, and why it is so hard to improve the air quality in those places. You will need to learn a lot of chemistry to understand where air pollution comes from and how to manage it. You may already have some ideas about what air is and how it becomes polluted, and you may have some questions about air and air quality. You will have a chance to ask those questions and answer them in this Unit.

Poor air quality is a problem for many cities and regions.

air pollution: the introduction of chemicals, particles, or organisms to air that are harmful to living things and structures.

Welcome to Air Quality!
Enjoy being a student scientist.

Think About the *Big Question*

How Can You Improve Air Quality in Your Community?

In this Unit, you will investigate air quality in your community and how it can be improved. But first, you will need to identify what is meant by air quality, where pollution comes from, and how it can affect the environment. Scientists often find it useful to examine a variety of different cases to begin to understand new concepts. To begin to understand exactly what air quality is and where pollution might come from, you will begin the Unit by doing what a scientist would do. To investigate the processes occurring in some natural situations, scientists analyze case studies. A case study combines data about a variety of factors as they relate to a specific topic or issue. These results may make it possible for a scientist to identify the relationship between factors. Although you will not be able to take part in an extensive case study, you can use a similar procedure to analyze photos showing how humans impact air quality. Later in this Unit, you will read about air quality in California and New York State to help you understand more about how air becomes polluted and what can be done about it.

Most power plants burn fossils fuels, such as coal, to produce electricity for homes and businesses.

Vehicles clog the roads of many highways in the United States. The average American family owns 2.5 cars.

Some mass-transit trains run on electricity instead of gasoline.

At a gas station, a man pumps gasoline into his sport utility vehicle.

Wind turbines in many parts of the world stretch across open areas of land.

A compact fluorescent light bulb can be used in homes instead of a regular light bulb.

Solar panels on the roof of a house convert sunlight energy into electricity.

City workers plant a garden in a park.

Forest fires, some caused by humans, can burn for many weeks and kill many trees.

Large areas of the western United States have big herds of cattle and other livestock.

Get Started

Begin thinking about air quality by examining the pictures on this page and the previous pages. Each shows an example of a human activity or product that affects air quality. Identify the human activity or product as a *source* that has an impact on air quality. Then identify how each human activity or product might affect air quality to make it better or worse. In other words, identify its *effect*. Also, consider how the change in air quality might affect people, animals, or objects in the area. Record your ideas in the first two columns of a *Sources and Effects of Air Quality* chart like the one shown on the next page. You might think about the *Sources* column as answering the question: What activities and products make air quality good or poor? To complete the *Effects* column, think about the question: It what way does the activity improve or worsen air quality?

Sources and Effects of Air Quality		
Sources	Effects	How to improve the air

Conference

Share with your group the sources you identified and how you think those sources might affect a community. Discuss how you decided a source was good or bad for air quality and how you determined the effects of each source. It is important for every member of your group to discuss how they determined the effects of each source.

Create a group list of sources and effects. On the list, circle the ideas that some group members disagreed with. During your discussion, you may realize that there are some things you do not know about air quality. Record these as questions to share with your class.

Communicate

Share Your Ideas

As a class, make a *Sources and Effects of Air Quality* chart. When it is your group's turn to share your ideas, present the sources and effects your group discussed, why you think each is a source or effect, and the ones your group disagreed about. As you are listening, decide if you agree with the sources and effects that are presented. If you disagree, present your reasons for disagreeing. Circle the sources and effects the class disagrees about on the class *Sources and Effects of Air Quality* chart. Then, as a class, come up with a question that could be answered to help the class come to agreement about each circled item. Record the questions on the class chart. Throughout the Unit, you will investigate many sources and effects. Those investigations will help you come to agreement on ideas about which you may disagree now.

Observe

Look for Evidence of Air Quality in Your Community

The pictures gave you some ideas about what affects the quality of the air you breathe. You know enough now to begin to explore the air quality in your own community by taking an "air walk" with your class. Before you take your "air walk," make a list of the sources and effects of air quality that you expect to see. Then, working with a partner on your walk, you will look for evidence of humans affecting air quality and the sources of these effects.

Many things you observe in nature can be an indication of good air quality or bad air quality.

As you walk around, it will help to notice small details. You may notice soot on a building or see a solar panel on a roof. You may smell wood burning in a fireplace, or you may observe butterflies on flowers. Look carefully as you walk around, and try to find examples other students have not noticed. Your *Sources and Effects of Air Quality* chart will give you some ideas about what you should be looking for.

Working with your partner, identify at least four sources that improve air quality and four sources that worsen air quality.

Recording Your Observations

Record your examples on an *Air-Walk Field Notes* pages. You will be able to fit four observations on each page, so each pair of students will have room to record eight examples.

For each example you identify,

- describe the source you identified. If you can see it, use words and a sketch to give details about your observations. If you cannot see it, describe what you think the source might be.

- record the location of the source.

- describe the effect of the source. If you can see the effect, describe what you see. If you cannot see the effect, describe what you think the effect might be.

Record enough information so that you will be able to share your observations with others. If a camera is available, someone should take pictures of the sources and effects that you identify on your walk. The sketches and photographs will help you throughout the Unit.

Stop and Think

Working with your group, use your observations to answer these questions. As your group discusses the answers to the questions, record the answers on a new *Sources and Effects of Air Quality* chart. At the top of the chart, record that these sources and effects came from your air walk. Be sure to give all members of your group a chance to report their observations.

1. What sources that improve air quality did you observe on your air walk? For each, how did you decide it improved air quality? Record these sources in the *Sources* column of your air walk *Sources and Effects of Air Quality* chart. As you did earlier, circle any sources that members of your group disagree about.

2. What sources that worsen air quality did you observe? For each, how did you decide it made air quality worse? Record these sources in the *Sources* column of your air walk *Sources and Effects of Air Quality* chart. As you did earlier, circle any sources that members of your group disagree about.

Air-Walk Field Notes   0.0.1

Name: _____   Date: _____

Source _____
Description _____

Location _____
Effect _____

Source _____
Description _____

Location _____
Effect _____

Source _____
Description _____

Location _____
Effect _____

Source _____
Description _____

Location _____
Effect _____

© It's About Time

---

3. For each source you observed, what effects did you observe or suggest? Record those in the *Effects* column of your air walk *Sources and Effects of Air Quality* chart. For each, how did you identify it as an effect? If you did not observe effects, record any effects you think might result from the source you observed. Put parentheses around any effects that you did not directly observe. As earlier, circle any effects that members of your group disagree about.

4. How did what you actually observed differ from what you expected to see?

5. What evidence did you observe to show that people in your community are working to improve air quality? Record these efforts in the *How to improve the air* column of your air walk *Sources and Effects of Air Quality* chart.

Communicate

Share Your Ideas

You are now ready to share your observations with the class. As you did earlier, create a class *Sources and Effects of Air Quality* chart. Each time you share an idea with the class, be sure to tell the class why you think what you observed was related to air quality. Others may have different ideas about what they observed. They may have observed different things, or they may have interpreted what they saw differently than you did. Listen carefully as others present their ideas. Ask questions if you do not understand how others came to their conclusions. Be sure to ask your questions respectfully.

Reflect

The *Big Question* for this Unit is *How can you improve air quality in your community?* To answer this question, you will have to identify how good the quality of the air is in your community, what might be causing poor air quality in your community, and what can be done to improve air quality. Then you will make recommendations for improvement. Working with your group and using the ideas on the *Sources and Effects of Air Quality* charts, identify what you already know about sources and their effects on air quality and what you need to learn more about. Use the following questions as a guide.

1. What are the three most important things your class has identified about the quality of air in your community?

2. What are the three most important things your class has identified about sources that affect air quality in your community?

3. What are the three most important things your class has identified about the effects of human activities and products on air quality in your community?

4. What else do you need to know about sources and their effects on air quality to decide if your community has good or poor air quality?

5. What else do you need to know to decide how the air quality in your community can be improved?

As you work with your group, share ideas about what you need to do to answer the *Big Question*. Look back at the parable you read and the observations from your *Sources and Effects of Air Quality* charts. What does your community have in common with Malaire? How is it different? Refer back to the parable for examples of how the air quality can become bad. Discuss how what you do every day affects air quality. If you lived in Malaire, what could you do to improve air quality? Would you be willing to give up some things for better air? What would you give up? What would happen if you did that? What would happen if everybody did that? How can you have the things you want and still have good air quality? These are all questions you should be thinking about as you consider the *Big Question, How can you improve air quality in your community?*

Create a *Project Board*

When you are trying to answer a difficult question or solve a hard problem, it is helpful to organize your work. You will be using a *Project Board* throughout this Unit to keep track of your progress and the things you still need to do. Your class will keep a class *Project Board,* and you will use your own copy of the *Project Board* for reference.

Remember that the *Project Board* has space for answers to five guiding questions:

- What do we think we know?
- What do we need to investigate?
- What are we learning?
- What is our evidence?
- What does it mean for the challenge or question?

How can you improve air quality in your community?				
What do we think we know?	What do we need to investigate?	What are we learning?	What is our evidence?	What does it mean for the challenge or question?

To begin this *Project Board,* identify the *Big Question* for this Unit: *How can you improve air quality in your community?* Record it across the top of the class *Project Board.*

What do we think we know?

In the first column of the *Project Board,* record what you think you know about air and air quality. You will want to think about what is meant by good-quality air and poor-quality air, and what are the sources that impact air quality. How does poor-quality air make you sick, and how can it change the quality of your life? How does it affect animals and objects? Think about the air-quality problems facing your community. What kinds of air pollution would you expect to find in your community? What are the people of your community doing now to improve air quality? What do you think they can do in the future?

How does poor-quality air make you sick?

What do we need to investigate?

Perhaps not all students in your class agree on the main problems your community faces in trying to improve air quality. Or, maybe you and other members of your class have different opinions about how scientists and engineers can solve the air-quality problems in your community. Use this column to keep track of what you need to investigate to answer the *Big Question.* Make sure you also record what you need to find out about air and air quality. Record things you are not sure about and need to find out more about.

You will return to the rest of the *Project Board* throughout the Unit. For now, work with your class to fill in the first two columns.

Learning Set 1

What Is Air?

In the parable about Malaire, you explored pollution. Before you can fully understand air pollution, you must first learn about air. You may not have thought much about air in the past, but you probably know something about it. You might tell people that you breathe air. You blow air into a balloon and pump air into your bike tires. How much do you really understand about air? It is important to think about what you know about air before you answer the *Big Question* for this Unit. The demonstrations in this section will help you learn more about air.

Wind is moving air that blows the leaves of trees and the sails of sailboats.

1.1 Understand the Question

What Is Air?

Imagine you could look at a sample of good-quality air through an extremely powerful magnifying tool, so powerful it could see the smallest parts that make up air. What do you think the air would look like? What would a sample of poor-quality air look like? How might good-quality air look different from poor-quality air?

Sketch two pictures. In one, sketch your idea of what clean (good-quality) air would look like if you could see it through the powerful tool. In the second picture, sketch what you think polluted (poor-quality) air would look like through the same tool. Put as much detail as you can into your pictures. Be prepared to present your sketches to your group. Do not worry if you do not know a lot now. You will add to your knowledge as you complete this Unit.

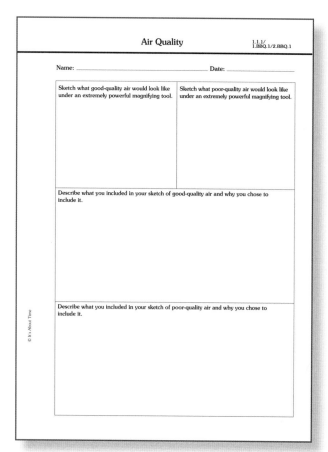

Conference

Share your sketches with your group members. When you present your sketches, be as clear as you can about what each item in your drawing represents and how any parts in your sketch are related to one another.

In your group, make one list of similarities and another of differences among the sketches. If you are not sure about the details of someone's sketch, ask questions to help you understand. For example, ask what the different parts of the sketch represent. How big are the parts shown in the sketch? What shape are they? Find out if the parts are moving or still.

Communicate

Investigation Expo

Make a poster with your sketches, and post it so others can examine it. On your poster, include your group members' sketches and the lists of similarities and differences you developed. Use the sketches that members of your group created to show examples of what your list items mean.

As you walk around and look at the other posters, compare your ideas about what air looks like with the other groups' ideas. Ask questions if you do not understand another group's sketches. Be sure to ask your questions respectfully. As you examine the other sketches, make lists of similarities and differences among the sketches. Then, as a class, answer the following questions:

1. What are common components of the sketches of good-quality air? What unique ideas do students have?

2. In the sketches, what are the most common components of poor-quality air? How are these sketches different from the sketches of good-quality air?

Reflect

It is difficult to draw air. Your class probably has many different ideas about what good-quality air and poor-quality air look like. Some students probably think clean air is empty space or is not made of anything. Some students probably described many different substances in clean air, and others described only one. Some of you sketched air with particles shown by dots, and in some of those sketches, the particles were moving. If scientists were arguing about whether air is empty space or made of particles, they would collect data and use it as evidence to find out what air is. Answering the questions below will help you identify evidence that will tell you if air is empty space or made of particles. Be prepared to discuss your answers to the questions with the class.

1. You cannot see air. What evidence, then, could help you determine if clean air is made of particles or is just empty space?

2. If air is made of particles, what do you need to investigate to find out if the particles are moving or still?

Update the *Project Board*

In this section, you sketched and described what you think good-quality air and poor-quality air look like. Update the *Project Board* by adding ideas from your sketches and discussions in the *What do we think we know?* column. You have also discussed what makes up air. Some students may think it is empty space, and some students may think that substances make up air. Be sure to add the ideas your group agreed on and ideas you are not sure about to the *Project Board*. You may have questions about what air looks like, what it contains, and the relationship between air and pollution. You may have ideas for investigations to find out more about what air is. Record your questions and ideas for investigations in the *What do we need to investigate?* column.

What's the Point?

You imagined you were looking through an extremely powerful magnifying tool at samples of good-quality air and poor-quality air. Your ideas may have differed from the ideas of others. You may have thought air looks like dots, or you may have thought that air looks more like a cloud. Your sketch may have contained particles that were moving or particles that were still. Or, you may have thought that air looks like empty space. Before scientists can fully describe a new substance, they must gather evidence.

1.2 Investigate

Does Air Take Up Space?

When scientists examine a substance, they investigate its properties, or its characteristics. One property they might investigate is how much space it takes up. Investigating this property of air will help you understand more about what air is.

Demonstrations

You will observe three demonstrations to help you think about whether air takes up space. In each demonstration, a cup that contains a paper towel is pushed into a bowl of water. Pay attention to the paper towel and whether or not it gets wet. Look for evidence of the role air may play in whether the paper towel gets wet. In each demonstration, ask yourself where the air is in and around the cup, and what happens to the air as the cup enters the water.

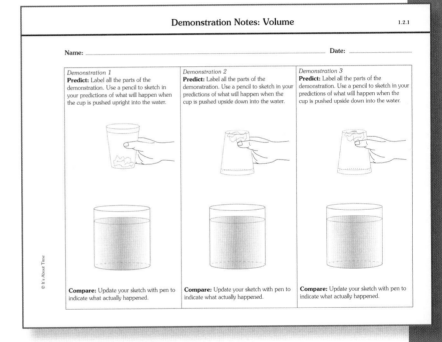

During each demonstration, you will be asked to do three things:

Predict—Make a prediction about what will happen based on your ideas about whether air takes up space.

Observe—Observe the demonstration and record your observations.

Compare—After the demonstration, you will compare your predictions to what you observed. Note what you predicted correctly and what surprised you.

You will record all of your predictions, observations, and comparisons on a *Demonstration Notes: Volume* page. After you have seen all of the demonstrations, you will make a claim about whether air takes up space.

Demonstration 1: Upright Cup, Paper Towel, Water

In this demonstration, a cup with a paper towel taped inside will be pushed upright (open end up) into a bowl of water until the water is above the rim of the cup.

Demonstration 1

Predict—In the *Demonstration 1* sketch on your *Demonstration Notes: Volume* page, use a pencil to label all the parts of the demonstration: cup, paper towel, bowl of water, and where you think there is air in the cup.

- Use a pencil to sketch your prediction of what will happen to the air in the cup after the cup is pushed upright into the water.

- Label the drawing to show what will happen to the paper towel when the cup is pushed upright into the water.

Observe—Observe what happens when the upright cup is pushed into the water. Watch the level of the water in the bowl. Does it go up, down, or stay the same? If it changes, how much does it change? Pay special attention to what happens to the paper towel and what happens to the air in the cup.

Compare—Update your original sketch under *Demonstration 1*. Use a pen to label the actual location of air and water in the cup. Think about how the results compare with your prediction. If your prediction differs from the actual results, record why you think the actual results were different.

Stop and Think

1. Describe what happened to the paper towel in the cup when the cup went into the water.

2. Describe what happened to the air when the cup was put into the water.

3. What happened to the level of the water in the bowl? If it changed, how much did it change? How did you observe this result?

4. How do you think what happened to the air affected the paper towel?

Demonstration 2: Upside-down Cup, Paper Towel, Water

In *Demonstration 2,* a dry cup with a dry paper towel taped inside will be pushed into the water upside down until the cup is completely below the water.

Demonstration 2

Predict—When you are making your predictions, begin by thinking about the results of the first demonstration and what you observed that might help you make a good prediction for this demonstration. Think about how the position of the cup (upright or upside down) affects the air in the cup.

In the *Demonstration 2* sketch on your *Demonstration Notes: Volume* page, label all of the parts of the demonstration: cup, paper towel, bowl of water, and where you think there is air in the cup.

- Use a pencil to sketch your prediction of what you think will happen to the air in the cup after the cup is pushed upside down into the water. Label the location of where air will be in the cup when the cup is underwater.

- Label the drawing to show what will happen to the paper towel when the cup is pushed upside down into the water.

Observe—Observe what happens when the cup is pushed upside down into the water. Watch the level of the water in the bowl. Does it go up, down, or stay the same? If it changes, how much does it change? Pay special attention to what happens to the paper towel and what happens to the air in the cup.

Compare—Update your original *Demonstration 2* sketch based on what you saw in the demonstration. Use a pen to label the actual location of air and water in the cup. How did the results compare with your prediction? If your prediction differed from the actual results, record why you think the actual results were different.

Stop and Think

1. Describe what happened to the paper towel in the cup when the cup went into the water.

2. Describe what happened to the air when the cup was put into the water. How did what happened to the air affect the paper towel?

3. What happened to the level of the water in the bowl? If it changed, how much did it change? How did you observe this result? Why did the result differ from *Demonstration 1*?

4. How did the results of *Demonstration 2* differ from the results of *Demonstration 1*? How did the position of the cup affect the results?

These demonstrations helped you think about whether air takes up space. Only if air takes up space would the paper towel in *Demonstration 2* stay dry. The results of *Demonstration 2* might have surprised you. These results should help you think about whether air takes up space.

Demonstration 3: Upside-down Cup With Hole, Paper Towel, Water

Demonstration 3 is the same as *Demonstration 2,* except the cup now has a hole in the bottom. This cup, with a paper towel taped inside to the bottom, will be pushed upside down into a bowl of water until the cup is completely below the water. Before you make your predictions, think about the other demonstrations. Think about how having a hole in the bottom of the cup will affect the paper towel and the air in the cup.

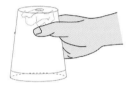

Demonstration 3

Predict—In the *Demonstration 3* sketch on your *Demonstration Notes: Volume* page, label all of the parts of the demonstration: cup, paper towel, bowl of water, and where you think there is air in the cup.

- Use a pencil to sketch your prediction of what will happen to the air in the cup after the cup is pushed upside down into the water. Label the location of air in the cup when the cup is under water. Indicate in your drawing how the hole in the cup affects the air in the cup.

Observe—Observe what happens when the cup with the hole is pushed upside down into the water. Watch the level of the water in the bowl. Does it go up, down, or stay the same? If it changes, how much does it change? Pay special attention to what happens to the paper towel and what happens to the air in the cup.

Compare—Update your original *Demonstration 3* sketch based on what you saw in the demonstration. Use a pen to label the actual location of air and water in the cup. How did the results compare with your prediction? If your prediction differed from the actual results, record why you think the actual results were different.

Stop and Think

1. Describe the results of *Demonstration 3*. What happened to the paper towel in the cup? What happened to the air in the cup?

2. What happened to the level of the water in the bowl? If it changed, how much did it change? How did you observe this result? Why did the result differ from *Demonstration 2*?

3. How did the results of this demonstration differ from the results of the other two demonstrations?

4. In the sketch for *Demonstration 3*, trace the path the air took during the demonstration.

Reflect

Discuss the answers to the following questions with the class.

1. What made the results of the three demonstrations so different?

2. You were looking for evidence that air takes up space. What did these three demonstrations tell you about whether or not air takes up space?

volume:
a measure of
how much
space something
takes up.

Volume

In the demonstrations, you were looking for evidence that air takes up space. You may have made some conclusions about this based on the demonstrations. Scientists call the amount of space a substance takes up **volume**. The cup and the water in the demonstrations took up space. The paper towel also took up space. It makes sense that all these parts of the system have volume. The question is whether air takes up space as well.

When an object takes up space, only that object can be in that space at any one time. For example, if you sit in a chair, another person cannot sit in that same chair at the same time. You are already taking up the space in the chair. You have volume. Does air have volume, too?

The three demonstrations you observed provide evidence that air takes up space, and therefore, has volume.

- When a cup containing air and a paper towel is pushed upright into a bowl of water, the water rushes into the cup and pushes out the air. Only one object can be in one place at a time. The water rushing into the cup takes the place of the air that was in the cup. As a result, the paper towel in the cup gets wet. The level of the water in the bowl rises a very small amount because the cup and paper towel take the place of some of the water.

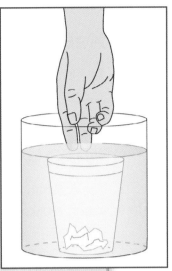

Demonstration 1

- When a cup is pushed into the water upside down, the paper towel stays dry. In the upside-down cup, air takes up space in the cup and stays in the cup as it is lowered into the water. The water cannot push the air out. There is no way for the air to escape from the cup. The paper towel does not get wet because the water cannot reach it. In *Demonstration 2*, air takes up the space inside the cup. Because two things cannot occupy the same space, water cannot fill the space inside the cup if air is already there. The level of water in the bowl rises higher than in *Demonstration 1* because now the cup, the paper towel, *and* the air are taking the place of some of the water.

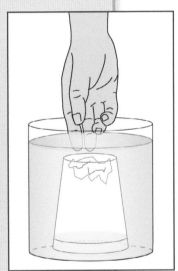

Demonstration 2

- The hole in the cup in *Demonstration 3* allowed the air in the upside-down cup a way to escape. The air in the space in the cup is pushed out of the hole by the water. The cup fills with water, and the paper towel gets wet. The level of the water in the bowl will rise the same distance as in *Demonstration 1*. The bubbles you saw are an indication of air escaping from the cup.

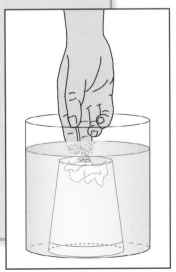

Demonstration 3

Reflect

1. Using the information from the demonstrations and from the reading, describe why you think air takes up space.

2. Describe another example that tells you that air has volume.

What's the Point?

To determine if air takes up space, you observed demonstrations involving water, a cup, and a paper towel. The demonstrations supported the idea that air takes up space. A measure of how much space something takes up is its volume. Volume is a property of any substance. The demonstrations provided evidence that air has volume.

You cannot see air with the unaided eye. Therefore, it is difficult to determine if air has volume.

1.3 Investigate

Does Air Have Mass?

A water bottle with no water in it is sitting on the table. Your friend says the bottle is empty. What would you tell your friend about the bottle? Would you describe the bottle as empty?

You know that one property of a substance is volume (how much space it takes up). Another property of a substance is how much "stuff" it contains. How much "stuff" something contains is its **mass**. Think about the "empty" bottle again. Do the contents of the "empty" bottle have mass? How would you find out?

Scientists measure mass using an instrument called a **balance**. In investigations of substances, scientists have discovered that some things have more mass than other things. A bowling ball has more mass than a golf ball. A golf ball has more mass than a table-tennis ball.

mass: the amount of "stuff" something contains.

balance: an instrument used by scientists to measure mass.

Is the bottle empty?

Using a Balance to Measure Mass

If you were a scientist and wanted to investigate a substance, you would probably measure its mass.

Scientists can use two types of balances to measure mass: a triple-beam balance or an electronic balance. A triple-beam balance acts like a scale in a doctor's office. In the doctor's office, you step onto the scale, and the nurse slides weights along beams until the scale is balanced.

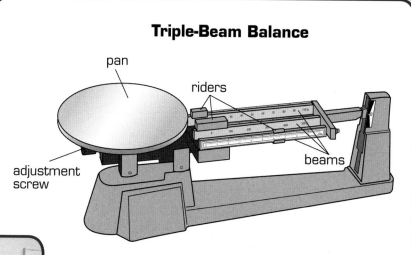

Triple-Beam Balance

pan

riders

beams

adjustment screw

Most doctors use a triple-beam balance to determine a patient's weight.

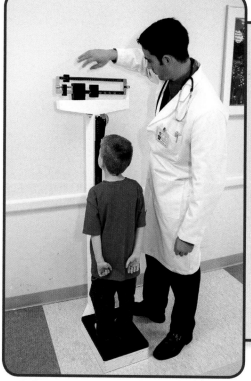

The first step to measuring the mass of a solid object is to make certain the pointer is lined up with 0.00 g. The next step is to put the object on the pan. Once the object is on the pan, move the riders along the beams until the pointer again lines up with 0.00 g. Then you add the masses on each rider to find the total mass of the object.

To measure the mass of a liquid such as water or a loose substance such as salt, you must put the substance in a container before measuring its mass. You do not want to include the mass of the container in your measurement. You must first measure the mass of the empty container. Then, measure the mass of the substance in the container. This is called "taring" the container.

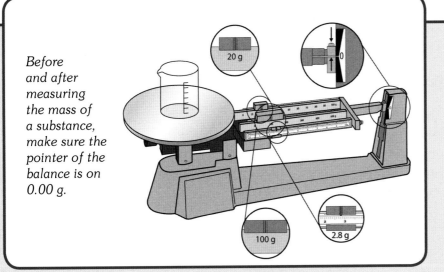

Before and after measuring the mass of a substance, make sure the pointer of the balance is on 0.00 g.

20 g

0

100 g

2.8 g

Subtracting the mass of the container from the mass of the substance and container will give you the mass of the substance alone.

When measuring mass using an electronic balance, you place the object you are measuring on the pan. Then you turn on the device and choose the unit of measurement. You read the measurement on the digital display. Some electronic balances have a tare button. This button lets you place a container on the balance and automatically subtract out the mass of the container. This saves you from having to take separate measurements and then subtract the mass of the container from the total mass.

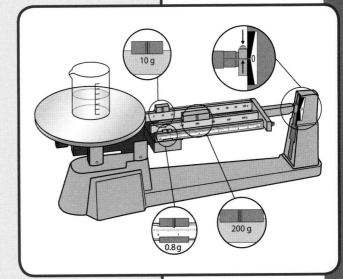

10 g

0

200 g

0.8 g

Electronic Balance

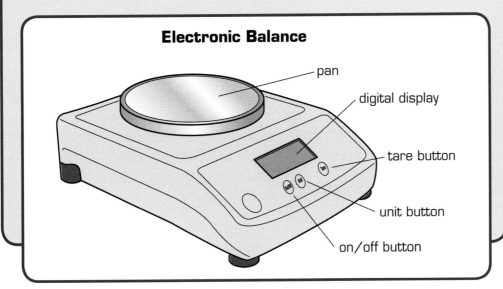

pan

digital display

tare button

unit button

on/off button

In this section, you are trying to determine if air, like other objects, has mass. Think about this as you are observing the demonstration.

Demonstration

In this demonstration, air will be added to a deflated ball. The process is similar to the one described for measuring the mass of objects in a container. First, a balance will be used to measure the mass of a deflated ball. Then, air will be added to the ball, and the mass of the ball will be measured again.

During the demonstration, as a class, you will be asked to predict, observe, and compare.

You will record all of your predictions, observations, and comparisons on a *Demonstration Notes: Mass* page.

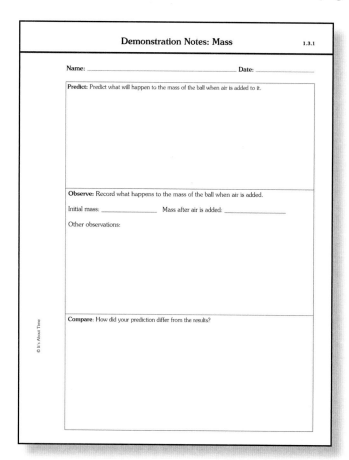

Predict—Predict what will happen to the mass of the deflated ball when air is added to it. Think about what the results should be if air has mass. After air is added, will the mass of the inflated ball be more, less, or the same as the mass of the deflated ball?

Observe—Record the mass of the deflated ball. Now observe what happens to the mass of the ball when air is added and the mass of the ball is measured again. Is the mass of the ball now more, less, or the same? If the mass has changed, how much did it increase or decrease?

Compare—How did the results of the demonstration compare with your prediction? Describe what happened to the ball when air was added. If your prediction differed from the actual results, record why you think the results were different.

Reflect

1. Come to a class agreement on the question for this section, *Does air have mass?*

2. How did the results of the demonstration help you determine if air has mass? Support your conclusion with evidence from the demonstration.

Matter

Anything that has both volume and mass is called **matter**. Matter is a term used to describe every substance that takes up space and has mass. Rocks, lemonade, and helium in a balloon are examples of matter because they have volume and mass.

matter: anything that has volume (takes up space) and has mass.

Properties of Matter

Volume and mass are two examples of physical properties of matter. A physical property of matter is a characteristic that you can observe without changing the nature, or composition, of the matter. Shape, color, odor, texture, and temperature are other physical properties of matter.

A train is matter. It has mass and volume.

Reflect

Think about all the demonstrations you have seen.

1. What evidence do you have that air has volume?

2. What evidence do you have that air has mass?

3. Now that you have learned what matter is, how can you use the evidence from the demonstrations to decide if air is matter?

Create Your Explanation

1.3.2/2.BBQ.2/3.5.2
4.2.2/4.6.7/4.7.1/ABQ.2

Name: _____ Date: _____

Use this page to explain the lesson of your recent investigations.

Write a brief summary of the results from your investigation. You will use this summary to help you write your Explanation.

Claim – a statement of what you understand or a conclusion that you have reached from an investigation or a set of investigations.

Evidence – data collected during investigations and trends in that data.

Science knowledge – knowledge about how things work. You may have learned this through reading, talking to an expert, discussion, or other experiences.

Write your Explanation using the *Claim*, *Evidence*, and *Science knowledge*.

© It's About Time

Explain

You have investigated whether air has mass. Earlier you investigated whether air has volume. Now use the evidence from your observations to make a claim about whether air is matter. Use a *Create Your Explanation* page to develop an explanation of your claim and support it with evidence. The results from the demonstrations are your evidence. You may have some science knowledge from your own experiences or from readings. Record all this information in the appropriate boxes. Then write a statement connecting your evidence and science knowledge to support your claim. This is your explanation. You do not know a lot of science knowledge to record yet. You will have a chance later, after you know more about air, to revise your claim and explanation.

Communicate

Share Your Explanation

Share your group's claim and explanation with the class. Share how you supported your claim with evidence and science knowledge. Pay special attention to how the other groups have supported their claims with science knowledge. Ask questions or make suggestions if you think a group's claim is not as accurate as it could be or if the group has not supported their claim well enough with evidence and science knowledge.

Reflect

1. Think back to the "empty" bottle at the beginning of this section. When your friend says the bottle is empty, you disagree. Using your explanation of air as matter, describe why the water bottle is not empty.

2. Describe a different way you might teach another student that air is matter.

3. Air has volume and mass. Air is matter. What is the relationship between air as matter and air quality? How does this change what you think about air quality?

Update the *Project Board*

In the demonstrations, you explored the volume and mass of air. You also made a claim about the properties of air. Add to the *What are we learning?* column of the *Project Board* what you now know about the relationship between volume, mass, and matter. Use the results from the demonstrations as supporting evidence in the *What is our evidence?* column. You may have ideas about investigations to find out more about what air is. Record your questions and ideas for investigations in the *What do we need to investigate?* column.

How can you improve air quality in your community?				
What do we think we know?	**What do we need to investigate?**	**What are we learning?**	**What is our evidence?**	**What does it mean for the challenge or question?**

What's the Point?

Matter is defined as anything that has volume and mass. In the previous section, you found that air has volume. In this section, you investigated whether air has mass. When air was added to a deflated ball, the mass of the ball increased. Because only air was added to the ball, the change in mass must have come from the air. Therefore, air has mass. Because air has volume and mass, air is matter.

1.4 Investigate

What State of Matter Is Air?

state: form, type, or kind.

When you look around, everything you see is matter. Everything takes up space and has mass. You can sit in a chair. It is hard and always the same. It has mass and takes up space. You can fill a sink with water, and when you spill water on the floor, it forms a puddle. Whether in the sink or on the floor, the water has mass and takes up space. The air you breathe is also matter. But air is a very different type of matter than a chair or water. You cannot sit on air, and you cannot see it. It does not form puddles on the floor. Chairs, water in a puddle, and air are examples of different **states** of matter. These states differ in very specific ways.

Two characteristics of matter—volume and shape—can help you determine its state. Volume and shape are different for each state of matter. You may already have some ideas about the volume and shape of different states of matter. In this section, you will investigate these properties of states of matter.

Demonstration

How Can You Describe States of Matter?

You will observe the contents of three bottles similar to the ones in the diagram below. Each bottle contains matter in a different state. One bottle contains a wooden dowel, one contains water from a faucet, and one contains air.

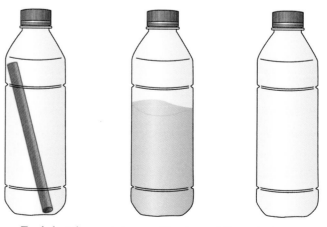

Each bottle contains matter in a different state.

Before observing the demonstration, discuss with your group the contents of each of the bottles.

- How do you know that each bottle contains matter? Support your answers using the results of the demonstrations in the previous sections.

You will be observing while the contents of each bottle are moved from the bottle to a beaker, and then, from the beaker to a bowl. As you observe this demonstration, pay close attention to what happens to the shape and volume of the matter in each bottle as it moves from one container to another. After observing the demonstration, you will decide how to describe a state of matter by its volume and shape.

During the demonstration, you will be asked to predict, observe, and compare.

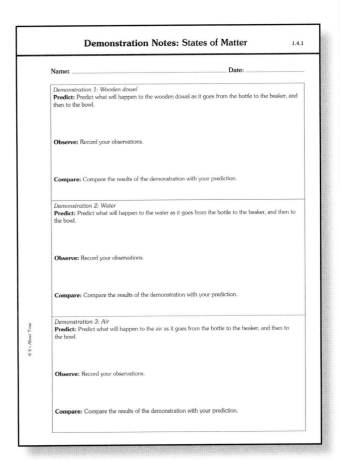

Demonstration Notes: States of Matter 1.4.1

Name: _____ Date: _____

Demonstration 1: Wooden dowel
Predict: Predict what will happen to the wooden dowel as it goes from the bottle to the beaker, and then to the bowl.

Observe: Record your observations.

Compare: Compare the results of the demonstration with your prediction.

Demonstration 2: Water
Predict: Predict what will happen to the water as it goes from the bottle to the beaker, and then to the bowl.

Observe: Record your observations.

Compare: Compare the results of the demonstration with your prediction.

Demonstration 3: Air
Predict: Predict what will happen to the air as it goes from the bottle to the beaker, and then to the bowl.

Observe: Record your observations.

Compare: Compare the results of the demonstration with your prediction.

© It's About Time

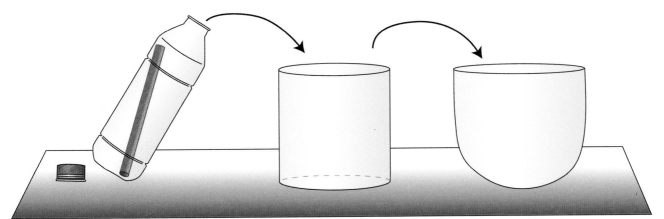

Predict—Make three predictions.

- Make a prediction about the wooden dowel in the bottle. What do you think will happen to the wooden dowel when it is moved from the bottle to a beaker, and then to a bowl? How will the volume of the wooden dowel change? How will the shape of the wooden dowel change?

Include the reasons for what you think will happen. Record your predictions and reasoning on your *Demonstration Notes: States of Matter* page.

- Make a prediction about the water in the bottle. Predict what will happen to the water when it is moved from the bottle to a beaker, and then to a bowl. How will the volume of the water change? How will the shape of the water change? Include the reasons for what you think will happen. Record your predictions and reasoning on your *Demonstration Notes: States of Matter* page.

- Make a prediction about the air in the bottle. Predict what will happen to the air when it is moved from the bottle to a beaker, and then to a bowl. How will the volume of the air change? How will the shape of the air change? Include the reasons for what you think will happen. Record your predictions and reasoning on your *Demonstration Notes: States of Matter* page.

Observe—Record your observations of any changes in shape or volume as the wooden dowel is moved from the bottle to the beaker, and then to the bowl, on your *Demonstration Notes: States of Matter* page. Repeat your observations for the bottles of water and air.

Compare—Compare the results of the demonstration with your predictions.

Wooden dowel

- What happened to the volume of the wooden dowel as it was moved from one container to another? What happened to the shape of the wooden dowel as it was moved from one container to another? What conclusions can you make about this state of matter from your observations? How did the results of the demonstration compare with your prediction? If your prediction differed from the results, record why you think they were different.

Water

- What happened to the volume of the water as it was moved from one container to another? What happened to the shape of the water as it was moved from one container to another? What conclusions can you make about this state of matter from your observations?

How did the results of the demonstration compare with your prediction? If your prediction differed from the results, record why you think they where different.

Air

- What happened to the volume of the air as it was moved from one container to another? What happened to the shape of the air as it was moved from one container to another? What conclusions can you make about this state of matter from your observations? How did the results of the demonstration compare with your prediction? If your prediction differed from the results, record why you think they were different.

Communicate

With the class, discuss the results of the demonstration and your conclusions about the states of matter you observed.

- Come to an agreement about how the shape and volume of the different states of matter you observed changed because of the container.

- Develop a statement about how each state of matter can be described by its shape and volume.

How Is One State of Matter Different From Another?

The word **macroscopic** is used to describe observations that you can see with your unaided eye. In the demonstration, you observed the three states of matter.

The wooden dowel represented the **solid** state of matter. A solid maintains its shape and volume regardless of its container. Its shape and volume do not change whether it is in a bottle, a beaker, a bowl, or any other container.

Water from the faucet represented the **liquid** state of matter. A substance in the liquid state does not change its volume, but its shape can change. A liquid takes on the shape of its container. Whether in a bottle, a beaker, or a bowl, the water will have the same volume. However, its shape is the same as its container. This is true for all liquids.

---

macroscopic: a word used to describe an observation that can be seen by the unaided eye.

solid: matter that has a definite shape and volume and an organized arrangement of particles that remain very close together and vibrate slowly.

liquid: matter that has a definite volume but not a definite shape. A liquid takes the shape of its container. The particles remain close together and slide past each other in a fluid motion.

gas: a gas: matter that has no definite shape or volume. A gas takes the shape and volume of its container. The particles are far apart and move rapidly and randomly.

microscopic: things you cannot see with your unaided eyes.

atom: the basic building block of matter.

element: the simplest type of substance made up of identical atoms.

molecule: a combination of two or more atoms.

particle: atoms and molecules that make up substances.

thermal energy: the energy of motion of the particles of matter in a substance.

heat: the transfer of thermal energy from a warmer substance to a cooler one.

The air in the bottle represented the **gas** state of matter. Neither the volume nor the shape of a gas is constant. At first, the volume and shape of the air were determined by the bottle. A gas must be enclosed in some kind of closed container to have a measureable volume or a definite shape. When the bottle of air was emptied into the beaker, you could not see what happened to the air. The air took the volume and shape of its new container—the room, not the beaker. Some of it may have gone into the beaker, but you could not tell because you could not see the air.

What is it that makes one state of matter different from another? The answer has to do with the structure of matter that you cannot see with your unaided eyes. Characteristics you cannot see with your unaided eye are called **microscopic** characteristics. All matter is made up of very small particles. The building blocks of matter are known as **atoms**. An atom is so small that trillions of atoms can fit on the head of a pin. You cannot see an atom.

The simplest type of substance made up of identical atoms is called an **element**. Hydrogen, oxygen, and helium are some elements with which you may be familiar. There are over 100 known elements.

Atoms of different elements can combine to form a variety of substances. A combination of at least two atoms can form a **molecule**. Substances such as water are made up of individual molecules. Each water molecule consists of two atoms of hydrogen and one atom of oxygen.

The atoms and molecules of substances are generally known as **particles** of matter. The particles within a substance are held together by forces of attraction. In other words, they are pulled together. The strength of the forces between them depends on the energy they have. Energy exists in many forms. Some objects have energy because they are moving. Other objects have stored energy in them. The energy of the motion of the particles in a sample of matter is known as **thermal energy**.

Thermal energy can be transferred from one sample of matter to another as **heat**. When you heat a sample, you increase the thermal energy of its particles. When a sample cools, the thermal energy of its particles decreases. How does this affect the state of matter? To figure it out, consider water as an example.

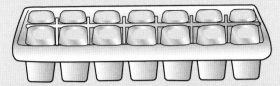

When the temperature of liquid water reaches the freezing temperature, it changes from liquid to a solid.

You may have made ice cubes in a freezer. The ice cubes are water's solid state. The particles in the ice cubes barely move. They can only vibrate in place. The force of attraction between the particles is strong, and they are held together. They retain a constant shape and volume.

Suppose you place the ice cubes in a pot on a stove. As you heat the ice, you transfer thermal energy to the water molecules. This causes the molecules to vibrate faster and faster. Their energy of motion increases. **Temperature** is a measure of the average speed of the molecules. The temperature of the ice cubes increases as they are heated.

At a certain temperature, the molecules become so energetic that they overcome the forces of attraction between them. The solid ice becomes liquid water. The particles of the liquid are still strongly attracted to one another, but they are not held as tightly together as those in the solid. Now they are free to flow smoothly past one another.

The temperature at which a solid changes into a liquid is known as the **melting point** of a substance. The melting point of water is 0°C (32°F). The process of melting occurs at the melting point. Once a substance reaches the melting point, it continues to absorb energy. However, the temperature does not change. The increased energy is used to overcome the forces of attraction. Once the solid is completely changed into a liquid, any additional energy causes the temperature to start rising again.

If you continue to heat the liquid water, the molecules will move even faster. At a certain temperature, the molecules become so energetic that the forces of attraction can no longer hold the molecules together. The liquid changes into a gas. The gaseous state of water formed in this way is known as steam. The temperature at which a liquid changes into a gas is known as the **boiling point**. The boiling point of water is 100°C (212°F). The process of boiling occurs at the boiling point.

When the temperature of ice reaches the melting point, ice changes from a solid to a liquid.

temperature: a measure of the averge speed of the particles of matter. Temperature changes as the particles move faster (warmer) or slower (colder).

melting point: the temperature at which a solid changes to a liquid.

boiling point: the temperature at which a liquid changes to a gas.

When water becomes hot enough, it changes from a liquid to a gas.

evaporation: a change from a liquid to a gas at a temperature that is lower than the boiling point.

condensation: the process in which a gas cools to form a liquid.

freezing: the process in which a liquid cools to form a solid.

freezing point: the temperature at which a liquid turns into a solid.

sublimation: the process of a substance changing directly from a solid to a gas.

You might know that a puddle of water can slowly disappear throughout the day. The water does not actually disappear, however. The liquid water in the puddle changes into a gas in the air without boiling.

A change from a liquid to a gas at a temperature that is lower than the boiling point is known as **evaporation**.

A change from one state of matter to another is known as a change of state. The changes of state can be reversed by cooling a substance. When a substance cools, thermal energy is transferred out of it. When a gas loses energy, the particles slow down and stay closer together. When the particles slow down enough so that the forces of attraction can hold them together, the gas changes into a liquid. The process in which a gas cools to form a liquid is known as **condensation**. The temperature at which a gas condenses is the same as the boiling point.

If the liquid cools, the particles slow down even further. When the particles slow down enough, the forces of attraction between them can hold them tightly enough to form a solid. The process in which a liquid cools to form a solid is known as **freezing**. The temperature at which a liquid freezes is the same as the temperature at which a solid changes into a liquid. This temperature is called the **freezing point**.

Generally, substances change from solid to liquid to gas, or they change from gas to liquid to solid. Some substances, however, can change directly from a solid to a gas in a process known as **sublimation**. The solid ice in a comet, for example, changes into a gas when the comet travels near the Sun. This sublimation forms a streak behind the comet that people on Earth can see.

The tail of a comet is the sublimation of ice to gas.

Stop and Think

1. List three solids not discussed in this section. How do you know they are solids? Discuss the characteristics that indicate they are solids.

2. List three liquids not discussed in this section. How do you know they are liquids? Discuss the characteristics that indicate they are liquids.

3. List three gases not discussed in this section. How do you know they are gases? Discuss the characteristics that indicate they are gases.

4. List two characteristics that solids, liquids, and gases have in common.

Conference

To understand the differences between the particles in solids, liquids, and gases, study the three diagrams below. In these diagrams, each small circle represents one particle. In general, matter can exist in three states: the solid state, the liquid state, and the gas state. Each of these diagrams represents one of these states of matter. Discuss the diagrams in your group and come to an agreement about which state of matter each diagram represents. Use evidence from the demonstrations and your reading.

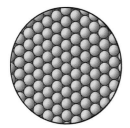
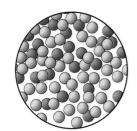
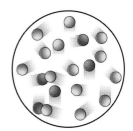

You have read about particles of matter and the forces of attraction between them. You know some of the characteristics of states of matter. You should now have more of an idea of what air looks like. When you began this Unit, you sketched what you thought air looks like if seen through a powerful tool.

Most of your sketches were probably like one of these.

Now that you have more information about states of matter, discuss the pictures with your group. Which of the pictures do you think is more accurate, based on what you now know about air? Use evidence from the demonstrations and your reading.

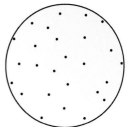

How do you see air?

Reflect

1. When workers make gold bars, they must first melt the gold by heating it to a very high temperature. Describe what is happening to the particles that make up the gold when it is melted. In your answer, use the terms: states of matter and forces of attraction.

2. You put mothballs in a closet and leave them for a long time. Mothballs are made of a solid chemical substance called camphor and are used to keep moths out of clothing. They have a very strong smell. When you open the closet again, the mothballs are much smaller. You cannot find any evidence of liquid on the floor. What do you think happened to the mothballs? Why are they smaller?

What Is the Fourth State of Matter?

plasma: a state of matter that forms from gases at very high temperatures.

You have investigated three states of matter: solids, liquids, and gases. Almost all the matter on Earth is in a solid, liquid, or gas state. But scientists have studied the universe and found another type of matter that is rare on Earth. Scientists call this state of matter **plasma**. Plasma is closely related to gases and forms from gases only at very high temperatures. Ninety-nine percent of all the matter that can be observed in the universe is plasma. At extremely high temperatures, such as those on the Sun and other stars, matter exists as plasma. On Earth, plasma exists naturally only in the outer atmosphere and is responsible for the Aurora Borealis (Northern Lights) that can be seen in the sky in Earth's Northern Hemisphere. Through technology, scientists have developed "cool" plasma to make neon signs, fluorescent lights, and plasma (television and computer) displays.

The Aurora Borealis is an example of plasma, the fourth state of matter.

Model and Simulate

States of Matter

The demonstrations you observed and the reading you did provided information to help you describe the characteristics of states of matter. Now you will design and run a simulation to show how the molecules are arranged and move in solids, liquids, and gases. In your simulation, 12 students will use their bodies as model particles. They will simulate the arrangement and motion of particles in solids, liquids, and gases, and they will stay within a "container," a designated area on the floor.

Plan Your Simulations

1. Your goal is to arrange 12 classmates in a "container" and have them simulate the arrangement and motion of particles in solids, liquids, and gases. Agree about how you want to arrange and move your student "particles" for each state of matter—solid, liquid, and gas. The diagrams you analyzed, the demonstrations you observed, and your class discussions should help you as you plan.

2. With your group, write detailed instructions stating how the students should arrange themselves and how they will move when they simulate each state.

Run Your Simulation

When everyone has finished writing their simulation plans, 12 classmates will run each simulation. When it is your group's turn, read your instructions to the simulators. They will do what your instructions say.

When you observe the students running your simulation, pay attention to exactly how they are carrying out your directions. Note any differences in what you think you wrote and how the students are following your plan. Pay attention to what the students find simple and what they find more difficult. Also pay attention to how the simulation is similar to, or different from, the information you read earlier.

When it is time for your group to act as model particles in another group's simulation, follow the directions in their simulation plan as exactly as you can.

After the simulations are run, compare what you think you wrote in your simulation to what actually happened during the simulations. Compare the simulations run from your instructions to other simulations. Identify places where your simulation plan needs to be more specific or accurate.

Communicate

As a class, discuss the accuracy of the simulations. Use your notes to discuss how each simulation matched the information you read on particle arrangement and movement. How did each simulation differ from what you read and understood about characteristics of states of matter? How could you rewrite each simulation plan so that it is more accurate?

Together, write a simulation plan that accurately shows the arrangement and movement of particles in each of the states of matter you studied. Check to see that all the directions make sense. Come to an agreement about particle arrangement and movement for each of the states of matter.

Characteristics of the States of Matter

In class, you observed the characteristics of model particles in three different states of matter by observing a simulation of how the particles are arranged and how they behave.

When your classmates were simulating molecules in the solid state, they

- were lined up orderly;
- were closely packed together;
- moved a little bit, but very slowly (vibrated, rocked back and forth); and
- could not move to a different location in the container.

When your classmates simulated molecules in the liquid state, they

- were close together but randomly arranged;
- moved slowly but randomly about the "container"; and
- slid past one another.

When your classmates simulated molecules in the gas state, they

- were spread as far apart as possible within the container;
- were randomly arranged; and
- moved rapidly and randomly, bumping gently into one another.

Think about the air you investigated. Air is a gas. You are already familiar with the properties of some gases. When a balloon is filled with a gas such as helium, the balloon looks round. The gas inside the balloon takes the shape of its container. You could measure the balloon and determine the volume of gas inside. If you pop the balloon, the gas rushes out, and the balloon deflates. A gas cannot keep its shape without being in a container. When the balloon is popped and the gas is released, the gas particles move farther and farther apart until they are prevented from moving any farther apart by another container, such as the walls of a room, or until they reach a point where they are equally spread apart. When this happens, the gas particles continue to move quickly but will stay far apart.

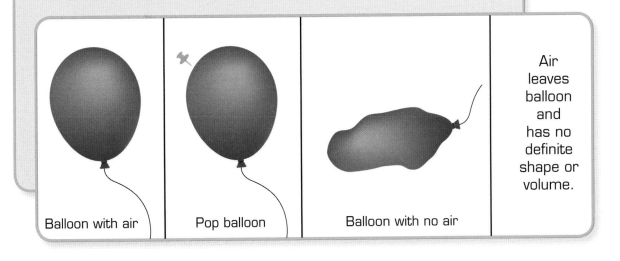

Air leaves balloon and has no definite shape or volume.

Balloon with air | Pop balloon | Balloon with no air

Reflect

You now know how the particles of a solid, liquid, and gas are arranged and how they move. Use what you know about these states of matter to answer the following questions. Discuss the answers to the questions in class.

1. A factory located 16 km (about 10 miles) out of town releases gases into the air through its smokestack. What happens to these gases?

2. A truck on the highway 16 km (about 10 miles) out of town spills a liquid pollutant onto the roadway. This liquid changes to a gas at 26.6°C (80°F). What happens to this pollutant if the temperature outside is 7.2°C (45°F)? 32.2°C (90°F)?

3. Another truck on the same highway carries garbage. This waste releases pollutants into the air when it is burned. The truck runs off the road, spills its cargo into a ditch, and catches on fire. What happens to the particles in the garbage?

Update the *Project Board*

In this section, you explored the characteristics of solids, liquids, and gases. Use what you learned about how particles of matter are arranged and move to update the *What are we learning?* column of your *Project Board.* The demonstration, reading, and simulation are your evidence. Be sure to add this evidence to the *What is our evidence?* column. You should be coming to a better understanding of what air is, but you probably still have some questions and investigations you would like to carry out. Enter these in the *What do we need to investigate?* column.

What's the Point?

Matter commonly exists in three states on Earth: solid, liquid, and gas. Solids have a definite volume and definite shape that does not depend on the container. Liquids have a definite volume but not a definite shape. Liquids take on the shape of their container. Gases have no definite volume or shape. They take on the volume and shape of any container.

The arrangement and movement of particles of matter are different for different states of matter. In solids, the particles are organized, tightly packed, and vibrate slowly. The particles of a liquid are less organized than in solids and slightly farther apart. The particles can move about and slide past one another instead of just vibrating in place. In a gas, the particles have no organization and move rapidly, collide with one another, and expand to fill the available space.

The particles of matter in a substance are held together by forces of attraction. As a sample of matter gains or loses energy, the particles are held more tightly together or more loosely. As a result, the sample can change from one state to another. Matter can change from a solid to a liquid to a gas by gaining energy through heating. Matter can change from a gas to a liquid to a solid by losing energy through cooling.

More to Learn

Investigate Changes in State

A change in thermal energy can cause matter to change state. Increasing the amount of energy of the particles of matter can make a solid change to a liquid or make a liquid change to a gas. In this investigation, you will heat ice cubes on a hot plate and record the changes in temperature and make observations about the changes in state. Record all your data in the data table on a *Changes in State* page. Your teacher may run the investigation as a class demonstration.

Before you get started, set up your equipment like the equipment in the picture. Be sure you attach the clamp firmly to your thermometer, and attach the clamp to the ringstand.

Get Started

1. Place five ice cubes in a beaker. Set the beaker on the hot plate. Insert a thermometer in the ice cubes.

2. Stir the ice cubes with the stirring rod and record the temperature on your *Changes in State* page in the box for 0 min time.

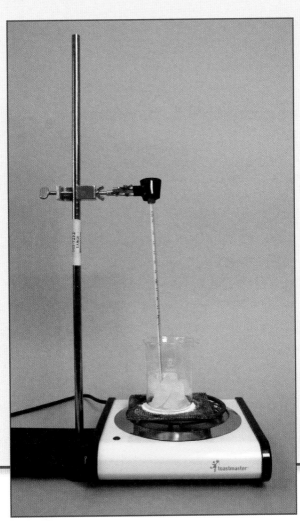

Materials

- **5 ice cubes**
- **250-mL beaker**
- **hot plate**
- **ringstand with thermometer clamp**
- **thermometer**
- **stirring rod**
- ***Changes in State* page**
- **pencil**
- **pen**
- **stopwatch**
- **safety glasses**

Be sure to wear your safety glasses. After turning on the hot plate, do not touch the hot plate or the outside of the beaker with your fingers. When stirring the ice cubes with the stirring rod, be careful that you do not break the thermometer. Leave the thermometer attached to the rod, as shown in the picture.

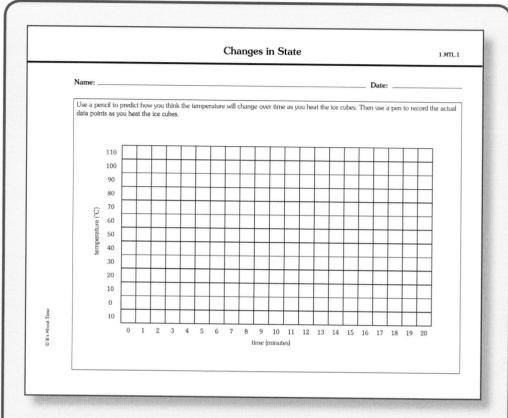

Changes in State   1.MTL.1

Name: _____   Date: _____

Use a pencil to predict how you think the temperature will change over time as you heat the ice cubes. Then use a pen to record the actual data points as you heat the ice cubes.

3. Look carefully at the graph on your *Changes in State* page. This graph will show the changes in temperature compared to the time that the ice in the beaker is on the hot plate. Make an X on the graph at time 0 min for the temperature you recorded.

4. Using a pencil, predict the shape of the graph over the time the beaker is on the hot plate. Sketch the shape you think the graph will be.

Increase the Energy

1. Turn the hot plate on medium heat.

2. While stirring the ice cubes with the stirring rod, record measurements of temperature and changes in shape or volume in the data table. Record the temperature every minute and record changes as they appear.

3. Continue heating and recording until the matter in the beaker reaches a temperature of 100°C (212°F) or your teacher instructs you to stop.

Do not touch the hot plate or the beaker with your fingers.

Analyze Your Data

One way to analyze data is to create a graph. Put a dot on your graph for the temperature at each time (0 min, 1 min, 2 min, and so on). Using a pen, connect the dots with one line, beginning at time 0 until 20 min. Place an X on the line in each place where the direction of the line changes. Then answer the following questions.

1. How does the shape of your temperature line compare to your prediction?

2. What about the two lines was the same? What was different?

3. What was the temperature at the points where you placed an X? What observations did you make about the state of matter in the beaker at each of the X's?

4. How do the points where you put the X's match up to the melting and boiling points of water?

Reflect

Discuss with your group the data you graphed.

1. What happened when the temperature began to change the first time? What do you think scientists call that point?

2. What happened when the temperature stopped changing the second time? What do you think scientists call that second point?

3. How many state changes did you observe?

4. The temperature and your observations indicate what is happening at the macroscopic level. What do you think is happening to the ice at the microscopic level? That's is, what do you think is happening to the particles of matter? Describe the motion of the molecules of water at each place where you put an X on your graph.

Communicate

Share your group's graph of the temperature data. Also share your ideas about the X points and what you think is happening to the water molecules.

Reflect

1. Some parts of the world are much warmer than others. Some days or times of the year are warmer than others. How do you think air temperature might affect air pollution?

2. How do you think heating or cooling could be used to remove pollutant gases from a factory's exhaust before that smoke leaves the smokestack? What would happen to the pollutants?

3. Scientists have found pollutants even in the ice of Antarctica. How might a warming of Earth's climate affect air pollution?

Heating Curve of Water

A type of a graph known as a heating curve can be used to trace changes of state for a specific substance. The graph below shows the heating curve of water. You can see that temperature is plotted along the vertical axis, or *y*-axis. Thermal energy is plotted along the horizontal axis, or *x*-axis. As thermal energy is added to solid ice, its temperature increases until it reaches 0°C—water's melting point. At this temperature, the graph becomes a flat line. The line shows that the temperature does not change, even though thermal energy is being absorbed. You read earlier that this thermal energy acts to overcome the forces of attraction between the water molecules. When the graph is flat at 0°C, water is changing from a solid to a liquid as thermal energy increases.

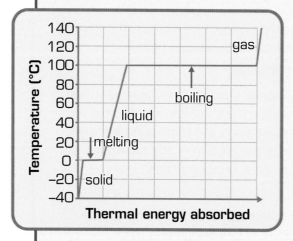

Once the sample of water is a liquid, the temperature rises again as it absorbs thermal energy. The temperature rises until it reaches 100°C—water's boiling point. Again, the graph becomes flat because the temperature stays the same, even though more thermal energy is absorbed. At this temperature, the thermal energy acts to overcome the forces of attraction holding the molecules in the liquid state.

The liquid changes to a gas. Once the sample is in the gas state, the temperature rises again as it absorbs thermal energy.

You can trace the heating curve in the opposite direction to find out what happens as gaseous water loses thermal energy to become a liquid, and liquid water loses thermal energy to become a solid.

Learning Set 1

Back to the Big Question

How can you improve air quality in your community?

To understand air quality, you must first understand that air is matter and that samples of matter can be described by their physical properties. Matter is one of the many words that have a specific meaning in science. A person may say that a bottle of soda is empty or that a bus is empty. Even though the bottle does not have any soda in it or the bus has no passengers in it, neither object is "empty" in a scientific sense—they still contain air.

When you investigated whether air has volume, you started with a cup that looked empty. From your investigations, you determined that the cup was not really empty; it contained air. Then, when water entered the cup, it pushed out the air and occupied the space the air had initially taken. In this way, you were able to conclude that air has volume.

Then you observed a demonstration with a deflated ball. When air was added to the ball, the total mass of the ball increased. After observing that, you were able to conclude that air has mass.

Everything on Earth is matter—air, water, soil, and all living things.

Because air has volume and mass, air is matter. You read about matter being made up of particles. These particles may be packed tightly together or spread far apart. Because air is matter, air is also made up of particles. Air can be described as a gas because of the arrangement and motion of its particles. The motion and arrangement of the particles of matter determines the state of matter.

Update Your Sketch

What Does Air Look Like?

In your first sketch of good-quality air, you may have sketched air as an empty space because you cannot see air. After your investigations and readings, how would you now sketch good air?

Again, imagine you had a very powerful tool and that you could use it to look at samples of air. What do you now think good-quality air would look like?

Using what you know about air, update your sketch of good-quality air. Sketch your picture using as much detail as you can. Use a new *Air Quality* page for your sketch. Be prepared to describe what you included in your sketch and why you chose to include those specific details.

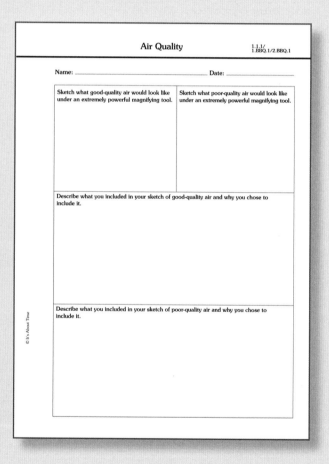

Conference

In your group, discuss what you now think good-quality air looks like. Share and discuss your sketch and the descriptions of what you included in your sketch. Compare your new sketch with the first one you completed earlier in the Unit. How do they differ? What things does your new sketch include that your first sketch did not include?

Communicate

Share your sketches of air with the class. Compare them to the sketches of others in the class. As a class, come to an agreement about what good-quality air would look like under an extremely powerful magnifying tool.

Revise Your Explanation

As a class, revise your claim and explanation of air as matter. Be specific about the type of matter air is. Make your claim based on the results of the investigations and demonstration, your class's previous explanations about whether air has volume and mass, and other class discussions. Then identify the evidence and science knowledge that support your claim. The results from investigations and demonstrations are your evidence. Then, as a class, develop a new statement that connects the evidence and science knowledge to your claim. This is your explanation.

Communicate

Share Your Explanations

When everyone is finished, you will share your explanations with the class. As each group shares theirs, record the explanation. You might also create a poster for the classroom that has a full set of explanations on it.

Revise Your Explanation

As a class, develop a class claim. Be sure to identify the supporting evidence and science knowledge. The results from investigations and demonstrations and your class discussions are your evidence. Then develop an explanation statement that connects the evidence and science knowledge to the claim in a way that convinces others that the claim is correct.

Reflect

Work with your group to answer the following questions. Be prepared to share your answers with the class.

1. Look back at the pictures from the beginning of this *Learning Set*. You now know that air is matter in the gas state. Use what you know to critique your decisions about which pictures represent sources that improve air quality. Which of your decisions would you now change? Support your answer with evidence.

2. Use what you know to critique your decisions about which pictures represent sources that worsen air quality. Which of your decisions would you now change? Support your answer with evidence.

3. Which of the pictures remind you of scenes in your community? Why?

4. What new questions do you have about air now that you know it is matter in the gas state?

5. Think about air as matter with volume and mass. What new questions do you have about air pollution?

6. Think about the characteristics of the different states of matter and how they are affected by temperature. What new ideas and questions do you have about managing air pollution in your community?

Update the *Project Board*

In this *Learning Set,* you investigated air to determine if it is matter. You looked at two characteristics of matter—volume and mass. You also investigated three different states of matter, how the particles in them move, and how the states of matter are related. Now it is time to update the *Project Board*. Add to the *What are we learning?* column what you have learned about air. Be sure to add your evidence to the *What is our evidence?* column to support your new knowledge. Record in the *What do we think we know?* column anything you now think you know about air pollution and about air pollution in your community. Record questions you have about air, about air quality in your community, and about managing air quality in your community in the *What do we need to investigate?* column.

What items in this picture have volume and mass?

Learning Set 2

What Is in Air?

To evaluate air quality in your community and suggest ways to improve it, you will need to know what *is in* air. You know that air is a gas with volume and mass. Volume and mass are properties of all matter. But what exactly is air made of—just one or more than one substance?

You probably already know that oxygen is in air. However, is good-quality air made up of only oxygen, or are air and oxygen different substances?

Can you tell what air contains just by looking at it?

2.1 Understand the Question

What Is in Air?

Get Started

Observe

You will observe a video that shows two stoppered test tubes. One test tube contains air. The other test tube contains pure oxygen. A glowing splint will be put into the test tubes. In this video, you will be observing the properties of two substances. Both substances are gases. The way a gas reacts with a glowing splint is one property of a gas. Pay close attention to what happens to the glowing splint in each of the test tubes. Record what happens to the splint.

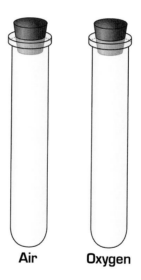

Air   Oxygen

Communicate

Share Your Observations

What happened to each splint in the video? For example, did the splint go out, did the splint burst into flames, or did nothing happen? How do your observations help you compare air and oxygen? Think about how the demonstration in the video provides evidence about what makes up air. Share your ideas about how you might describe the gas in the test tube with air. As you listen to the ideas of others, decide if you agree with what is being presented. If you do not agree with a group's idea or supporting statement, ask questions or offer advice.

Mixtures

You may have thought that air and oxygen were the same thing. The results of the test tube demonstration show that the splint reacted differently in oxygen alone than in air. Therefore, it seems that air must be more than oxygen alone. Oxygen is an example of a **pure substance**. A pure substance is made up of only one type of particle. Oxygen is made up of only oxygen atoms. Water is a pure substance made up of only water molecules.

Based on your observations, air appears to be a **mixture** rather than a pure substance. A mixture is a combination of different substances. In a mixture, the substances themselves do not change when they are combined. Instead, they retain their individual properties, and they can be separated from one another.

There are many types of mixtures in the world. You can sort them into different categories based on the way the mixture is made and how it might be separated. For example, your breakfast may contain two types of mixtures. The milk you pour on your cereal is a mixture. The milk you buy at the grocery store is a **homogeneous** mixture. A homogeneous mixture has the same amounts of its different substances in every part of it. In other words, it has the same composition throughout. The milk on one side of your bowl is not different from the milk on the other side of your bowl. All of milk is the same.

pure substance: a type of matter composed of a single type of particle.

mixture: two or more substances combined such that each substance may retain its own identity.

homogeneous: any mixture that has a uniform composition of substances.

Your breakfast cereal of strawberries, cornflakes, and blueberries is a heterogeneous mixture. The milk you put on your cereal is a homogeneous mixture.

heterogeneous: a mixture that varies in composition from one part to another.

Your cereal with strawberries, cornflakes, and blueberries is another type of mixture, called a **heterogeneous** mixture. A heterogeneous mixture does not have the same composition throughout. The number of blueberries in each spoonful will likely vary from spoonful to spoonful. You can usually tell by looking at a mixture whether it is heterogeneous or homogeneous.

The three states of matter you observed in *Learning Set 1*—solid, liquid, and gas—can combine to form mixtures. These mixtures can be heterogeneous or homogeneous. For example, if you place a spoonful of sand (a solid) in a glass of water (a liquid) and stir, the sand will sink to the bottom. This is a heterogeneous mixture of a solid and a liquid. The water at the bottom of the cup has more sand than the water at the top. However, if you place table salt in water and stir, the salt mixes with the water and forms a homogeneous mixture called salt water. Every spoonful of the mixture contains the same amount of salt and water.

Salt and water make a homogenous mixture. Sand and water make a heterogeneous mixture.

Reflect

You observed two test tubes, one containing air and one containing pure oxygen. You also read about different kinds of mixtures. With your group, answer the following questions. Be prepared to share your answers with the class.

1. List two homogeneous mixtures of liquids in liquids. Present your reasoning to support why you think the mixtures are homogeneous.

2. List two heterogeneous mixtures of solids in solids. Present your reasoning to support why you think the mixtures are heterogeneous.

3. Do you think clean air is a homogenous or heterogeneous mixture? What evidence do you have for your answer? How do you think you could find out if your answer is correct?

Predict

What substances are in air? Everyone probably agrees that oxygen is in air. It is important to think about what other gases, liquids, or solids might also be in the mixture called air. On your *Substances in Air* page, make a list of the substances you think are present in air. Use your reading and the video you observed to help you.

In the first circle on your *Substances in Air* page, create a pie chart to show the **percent** composition of each substance you think is in air. Percent composition relates the amount of a substance to the amount of the entire substance. Sketch and color what you think is the amount of each substance in air. For example, if you think half of the particles in air are oxygen atoms, color one-half of the circle with one color and label it "oxygen." Add each of your substances to your pie chart, showing the percentage of each.

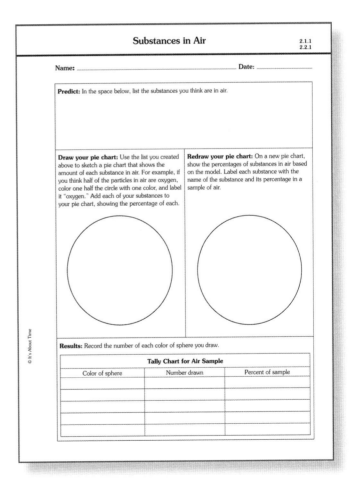

percent: out of one hundred.

Percent

A percent describes a number out of 100. You use the symbol %
to represent a percent. If 50 out of 100 people answer a survey,
50 percent (50%) of the people answered the survey. If you spend
$20 out of $100, you spent 20 percent (20%) of your money.

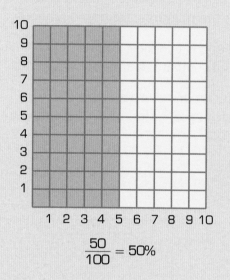

$$\frac{50}{100} = 50\%$$

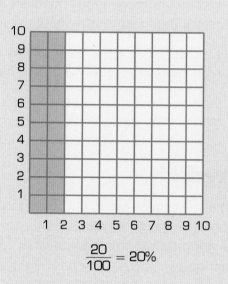

$$\frac{20}{100} = 20\%$$

Communicate

Share Your Ideas

Share with the class your ideas about what substances are in air and how
much of each substance you think is in air. Notice the similarities and
differences among your classmates' ideas. The disagreements you have
about what is in air will be good questions for the *Project Board*.
Save your *Substances in Air* page to use in the next section.

Update the *Project Board*

You now know that air is a mixture of oxygen and some other substances, but you do not know what those substances are. You also do not know yet whether air is a homogeneous or a heterogeneous mixture. In the rest of this *Learning Set*, you will be learning more about what is in air. But first, you will update the *Project Board*. In the *What do we think we know?* column, list what you think you know about what substances are in air. In the *What do we need to investigate?* column, list questions you need to investigate in order to fully understand what is in air. Your class probably had many disagreements about what is in air and how much of each substance is in air. Together with your class, formulate questions that you need to answer to come to agreement.

What's the Point?

A pure substance is made up of only one type of matter. A mixture is a combination of different substances. In a homogenous mixture, the substances are mixed evenly throughout. In a heterogeneous mixture, the composition varies throughout.

AIR QUALITY

2.2 Explore

What Substances Make Up Air?

sampling: to choose a part to examine.

sample: a small part of something or one of the many things in a set.

representative: typical or similar to, when referring to sampling.

One of the ways scientists learn about the composition of a substance is by **sampling** it. Sampling means selecting out a part to examine. A **sample** is a small part of something that can be used as an example of the whole thing. The best samples are **representative** of the whole. A sample is representative when it is similar to, or typical of, the whole.

If you wanted to find out how many yellow flowers were in this field, you would not count all the flowers. Instead, you would estimate. You would choose one part of the field and count the yellow flowers in that part of the field. From that, you would estimate how many yellow flowers are in the entire field.

To help you understand what substances are in air and how much of each substance is in air, you will begin this section by examining a container of spheres. The collection of spheres represents a sample of air. Then you will read about the different substances. There are a lot of some substances in air. There is only a very small amount of other substances. Whether there is a lot or a little, each substance in air plays an important role in the environment. Learning about the substances in air will help you understand how air becomes polluted. It will also help you identify how to improve the quality of the air in your community.

Investigate

What Is in Air?

You will use a container with 100 spheres in it to represent a sample of dry air. Each sphere represents one particle in the sample of air. Each color represents one substance in clean, dry air. Dry air does not contain water. Students in the class will take turns choosing a sphere from the container, and you will keep track of how many spheres of each color are in the sample.

Procedure

1. You will use your *Substances in Air* page. You have already recorded a prediction about what substances are in air. Now you will be keeping a tally on the same page of what substances are in the sample of air. A tally is a record of your count.

2. One by one, students will walk to the container that contains the model air sample, and choose a sphere. When it is your turn, choose your sphere and call out its color to the class. When a sphere is chosen and its color is announced, add a tally mark to the table at the bottom of your *Substances in Air* page. You will have to pay very careful attention to keep an accurate record.

3. Record the tallies for each color after 10, 25, and 50 spheres have been chosen. Calculate the percentage of the different colors in each case. To calculate the percentages, you can multiply the number for each color by 10 after 10 spheres have been chosen; by 4 after 25 spheres; and 2 after 50 spheres.

   These calculations are based on the following equations:

   $$\frac{x}{10} = \frac{x \times 10}{10 \times 10} = \frac{x \times 10}{100}$$

   $$\frac{x}{25} = \frac{x \times 4}{25 \times 4} = \frac{x \times 4}{100}$$

   $$\frac{x}{50} = \frac{x \times 2}{50 \times 2} = \frac{x \times 2}{100}$$

4. Continue until all the spheres are counted. You should have 100 tally marks in your table.

5. Since you began with 100 spheres, the final number of each color sphere is the percent of that substance's particles in the sample. Record the percent of each substance on your *Substances in Air* page. Then, sketch a new pie chart to show the percent of the different substances in air.

Analyze Your Data

Now that you know the percent composition for several substances in air, think about which substances the different spheres might represent. In your group, answer these questions. Be prepared to share your answers with the class:

1. How many different substances did you find in this sample of air? How did your actual results compare to your prediction?

2. How did the percentages of the colors in the sample compare to your prediction?

3. One of the colors in this sample represents oxygen. Which color do you think it is? Why do you think that?

4. What substances do you think the other colors represent? What information are you using to reach those conclusions?

Reflect

Discuss the answers to the following questions with your group. Be prepared to share them with the class.

1. After your discussion, what substances do you now think the three colors represent? Why?

2. Is a large sample more representative of the whole than a small sample? What evidence from your investigation do you have to support your answer?

What's the Point?

A sample is a portion of a whole substance that can be used to examine the properties of the substance. If the sample is representative of the whole substance, its properties will be very close to the properties of the whole substance. The composition of air can be examined by analyzing the numbers and kinds of particles in a sample.

2.3 Read

Some of the Substances of Air

In the 1700s, chemists were asking the same question as you: *What is air made of?* Like you, they found it a difficult question to answer, because you cannot easily see the particles in air. Chemists at that time wondered whether air was a pure substance made up of a single element or a mixture of different elements. For many centuries, people thought air was a single element. Scientists could not imagine how anything as basic as air could be made up of many different elements.

In 1771, an English chemist named Joseph Priestley came up with an experiment to investigate the composition of air. Priestley placed a glass jar over a candle. He observed that the flame slowly died out. Priestley reasoned that there must be something in air that is necessary to keep the flame burning. Because of the glass jar, that substance was present in a limited amount. When it was used up, the candle went out.

 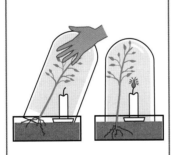 

Priestley used a candle, a plant, and a mouse to discover that plants could change the composition of air. Air, therefore, must be a mixture, because the composition of a single element does not change.

Priestley then placed a sprig of mint under the jar. Mint is a type of plant. After a few days, he lit the candle again. He was able to light the candle in the closed jar by focusing light from the Sun with a mirror onto the wick of the candle. The candle burned for a while. The mint must have produced the substance needed for burning.

Priestley went on to extend the experiment, using a mouse. He placed a mouse under the same glass jar with and without the sprig of mint. He observed that the mouse could not survive without the plant. Again, Priestley recognized that the plant must produce a substance that the mouse needed to survive.

Through his experiment, Priestley showed two very interesting things. First, the plant changed the composition of the air under the glass jar. This could not happen if air were made up of a single element. Instead, air must be a mixture, with a composition that can change. Second, plants must produce a substance that is needed not only for objects to burn, but also for living things to survive.

Oxygen

So what is the mystery substance produced by plants? It is oxygen. In your sample, the red spheres represent oxygen molecules. There are 21 red spheres out of the 100 spheres in the sample. That means that 21 percent of the sample is made up of oxygen. This result is representative of real air. Oxygen makes up about 21 percent of a sample of dry air.

chemical symbol: a one- or two-letter shorthand notation for describing a chemical element.

Oxygen is an element. Recall that an element is a pure substance made up of the same type of atoms. The element oxygen is made up of oxygen atoms. All elements are described by a **chemical symbol** made up of one or two letters. The chemical symbol for oxygen is O. The chemical symbol is usually based on the English name of the element, or its Latin or Greek origins. When an element is described, the chemical symbol is sometimes shown in parentheses after the name. Oxygen is in the air in molecules, and molecules of oxygen are made up of two oxygen atoms.

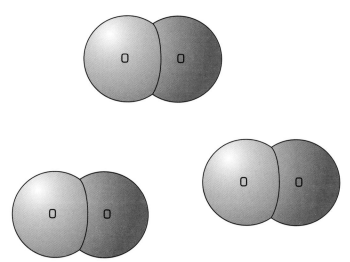

Each oxygen molecule is made up of two oxygen atoms.

At room temperature, oxygen is a colorless, odorless gas. Liquid and solid oxygen have a pale blue color. Oxygen is not only found in Earth's air, it is also found throughout the solar system. It is the third most abundant element in the Sun, and a small amount of oxygen surrounds Mars.

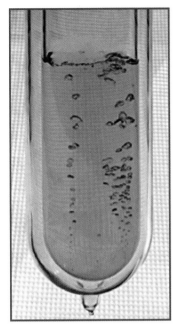

Liquid oxygen is pale blue.

Green plants on Earth produce oxygen in a process known as **photosynthesis**. During photosynthesis, green plants use energy from sunlight to make food in the form of sugar. Oxygen is released during the process.

Living things on Earth need oxygen to survive. The cells of living things use oxygen to release the energy stored in food. They use this energy to support their life processes. In this way, oxygen is an important link between plants and other living things in an ecosystem.

Now you can understand what happened in Priestley's experiment. Objects, such as the candle, need oxygen to burn. Living things, such as the mouse, need oxygen to survive. When placed under the glass jar alone, the candle and the mouse used up the oxygen present in the air. Once the oxygen was gone, the candle could not burn, and the mouse could not survive. That is where the sprig of mint comes in. The sprig of mint produced oxygen. When it was placed under the glass, it added oxygen to the air. The oxygen produced by the sprig of mint enabled the candle to burn and the mouse to survive.

photosynthesis: the process through which green plants use the energy of sunlight to make food and oxygen.

compound: a pure substance made up of two or more different elements.

Carbon Dioxide

When living things break down food, they produce a gas called carbon dioxide. Like oxygen, carbon dioxide is a colorless, odorless gas at room temperature. Unlike oxygen, carbon dioxide is not an element. It is a compound. A **compound** is a pure substance made up of two or more different elements. Carbon dioxide is made up of molecules that each contain a carbon atom (C) and two oxygen atoms (O).

Each carbon dioxide molecule is made up of two atoms of oxygen and one atom of carbon.

AIR QUALITY

Carbon dioxide is produced when animals and plants break down food. It is then used by plants during photosynthesis. In this way, oxygen and carbon flow in a cycle between living things and the environment. The substances produced when animals and plants break down food are used by plants to make food. The substances produced by plants during photosynthesis are used by animals and plants to break down food.

None of the spheres in your model represent carbon dioxide. This is because carbon dioxide makes up only a very small part of air. Only about 0.04 percent of air is made up of carbon dioxide. However, even though air has only a very small concentration of carbon dioxide, it is an important component of air.

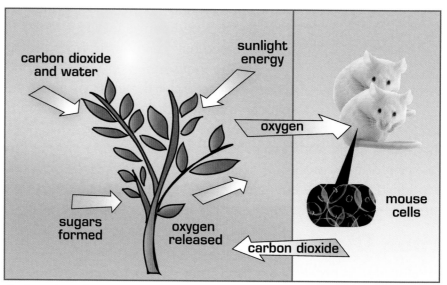

Carbon dioxide is important in the oxygen–carbon dioxide cycle that links plants and animals.

Nitrogen

The most abundant substance in air is a gas you may not have put on your list. It is the gas called nitrogen (N). In the model, nitrogen is represented by the blue spheres. Nitrogen accounts for 78 percent of dry air. Like oxygen, nitrogen is an element. Its molecules are made up of nitrogen atoms. Like oxygen, nitrogen molecules are each made up of two nitrogen atoms.

Although you breathe it in, your body cannot use nitrogen gas. You breathe nitrogen in, and you breathe it out again. The nitrogen you breathe out is the same as the nitrogen you breathe in.

Nitrogen is usually found in gas form. Nitrogen gas and nitrogen liquid are colorless and odorless.

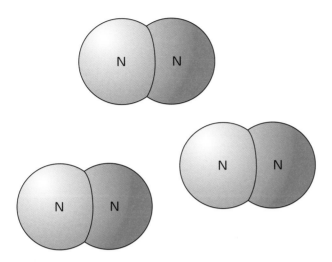

Each molecule of nitrogen is made up of two atoms.

Like oxygen and carbon, nitrogen cycles between living things and the environment. Living things need nitrogen to build many important substances, such as proteins. Even though nitrogen makes up a large part of air, it exists in a form that cannot be used by plants and animals. To be useful to plants and animals, nitrogen must be connected to other elements. Some organisms have developed a way to make nitrogen usable for plants and animals. Small organisms, called **bacteria**, some of which live in the soil, help plants by "fixing" the nitrogen so it can be used by plants. The bacteria take nitrogen from air.

bacteria: small organisms, some of which live underground on the roots of specific plants. Some bacteria can convert nitrogen into a form that plants can use.

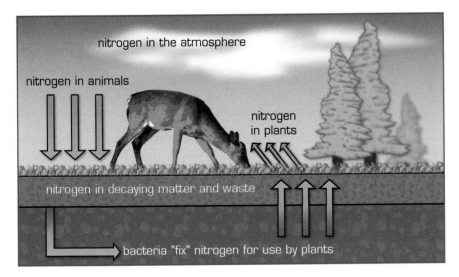

Nitrogen-fixing bacteria on the roots of plants convert nitrogen into substances that can be used by the plants.

They do not directly use the nitrogen. Instead, they convert it into substances that are carried in water and used by plants for growth. Plants that have these bacteria on their roots include peas, beans, clover, and alfalfa. Animals get the nitrogen when they eat the plants.

Animals return nitrogen to the soil through their wastes. Nitrogen is also returned to the soil when living things die and decay. Other bacteria then convert this nitrogen into the type of nitrogen found in the air so the cycle can continue.

Some nitrogen in the air is fixed during lightning strikes.

Argon and Other Gases

Nitrogen and oxygen make up about 99 percent of dry, good-quality air. Out of the 100 spheres in your model, 99 were either red or blue. So what does the silver sphere represent? It represents the other 1 percent of air. You know that a small part of that 1 percent is made up of carbon dioxide. A large part of that 1 percent of air—about 0.93 percent—is made up of argon. Argon is an element (Ar). It does not form molecules. Argon is in the air as single atoms. At room temperature, argon is a colorless, odorless gas. People use argon to fill light bulbs, to make lasers, and as insulation between window panes.

There is still another portion of air—about 0.04 percent. It consists of neon gas, helium gas, hydrogen gas, and methane gas, and it may include other substances. Water vapor, the gaseous form of water, is also found in air. You will read more about these substances later in the Unit.

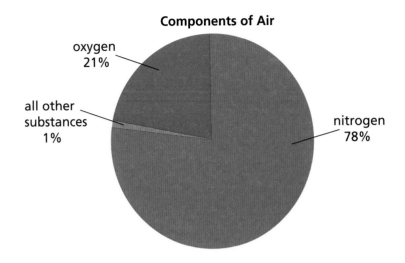

Components of Air

oxygen
21%

all other
substances
1%

nitrogen
78%

Your model of air contained three components: nitrogen, oxygen, and all other substances. Argon is a major part of the other substances.

Stop and Think

1. How do oxygen and carbon cycle between living things and the environment?

2. Nitrogen is one of the ingredients in fertilizers that you can buy to put on plants. Why do you think fertilizers contain nitrogen?

3. What does the silver sphere in your model represent? Why is there only one silver sphere?

Air Is a Solution

When you see the term *solutions*, you may think of answers to problems. In science, this term has a different meaning. A **solution** is another name for a homogeneous mixture. Recall that a homogeneous mixture is a combination of substances that are evenly spread throughout the mixture.

solution:
another term for
a homogeneous
mixture.

Solutions can be gases, liquids, or solids. Coffee, tea, soda, a brass doorknob, vinegar, and the filling in lemon cream pie are all solutions.

Air is also a solution. Air is a mixture of gases, and gases always combine to form homogeneous mixtures. If you took samples from different locations within a mixture of gases, every sample would have the same composition.

Each substance in a solution is known as a component. The component present in the greatest amount is called the **solvent**. Other components are called **solutes**. The solutes are said to be dissolved in the solvent. In salt water, salt is the solute and water is the solvent. In air, the solvent is nitrogen and all other substances are the solutes.

The amount of solute in a solvent is described as the **concentration** of the solution. A solution becomes more concentrated as more solute is added to it. For example, if you add a pinch of sugar to a glass of iced tea, the sugar dissolves in the tea. You can increase the concentration by adding more sugar. In this case, you can taste the increase in concentration. The drink becomes sweeter. If the drink becomes too sweet, you might add more tea. This makes the solution more **dilute**. A dilute solution is considered a weaker solution, whereas a **concentrated** solution is a stronger solution.

The ability of a solute to dissolve in a solvent is known as **solubility**. A solution is said to be **saturated** when no more solute can dissolve in the solvent at the given conditions. If you try to add more solute to a saturated solution, the additional solute will fall to the bottom of the container.

Not every pair of substances can form a solution. Oil and water, for example, simply do not mix. Even if you put them together and stir or shake their container, they will eventually separate into layers.

solvent: the component of a solution present in the greatest amount.

solute: the component of a solution said to dissolve in the solvent.

concentration: the amount of solute in a solvent.

dilute: to decrease the concentration of a substance in a mixture; a weaker solution.

concentrated: to increase the concentration of a substance in a mixture; a stronger solution.

solubility: the ability of a solute to dissolve in a solvent.

saturated: the condition in a solution when no more solute can dissolve in the solvent at the given conditions.

Reflect

1. The gases nitrogen, oxygen, and argon are colorless and odorless. Why would you expect this? Use what you know about air being a solution to answer this question.

2. Air is made of nitrogen, oxygen, and argon, along with some other substances. How does this list compare with the list you made at the beginning of this *Learning Set*? What, if anything, did you include in your list that turned out not to be a part of air?

3. How did the actual percentages of the gases in air compare to what you thought before you read this section?

Update the *Project Board*

In this section, you learned about four of the substances found in good-quality air—oxygen, carbon dioxide, nitrogen, and argon. Each of these gases is colorless and odorless, and to you, these gases may look the same. However, each gas plays a different role in the air mixture.

In the *What are we learning?* column, record what you now know about the properties of air, the substances in air, and air as a mixture. In the *What do we need to investigate?* column, record questions you still have about air and investigations you need to carry out to learn more about air.

What's the Point?

Good-quality air is a mixture of several pure substances that are odorless and colorless gases. Some of these gases are oxygen, carbon dioxide, nitrogen, and argon. Plants and animals require oxygen and nitrogen. Plants and animals, including humans, use oxygen to support life. Nitrogen is used to make complex molecules. The mixture of gases in air makes up a solution, which is a homogeneous mixture. In a solution such as air, the components are combined uniformly. The component present in the greatest amount is the solvent. All other components are called solutes. Solutes in air include oxygen, carbon dioxide, neon, helium, hydrogen, methane, and water vapor. The amount of solute in a solution is its concentration. The greater the amount of the solute, the greater its concentration is.

This field of soybeans can fix nitrogen in the soil.

2.4 Investigate

The Molecules in Air

Using Models to Observe Phenomena That Are too Small to See

You already know that scientists use models and simulations to explore processes and objects that are too small or too large, too fast or too slow, or too dangerous to experience easily. You will be using an atomic-model kit to explore how atoms interact with each other to form molecules. Actual atoms are so small that scientists can observe them only with

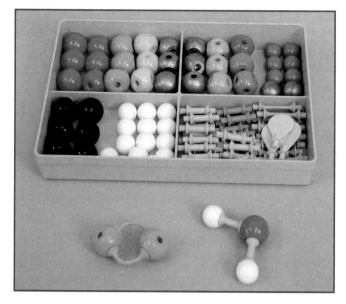

very specialized tools. Your atomic-model kit will allow you to experience the arrangements of these very small particles.

You will use small spheres with holes in them to represent atoms, and you will use gray rods to represent the connections between atoms to form molecules. Of course, real atoms do not have holes and are not connected by gray rods. However, using spheres and rods, you will be able to explore how atoms interact with each other. Understanding how atoms interact will help you understand how pollutants are formed and how, once formed, they cause problems.

In this investigation, you will use four different kinds of objects to build molecules: blue spheres with 3 holes, red spheres with 2 holes, silver spheres with no holes, and gray rods. The blue spheres represent nitrogen atoms, the red spheres represent oxygen atoms, and the silver spheres are argon atoms. The flexible gray rods will be used to connect the atoms together.

Materials

• **atomic-model kit**

• *Model Molecules* page

Investigation 1: Build Stable Molecules

A stable molecule is one with atoms that are fully connected. Stable molecules will tend to stay together. They do not easily break apart after they form. Using the atoms in your kit, you will be able to recognize stable molecules by following these two rules:

• A stable molecule will have all of its holes filled.

• Both ends of each gray rod will be attached to an atom.

Procedure

1. Using the blue, red, and silver spheres in your kit, build as many stable molecules as you can. Be sure that you follow the rules for making stable molecules. Remember that a molecule has at least 2 atoms.

2. As you complete each molecule, sketch a diagram of it on your *Model Molecules* page. Label the atoms.

Model Molecules

2.4.1/2.6.1
3.3.1/4.3.1

Name: _____ Date: _____

As you complete each molecule, sketch a diagram of it, and label the atoms. Record the molecular formula for each molecule you built next to each of your sketches. If you make more than six molecules, use a new *Model Molecules* page. Use a new *Model Molecules* page for each investigation.

Molecule 1	Molecule 2
Molecule 3	Molecule 4
Molecule 5	Molecule 6

© It's About Time

AIR QUALITY

Analyze Your Data

1. How many different stable molecules were you able to build? Why could you not build more molecules?

2. How many different molecules did you build with argon? What does this tell you about argon?

3. How many different molecules did you build that contain both nitrogen and oxygen? Why could you not build more?

molecular formula: a shorthand method of representing the types of atoms and the numbers of atoms in a molecule.

subscript: a number written below the line. In molecular formulas, it shows how many atoms of that type of element are in a molecule.

Molecular Formula

You sketched and labeled the atoms in each molecule. This is a time-consuming method of sharing your ideas with others. Scientists also sketch and label, but they do not spend time sketching and labeling common molecules like those you built. Instead, because scientists are already familiar with the form of those molecules, scientists use a shorthand method, called a **molecular formula**, to refer to those molecules.

A molecular formula requires two important pieces of information. First, it includes the chemical symbol for each element in a molecule.

Second, the molecular formula contains a number to show how many atoms of each element are in the molecule. This number is written below the line as a **subscript**. The subscript numbers in formulas show how many atoms of each type of element are in the molecule. An atom with no subscript represents one atom of that element.

As you saw in your models, an oxygen atom can be attached to another oxygen atom to make a stable molecule. The formula for an oxygen molecule is O_2. O is the chemical symbol for oxygen, and 2 (written as a subscript, below the line) shows how many atoms are connected to each other in an oxygen molecule.

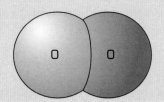

symbol for element

subscript shows the number of atoms of the element that are in a molecule

Reflect

Record the molecular formula for each molecule you built next to each of your sketches.

Investigation 2: Build Oxygen and Nitrogen Molecules

You will now use the modeling materials to build oxygen and nitrogen molecules. Make sure you follow the rules for building stable molecules when you build these molecules.

Red spheres represent oxygen atoms.

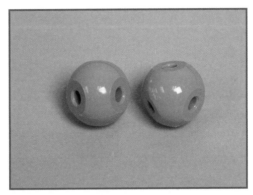

Blue spheres represent nitrogen atoms.

Procedure

1. Build a model of an oxygen molecule (O_2) and a model of a nitrogen molecule (N_2). Make sure you fill all of the holes to make the molecules stable. Have your teacher check your models after you have built them. Remember that the oxygen spheres are red, and the nitrogen spheres are blue.

2. Sketch the molecules on a *Model Molecules* page. Record the molecular formula for each molecule next to each sketch.

Analyze Your Data

1. How many oxygen atoms are in each of your oxygen molecules? How many gray rods did you use to make your oxygen molecules?

2. How many nitrogen atoms are in each of your nitrogen molecules? How many gray rods did you use to make your nitrogen molecules?

3. Why are there not more atoms in each molecule you made? Why is there a different number of gray rods in each molecule?

Investigation 3: Build More Molecules

Return to your atomic-model kit. This time you can break the rules and make molecules that have atoms with unfilled holes and unattached gray rods.

Procedure

1. Make at least 3 new molecules using N, O, and Ar. Remember, these molecules do not have to be stable.

2. Sketch the molecules on a *Model Molecules* page. Record the molecular formula for each molecule next to each sketch.

Analyze Your Data

1. Why do you think it is difficult to make a stable molecule that contains both nitrogen and oxygen?

2. Why do you think nitrogen molecules have 2 atoms? Why do you think oxygen atoms have 2 atoms?

What Do the Holes in Your Models Represent?

You have now used your atomic-model kit to build models of different molecules. You already know that the blue spheres represent nitrogen atoms, the red spheres represent oxygen atoms, the silver spheres represent argon atoms, and the gray rods represent connections between atoms. But what about the holes? What do the holes represent?

As you built molecules, you found that the holes have something to do with how atoms can combine with other atoms. In the kit you are using, the holes represent the ways atoms can connect to other atoms. An atom with holes in it forms molecules by combining with other atoms to fill the holes of all the atoms in the molecule. If all of the atoms in a molecule have their holes filled, then the molecule is stable.

You built stable oxygen molecules by using 2 rods to join one oxygen atom to another oxygen atom. You built stable nitrogen molecules by using 3 rods to join one nitrogen atom to another nitrogen atom. You know that stable molecules are molecules with all the holes filled.

But, if after combining, a hole remains in a molecule's atoms, then the molecule is **unstable**. Because it has a hole, it is incomplete. During the last investigation, you built some unstable molecules. When an unstable molecule is in a mixture, the molecule can combine with other atoms to fill the hole.

unstable: can easily change.

Reflect

With your group, answer the following questions. Be prepared to discuss your answers with the class.

1. Pollutants are very unstable molecules. Do you think N_2 and O_2 are pollutants? Use what you know about stable and unstable molecules to support your answer.

2. Do you think argon might be a pollutant? Why or why not?

3. What else do you think you need to know about atoms to know how air becomes polluted?

4. What else do you think you need to know about how atoms form molecules to know how air becomes polluted?

Update the *Project Board*

You know many things now about atoms and molecules. You also have generated questions about atoms and about molecule formation. Begin updating the *Project Board* by focusing on the *What are we learning?* column. Record in that column what you now know about atoms and molecules. Use the conclusions from building atomic models as evidence, and record your evidence in the *What is our evidence?* column.

Then think about the questions you generated about atoms and molecules. Add those questions to the *What do we need to investigate?* column.

As the class works on the class *Project Board*, remember to record the same ideas and questions on your own *Project Board*.

What's the Point?

Atoms form molecules by combining with other atoms. When a molecule contains atoms that are fully connected to each other, it is a stable molecule. In the atomic-model kit you are using, stable molecules are those for which all of the holes in the atoms are connected to other atoms by gray rods. Stable molecules tend to stay bound together and do not easily break apart.

However, when a molecule contains atoms that are not fully connected to other atoms, the molecule is unstable. In the atomic-model kit you are using, unstable molecules are those that have atoms with empty holes or gray rods that do not connect at both ends to an atom. In a mixture, unstable molecules combine to fill any holes.

Because atoms are too small to see, you are doing what scientists do when they need to explore something too small to see. You are using an atomic-model kit with pieces large enough for you to see to build models of atoms and molecules. Atoms do not look exactly like the spheres in your kit, and the connections between them do not look like the gray rods in your kit. However, with the kit, you can experience the way atoms combine with each other and what affects the combinations they make.

Scientists use molecular formulas to communicate the names of molecules to each other. A molecular formula uses letters representing the names of elements to show what kinds of atoms are in the molecule. A molecular formula contains numbers to show how many of each type of atom are in a molecule. The formula N_2 represents a molecule that includes two nitrogen atoms. This is the formula for naturally occurring nitrogen. The formula O_2 represents a molecule that includes two oxygen atoms. This is the formula for naturally occurring oxygen. Argon does not form molecules. It exists as individual atoms of argon in the air mixture.

2.5 Read

What Are Atoms, and Why Do They Join Together?

The spheres you used to model molecules help you understand that atoms join together in different ways. But why? What causes atoms to join together? To answer this question, you need to know more about the structure of an atom.

The Atomic Theory

Atoms are extremely small. There is no tool that can enable scientists to look inside individual atoms. Instead, scientists have learned about atoms through logic and by observing how atoms behave in different conditions. The understanding that scientists have about the existence of atoms and their structure is known as the **atomic theory**. The atomic theory is the current answer to the question, *What is the structure of the atom?*

In science, **theories** help scientists organize what they know about the world. Theories are the big ideas in science, often developed over long periods of time, using evidence gained through observations and experimental data.

Scientific theories are continuously studied and investigated. If new evidence is discovered that cannot be explained by the theory, the theory must be changed. A small part of the theory might be changed, or the entire theory might be replaced. The development of the atomic theory has a long and interesting history. As new experiments were designed and new technology was developed, scientists made observations that led to changes in the atomic theory. The development was not always smooth. In fact, scientists often disagreed about the structure of the atom, but they continued to gather evidence to develop a more complete description of the atom. The theory that exists today represents the best understanding at the current time. If scientists make discoveries that are not explained by the current theory, the atomic theory will change yet again.

The origin of the atomic theory can be traced back more than 2000 years ago to Greek philosophers, such as Democritus. These philosophers did not conduct controlled experiments, but instead, they used logic to reach conclusions about the natural world. Democritus, for example, imagined cutting a sample of matter in half and then cutting each half again and again.

atomic theory: the idea that all matter is formed from atoms and that atoms have a unique structure.

theory: a big idea in science, often developed over time, using evidence gained through observations and experimental data.

He argued that eventually he would get to a particle that could not be divided any further. He named this particle an "atom," which is the Greek word for "uncuttable." Democritus's idea was accepted, but it would be many years before scientists could find evidence to support his ideas.

370 B.C.E.
Democritus imagined that all matter is made of smaller particles that contain the essence of a substance and cannot be divided. He called these particles atoms.

Rutherford Model
1911 Ernest Rutherford determined that there were two areas in each atom. He called the center of the atom the nucleus, which contained positively charged particles. In the outside area, negatively charged particles moved around the nucleus.

370 B.C.E.   **1803**   **1911**   **1913**

Dalton Model
1803 John Dalton developed an atomic theory from observations of experiments he conducted. He pictured atoms as tiny, solid particles that could not be destroyed and had no internal structure.

Bohr Model
1913 Niels Bohr found that the electrons (negatively charged particles) of an atom move in orbits at a fixed distance from the nucleus.

In the early 1800s, an English scientist named John Dalton gathered evidence that supported many of Democritus's ideas. In his experiments, he combined different substances to make new substances. Each time, he measured the mass of the substances. The total mass of the substances before he mixed them with each other was always the same as the total mass of the resulting substances. From this and other experimental results, he gathered evidence that supported the beginning of the atomic theory.

Dalton's atomic theory stated the following:

- All matter consists of small particles called atoms.

- Atoms of any element are identical to each other, and the properties of each of these atoms are identical. Atoms of different elements have different sets of properties.

- Atoms cannot be destroyed. Atoms can rearrange or combine, but they are not destroyed.

- When atoms of different elements combine to form molecules, they combine in predictable ways. The number of atoms you start with equals the number of atoms you end up with.

Scientists still did not know why atoms combined in predictable ways. In 1911, the English scientist Ernest Rutherford performed experiments that helped him uncover the structure of atoms. He found that the mass of an atom is concentrated in a central part, what is now called the **nucleus**. Around the nucleus was another, less dense part of the atom. Knowing that atoms have a nucleus was the first step in understanding why atoms combine as they do. But scientists still wondered what was in that region around the nucleus.

nucleus: the center part of an atom.

Rutherford's work was followed by discoveries made by the Danish scientist Niels Bohr in 1913. Bohr investigated the space around the nucleus of an atom, and the particles that exist in that space.

How Big Is an Atom?

Some ideas in science are difficult to picture. Things that are really big or really small are often difficult to imagine. Atoms are a good example of this. They are so small, it is difficult to grasp their size. Comparing atoms to other things might help. For example, it would take about one hundred million (100,000,000) oxygen atoms to form a line one centimeter long.

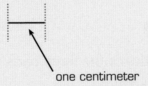

one centimeter

Compared with the size of the nucleus, the electrons of an atom are very far away. For example, if the period of this sentence were the nucleus of one type of atom, the closest electrons would be orbiting the period about 50 m (150 ft) away. There is nothing in the space between the nucleus and the electrons.

All matter is made of atoms, but most of the volume of an atom is empty space. This last fact is surprising, but it is true.

The Parts of Atoms

Through the contributions of many individuals, scientists developed an understanding of what atoms are and how they behave. In particular, they learned that while atoms are the smallest particles that have the properties of an element, atoms are made up of even smaller particles. These particles, known as **subatomic particles**, are the *proton*, *neutron*, and *electron*.

Protons and electrons are electrically charged particles. The **proton** is a subatomic particle that has a positive charge. The **electron** is a subatomic particle that has a negative charge. The **neutron** is a subatomic particle that does not have an electric charge. It is said to be electrically neutral.

Protons and neutrons are located in the nucleus of an atom. These particles make up most of the mass of the atom. The mass of a proton is about the same as the mass of a neutron. Every element has a specific number of protons in its nucleus. For example, oxygen has eight protons in its nucleus. Any atom with eight protons would have to be oxygen. The number of neutrons in the nucleus of an element may vary. Most oxygen atoms have seven neutrons, but some may have slightly more or less neutrons. You cannot tell what element an atom is just by the number of neutrons.

The mass of an electron is much less than the mass of a proton or neutron, and it would take about 2000 electrons to equal their mass. Electrons once were thought to orbit the nucleus much like planets orbit the Sun. However, scientists later found out that it is impossible to predict the exact location of an electron at any specific time. Instead, the region in which an electron is most likely to be found is described as an electron cloud.

subatomic particles: particles that make up an atom.

proton: a subatomic particle of an atom found in the nucleus. It has a positive charge.

electron: a subatomic particle of an atom found outside the nucleus. It has a negative charge.

neutron: a subatomic particle of an atom found in the nucleus. It is electrically neutral.

Stop and Think

1. Describe the characteristics of the three parts of an atom.

Charged Particles

You may be wondering what electric charge possibly has to do with the atomic theory. Quite a bit of the modern atomic theory depends on electric charge.

Now, using what you know about opposite charges, think about protons and electrons. Because they have opposite charges, protons and electrons attract one another. Protons in the nucleus and electrons outside the nucleus pull together. The force of attraction (pull) helps hold the atom together.

Investigation

Electric Charges

You read that protons and electrons are electrically charged particles. Protons have a positive charge and electrons have a negative charge. Why is it important that there are two different types of charges? You will use invisible tape to investigate what happens when charged objects are brought together.

Materials
• invisible tape

Procedure

1. Cut two strips of invisible tape about 12 cm long. Fold over a 1-cm section at one end of each strip to make a tab that you can hold.

2. Place one strip on a table with the sticky side facing down. Label the tab "B," for "bottom."

3. Place the second strip exactly on top of the first strip, sticky side down. Press it down firmly to make good contact. Label the tab "T," for "top."

4. Hold down the tab on the bottom strip and peel off the top strip. Then, with the other hand, pull off the bottom strip.

5. Hold the strips about 15 cm apart, allowing them to hang down. Slowly, bring the strips toward each other but do not let them touch.

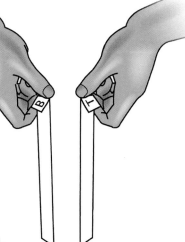

Analyze Your Data

1. What happened when you brought the strips close together?

2. What do your observations suggest about the electric charges on the two strips of tape?

3. How do you think the two strips of tape became electrically charged?

Predict

You are going to make a second set of top and bottom pieces of tape.

1. What do you think will happen if you bring two top pieces of tape together?

2. What do you think will happen if you bring two bottom pieces of tape together?

Record your predictions on a piece of paper.

Procedure

1. Make a second set of top and bottom strips as before. Be sure to label them with a "B" or a "T."

2. Bring the two top strips together without touching.

3. Bring the two bottom strips together without touching.

4. What is similar about the two top pieces of tape? The two bottom pieces?

Analyze Your Data

1. What happened when you brought the two top strips together? The bottom strips?

2. What do your observations suggest about the electric charges on the top pieces of tape? The bottom pieces?

Reflect

What test could you do to determine whether the top pieces of tape have a negative charge (more electrons) or a positive charge (less electrons). Why do you think this would work?

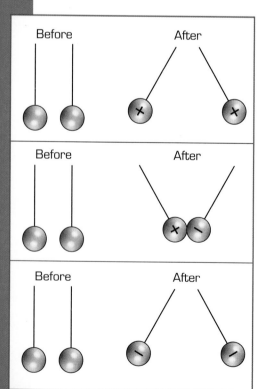

Metal spheres that have no charge, hang straight down. Spheres with opposite charges attract. Spheres with like charges repel.

Electrically Charged Particles

Perhaps you have walked across a carpet and received a "shock" by touching a metal doorknob. If so, you have experienced electric charge. Electric charge is a physical property of some objects. There are two kinds of charge—positive charge (+) or negative charge (–). Electric charges can build up on an object. This buildup of charge is known as static electricity. When the charges return to their normal, or neutral, condition, the release of charge can be experienced as a shock. The release of electric charge on a greater scale can be seen as lightning.

You may have heard the saying "opposites attract." This is true when it comes to electric charges. Opposite charges are attracted to one another. So a positive charge and a negative charge will be pulled together. Like charges repel one another. So two positive charges or two negative charges will push each other apart.

Atomic Bonding

The number of protons, neutrons, and electrons in an atom depends on the element. No two elements have the same number of protons. In a neutral atom, the number of protons is the same as the number of electrons. A carbon atom, for example, has 6 protons, 6 neutrons, and 6 electrons. An oxygen atom has 8 protons, 8 neutrons, and 8 electrons.

Atoms are most stable when they have a complete set of electrons in their outer level. For most atoms, a complete set includes eight outer electrons. One way atoms get a complete set of outer electrons is to share electrons. The attraction between atoms that share electrons is known as a **chemical bond**. Atoms in molecules are held together by chemical bonds. For now, the discussion about chemical bonds will be limited to sharing electrons. There are, however, other types of chemical bonds that do not involve sharing.

Earlier, you used your atomic-model kit to build molecules. The gray rods represented chemical bonds between atoms. You were told that most atoms are unstable and combine with other atoms to become stable. Now you know that atoms bond together to get a complete set of outer electrons.

You may have also discovered that atoms can form different numbers of bonds. In your model of the nitrogen molecule (N_2), the nitrogen atoms were connected by three gray rods. The three gray rods represent a triple bond. In a **triple bond**, two atoms share six electrons—two for each bond. In the oxygen molecules (O_2), the atoms were connected by two gray rods. These rods represent double bonds. In a **double bond**, two atoms share four electrons. Later in this unit, you will form water molecules (H_2O) by attaching the atoms by single gray rods. These rods represent single bonds. In a **single bond**, two atoms share two electrons.

chemical bond: an attraction between atoms that share electrons.

triple bond: a bond where 2 atoms share 6 electrons (3 gray rods).

double bond: a bond where 2 atoms share 4 electrons (2 gray rods).

single bond: a bond where 2 atoms share 2 electrons (1 gray rod).

Hydrogen atoms in H_2 bond to each other with a single bond. Oxygen atoms in O_2 bond to each other with a double bond. Nitrogen atoms in N_2 bond to each other with a triple bond.

Reflect

1. Models allow you to see some features of an object well, but they are not completely accurate. What is accurate about the models you made?

2. What parts of the atomic-model kit are not accurate? Identify from the reading how you know which parts are not accurate.

3. Imagine that you had to describe an atom to your friend. You need to make a comparison using the word "like." What could you compare an atom to that would help your friend better understand what you are talking about? Describe also how your comparison is incomplete.

Update the *Project Board*

On the *Project Board,* record what you now know about what matter is made of, the subatomic particles, and how atoms combine to make molecules. Record this information in the *What are we learning?* column. Be sure to record your evidence in the *What is our evidence?* column. You may have some new ideas about what additional information you need to answer the *Big Question.* Record those questions in the second column, *What do we need to investigate?*

What's the Point?

Atoms are the smallest particles of matter that have the properties of an element. Every atom of an element has the same properties and the same number of protons. Molecules are made up of two or more atoms.

Much like molecules are made up of small particles called atoms, atoms are made up of even smaller particles—protons, neutrons, and electrons. Neutrons have no charge, protons have a positive charge, and electrons have a negative charge. The opposite charges in atoms attract each other and help hold the atom together. Charges also hold molecules together.

More to Learn

Periodic Table of the Elements

By the middle of the 1800s, chemists had identified a large number of elements. To keep track of all the elements, they needed a way to sort them into categories. Chemists had observed that some elements shared similar chemical properties. They looked for a way to arrange the elements according to these properties. The chemists that are given credit for successfully grouping the elements into a pattern according to their properties are Dimitri Mendeleev and Julius Meyer. Individually, they were responsible for arranging the first version of the **Periodic Table of the Elements**.

While the first periodic table grouped the elements according to properties, years later, the arrangement also revealed information about the structure of the atoms of those elements. For example, the modern periodic table, which has been updated since Mendeleev's time, shows that the elements are arranged according to their numbers of protons.

The element with the smallest number of protons, one, is hydrogen (H). You can find hydrogen on the top row in the left column. Another gas, helium (He), with two protons, is in the same row but in the column on the right. The pattern goes on like this for the rest of the table. Each element has one more proton than the element that came before it.

Because each element has a different number of protons, the number of protons can be used to tell one element from another. The number of protons in an atom is called its **atomic number**. The atomic number of hydrogen is 1, and the atomic number of helium is 2. Each element has a unique atomic number. In the periodic table shown at the back of this book, the atomic number of each element can be found in the upper left corner of each square. Remember that the protons and neutrons make up almost all the mass of an atom. The sum of the number of protons and neutrons in an atom of an element is the element's **atomic mass**. This can be found below the chemical symbol on each square.

Periodic Table of the Elements: a table listing all the known elements and their properties.

atomic number: the number of protons in an atom's nucleus.

atomic mass: the average number of total protons and neutrons in an atom's nucleus.

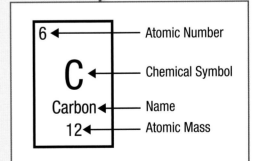

chemical family: group of elements found in a column of the periodic table. These elements exhibit similar properties.

noble gases: a family of elements with full electron energy levels. These elements do not undergo chemical reactions and are found in column 18 in the periodic table.

period: a word to describe something that repeats in a regular pattern.

In addition to being arranged in order of atomic number, the elements of the periodic table are organized into rows and columns. Each column represents a group or **chemical family**. The elements in a chemical family all have similar properties. The reason for this is that the elements in each column have the same number of outer electrons. Therefore, they are likely to behave in similar ways to become stable.

The elements in the first column of the periodic table (all the way to the left) have just one outer electron. They are very likely to combine with other atoms to become stable. On the contrary, the elements in the last column of the periodic table (all the way to the right) all have a complete set of outer electrons. Because they have a complete set of outer electrons, these elements are already stable and do not combine with other atoms. These elements are known as the **noble gases**. Notice that argon is a noble gas. In your atomic-model kit, the sphere for argon did not have any holes in it. Now you know why.

The rows of the periodic table are known as **periods**. Things that are periodic repeat in a regular pattern, such as time on a clock or ocean tides. The properties of the elements change in a pattern that repeats itself with each new row. This is how the table got its name. Mendeleev and other scientists observed periodic changes in the properties of the elements when they were arranged in rows and columns. The two rows of elements at the bottom of the periodic table, elements 57–71 (Lanthanide Series) and 89–103 (Actinide Series), actually fit into the sixth and seventh rows. They are separated from the rest of the table to make the table fit on a page. You will learn more about the periodic table later in this Unit and in future science courses.

Currently, there are more than 100 known elements. Each element has properties that make it unique. Scientists continue to search for new elements and for ways the periodic table might be improved.

Stop and Think

1. Find oxygen in the periodic table. What is its atomic number? What is the next element to the right of oxygen? How many protons does that element have?

2. Find nitrogen in the periodic table. What is its atomic number?

3. Find two other familiar elements in the periodic table. List their atomic numbers and atomic masses.

Development of the Periodic Table

Ca-40	Li-7	Cl-35
Sr-88	Na-23	Br-80
Ba-137	K-39	I-127

Numbers after the elements are atomic weights.

1829

German chemist **Johann Döbereiner** arranged the 55 known elements by atomic weight into groups of three, called a triad, based on similar properties. Döbereiner noticed that he could organize elements into groups of three in such a way that the atomic weight of one element was an average of the atomic weights of the other two elements.

English chemist **John Newlands** arranged the 56 known elements in order of increasing atomic weight. He observed similarities that repeated after each set of eight elements. As a result, he proposed the law of octaves, because an octave describes a group of eight notes in music.

1864

An octave of eight musical notes.

	F-19	Cl-35	Br-80	I-127
Li-7	Na-23	K-39	Rb-85	Cs-133
		Ca-40	Sr-88	Ba-137

Numbers after the elements are atomic weights.

1869

Russian chemist **Dmitri Mendeleev** developed a table of 63 known and predicted elements in order of atomic weight but arranged them in columns based on similar properties. He left spaces for elements that had not yet been discovered based on the properties he predicted. Mendeleev's table had columns and rows so that the properties of elements changed from left to right across a row and then repeated in a similar way in the next row.

German chemist **Lothar Meyer** also observed patterns of properties when he arranged the 56 known elements in order of atomic weight and developed his own periodic table. However, Meyer did not predict the existence of missing elements.

British chemist **Henry Moseley** determined the atomic number of each element, which is the number of protons in the nucleus. He changed the periodic table to arrange the 92 known elements in order of atomic number rather than atomic weight.

1914

Li-3		
Na-11		Cl-17
K-19	Ca-20	Br-35
	Sr-38	I-53
	Ba-56	

Numbers after the elements are atomic numbers.

Pu-94	Am-95	Cm-96	Bk-97	Cf-98
Es-99	Fm-100	Md-101	No-102	

Nine new elements discovered by Seaborg.
Numbers after the elements are atomic numbers.

1940

American chemist **Glenn Seaborg** discovered nine new elements after uranium, and his discoveries led to the current arrangement of the periodic table. He won the Nobel Prize in chemistry for his work.

2.6 Explore

The Other Components of Air

You learned that air consists of oxygen, nitrogen, and argon. It also contains very small amounts of carbon dioxide, neon, helium, hydrogen, methane, and water vapor. It may also include other substances. What are those other substances? Some of those substances are small, solid particles. In this section, you will examine some of those particles.

Particles in Air

Good-quality, clean air is a mixture of gases. But organisms and changes in nature can also cause small, solid particles to become part of the air. These particles can stay in the air because there is space between the molecules of the gases. This space leaves room for other materials to be part of the mixture. Scientists call small, solid particles in the air **particulate matter (PM)**.

particulate matter (PM): solid particles that become airborne and can be inhaled by people.

Demonstration

How Does Particulate Matter Form?

You will be examining one way particulate matter forms. Your teacher will hold a beaker above a lit candle. Watch the flame and the beaker carefully.

Procedure

1. Observe a beaker being held for 2–3 s above a lit candle. Record any changes.

2. When the beaker is moved away from the candlewick, observe and record what you see on the bottom of the beaker.

Stop and Think

1. Describe what you saw on the bottom of the beaker. What do you think caused this?

2. How do you think particulate matter gets into the air?

Formation of Particulate Matter

All air has some particulate matter. Particulate matter can be dust carried by the wind or can be the product of **combustion**, or burning. One type of particulate matter which you might be familiar with is **soot**. During combustion, a **fuel** reacts with oxygen and produces heat and light. For example, the wax in the candle was the fuel that burned in the demonstration you observed. If there is not enough oxygen available, the fuel will not burn completely, and soot is created. Soot is the particulate matter that forms as a product of combustion. You observed soot on the bottom of the beaker.

Some particulate matter is large and can easily be seen by the unaided eye or with a hand lens. Some particulate matter is so small that it can be seen only through a powerful microscope. Some areas of the country have more particulate matter in the air than other areas. The more particulate matter the air contains, the more polluted the air is. Particulate matter, such as soot, is breathed into the lungs with air.

Soot is made mostly of atoms of carbon. It may also contain hydrogen, oxygen, sulfur, and nitrogen. Soot can be like a molecule, but it is an unusual molecule. A molecule of soot can have many different sizes. It can contain from only a few carbon atoms to hundreds of carbon atoms. Remember that a molecular formula describes a molecule by showing the chemical symbol and a subscript. The subscript indicates the number of atoms of each element present in a molecule. Because the number of carbon atoms can vary in a molecule of soot, you cannot use any specific number as a subscript to describe soot. Instead, scientists use the letter x for the subscript, C_x. The C is the chemical symbol for carbon. The letter x shows that the subscript can change depending on the specific molecule. If the molecule has 2 atoms, the molecular formula becomes C_2. If the molecule has 200 atoms, the molecular formula becomes C_{200}. The x is replaced by the actual number of atoms in the molecule.

Soot is stable. It does not combine with atoms of other elements, and it does not damage plant or animal tissues. It is a pollutant, however, because the particles, when inhaled, are irritating to the lungs. Infants, older people, and people with asthma are particularly sensitive to particulate matter (PM), such as soot, in the air they breathe. Particulate matter, such as soot, may also cause cancer.

combustion: the process of burning. The reaction of a fuel with oxygen that produces light and heat.

soot: paticulate matter that is a product of combustion.

fuel: any substance that reacts with oxygen to produce light and heat.

Combustion

Combustion, also called burning, requires only fuel, oxygen, and a source of energy, such as a match, to get started. Power plants burn coal, oil, and natural gas to generate power for electricity. Even your own body uses oxygen and burns fuel (food) to release energy. The many places combustion happens include cars, trucks, buses, and airplanes. One product of combustion is particulate matter. Combustion also produces water, carbon dioxide, and small amounts of other substances, depending on what kind of substance is burned.

Combustion is an example of a change in matter. Matter can undergo two general types of changes. A **physical change** is a change in the form or appearance of matter. It does not affect the composition of the matter. When liquid water freezes into ice, for example, the state of matter changes. The solid ice looks and feels different from the liquid water. However, both the liquid and the solid ice are made up of water molecules. The composition of the matter does not change. A change of state is an example of a physical change. Bending a paper clip, tearing a sheet of paper, and crushing a sugar cube are other examples of physical changes.

A **chemical change** is a change in the composition of matter. During a chemical change, also known as a **chemical reaction**, matter changes into another type of matter. Recall that green plants make food during photosynthesis. During photosynthesis, carbon dioxide and water are changed into sugar and oxygen. Because the original substances are changed into different substances, photosynthesis is an example of a chemical reaction. The substances that enter into a chemical reaction are known as the **reactants**. The substances that are formed are known as the **products**.

Now think about the type of change that occurs during combustion. During combustion, a fuel is combined with oxygen. Substances such as carbon dioxide, water, and particulate matter (soot) are formed. Because the original substances change into different substances, combustion is an example of a chemical reaction. During combustion, a set of reactants produces a set of products.

Stop and Think

1. Think of an example in which something burns. Identify the fuel that is burned.

2. How is soot different from the other types of molecules you learned about?

physical change: a change in the form or appearance of matter, but not in its composition.

chemical change: a change in the composition, or chemical makeup, of a sample of matter. A chemical change is also known as a chemical reaction.

chemical reaction: a change in the composition, or chemical makeup, of a sample of matter. A chemical reaction is also known as a chemical change.

reactant: a substance that enters into a chemical reaction.

product: a substance that is formed by a chemical reaction.

3. What is an example of a physical change in matter? What is an example of a chemical change in matter? Why did you classify each change as you did?

Investigate: Molecules Formed During Combustion

You will use your atomic-model kit to build models of carbon dioxide (CO_2) and water (H_2O). To do this, you will have available the nitrogen, oxygen, and argon you used previously, along with spheres representing two new elements, carbon and hydrogen. The spheres representing carbon are black (like soot) and have 4 holes. The spheres representing hydrogen are white and have 1 hole.

The black spheres represent carbon atoms.

The white spheres represent hydrogen atoms.

Procedure

1. Using the materials in your kit, build a carbon dioxide molecule (CO_2). Use the gray rods to link the spheres together. Be sure that you follow the rules for making stable molecules. Remember that a molecule of CO_2 has three atoms. Use the subscript to help you determine how many of each atom of each element you have in carbon dioxide.

2. When you complete your molecule, sketch a diagram of it on a new *Model Molecules* page. Label the atoms in the molecule so you know which atoms you used.

3. Now build a water molecule (H_2O). Again, follow the rules for stable molecules. Sketch a diagram of it on your *Model Molecules* page. Label the atoms in the molecule so you know which atoms you used.

Why Are Carbon Dioxide and Water Stable Molecules?
When you worked with the models of molecules, you used gray rods and fitted them into holes in the spheres that represented atoms. The rods represented bonds between the atoms. When a sphere has all its holes filled, it is stable. Stable molecules do not easily form new molecules.

Stop and Think

1. Why do you think the water and carbon dioxide molecules are not pollutants when present in normal concentrations?

2. Of the other molecules you made, how many of those structures are stable? How do you know they are stable?

3. If you were to use your atomic-model kit to build a soot molecule, how would you build it? Why might your soot molecule look different from the soot molecules of other students?

Model Molecules

2.4.1/2.6.1
3.3.1/4.3.1

Name: _____   Date: _____

As you complete each molecule, sketch a diagram of it, and label the atoms. Record the molecular formula for each molecule you built next to each of your sketches. If you make more than six molecules, use a new *Model Molecules* page. Use a new *Model Molecules* page for each investigation.

Molecule 1	Molecule 2
Molecule 3	Molecule 4
Molecule 5	Molecule 6

© It's About Time

Update the *Project Board*

Use the *Project Board* to record what you now know about combustion and the sources of particulate matter in the *What are we learning?* column. Be sure to include the new components of air—carbon dioxide and water vapor, as well as soot. Record evidence from your investigations and reading in the *What is our evidence?* column. Now that you know about the stable molecules that are found in air, you may have questions about the unstable molecules. Some questions you might have are: Are all unstable molecules pollutants? How do they form? Include your questions in the column, *What do we need to investigate?*

What's the Point?

Air is mostly nitrogen, oxygen, and argon. These three gases make up 99.93 percent of dry air, but there are still other important components of air. Carbon dioxide, a component of the air you exhale, makes up about 0.04 percent of air. Water vapor is also present in the air you breathe in and out.

Some pollutants enter the air as a result of combustion. Combustion releases water and carbon dioxide into the atmosphere, along with soot. Water and carbon dioxide are not pollutants, but soot, a molecule made of carbon atoms, is a dangerous pollutant. Though soot is a stable molecule, the particles can be breathed in by organisms and can damage their lungs.

Even country air that looks clean contains the products of combustion and other particulate matter.

2.7 Investigate

How Much Pollution Is Combustion Causing in Your Community?

You know that combustion can create particulate matter, and that too much particulate matter in the air can damage the lungs of people and other living things. But you do not know exactly how much particulate matter is in the air. Combustion has many different sources, for example, vehicles in the streets and on the waterways use combustion to move. These vehicles usually burn oil. The heating systems of some of the buildings around you and in factories that might be in your community also rely on combustion. Buildings are usually heated by burning oil or natural gas. Sometimes they are heated by a stove that burns wood. When you light a fireplace, you are burning wood as fuel. The power plant that makes your electricity probably uses combustion to create electricity. It may burn coal, or it may burn natural gas. In addition, many different fuels can be used in combustion.

Combustion from brush fires produces particulate matter.

Almost every fuel used in combustion produces particulate matter. Some fuels, such as coal and wood, produce large amounts of particulate matter. Forest fires and large brush fires are events in which combustion gets out of control. These fires are common, particularly in California and other western states. Along with the damage to homes and forests, these fires produce a lot of particulate matter that can be carried very long distances.

Combustion from all types of vehicles produces particulate matter.

You will investigate how much particulate matter is in the air you are breathing. Later in the Unit, you will get a chance to think about how to get rid of some of that particulate matter.

Investigate: Particulate-Matter Collection

Materials
• colored index card
• white index card
• string
• scissors
• clear, wide packing tape
• hand lens
• hole punch

You will make a particulate-matter collector to examine particulate matter in the outside air. A particulate-matter collector traps the particulate matter so you can examine it.

You know that particulate matter is produced by combustion. When a fuel burns, particles are sent into the air. Other particulate matter comes from natural sources, such as dust carried by the wind.

Procedure

1. Before you build your particulate-matter collector, think about where to put your collector to measure the particulate matter in the air. As a class, discuss where there might be larger amounts of particulate matter and where there might be smaller amounts. Decide as a class where to put collectors so that you will be able to observe differences in the amount and type of particulate matter in different places.

2. Now begin working with your group. Cut a large square (4 cm, or 1.5 in., on each side) in the center of the colored index card.

3. On one side of the card, write the names of your group members (this will be the back of the card). On the other side of the card, record the exact location where you will place your collector and the start date and time of your collection.

4. Punch a hole in the top center of the card, and attach a piece of string to hang the card.

5. Cut a strip of clear, wide packing tape, and cover the back of the card so the sticky side shows through the square you cut out. Try not to touch the exposed sticky area.

6. Hang your collector.

7. Leave your collector in place for 48 h. If you can, check your collector after 24 h.

Record Your Data

1. After 48 h, collect your card. On your card, record the date and time you completed the particle collection.

2. Examine the particles trapped by your collector. It might be hard to see the particles on the tape. If so, lay a white card behind the tape to help you see the particles better.

3. Use a hand lens or microscope to examine the particles that are present. Determine the approximate size of the particles and amount of particulate matter on the card.

4. Sketch your data on paper. Try to draw the number and size of particles as accurately as possible.

Analyze Your Data

1. Look carefully at your collector. Approximately what percentage of the exposed area had particles on it? (Be careful here; insects are not particulate matter that contribute to air pollution.) Half, or 50 percent? One-quarter, or 25 percent? One-third, or 33 percent? Two-thirds, or 66 percent? Approximate as best you can.

2. Describe the types of particulates on your card. Describe what the particulate matter looks like. Use size, shape, color, and other properties you can see.

3. Which of the particles come from a particular place you can identify, and why? For example, you might have found a piece of red clay on a card that was hanging near the sports field, and maybe the field uses red clay on the running track.

4. What effect do you think wind conditions had on the particulate matter you collected on your card? Justify your answer.

5. You used a hand lens or microscope to examine your card. Do you think you were able to see all the particles trapped by the tape? Why or why not?

Communicate

Investigation Expo

You will display your particulate-matter collectors to the class in an *Investigation Expo*. Make a small poster to display along with your collector.

Include the following information on your poster:

- where you placed your collector
- your sketches of the particles on your collector
- a chart or description of your analysis of the amount and types of particulate matter you could see on your collector
- your answers to the questions on the previous page
- a short paragraph describing how your analysis of particulate matter might relate to air quality in your community

During this *Investigation Expo*, you will be walking around the room to see all the particulate-matter collectors. When you look at other groups' collectors and analyses, pay attention to the similarities and differences among them. Ask questions if you do not understand what others found or how they analyzed their data.

Reflect

1. After observing the results from other collectors, what conclusions can you draw about the overall amount of particulate matter in your community?

2. In what places is there more particulate matter? Why do you think there is more in those places?

3. What sources of particulate matter did the class identify?

4. During the Olympics in China, people wore nose and mouth masks because of high pollution. What do you think was the purpose of these masks?

5. If you were collecting particulate matter in another community, how do you think the particulate matter would be similar to and different from what you collected in the investigation? What things would make it similar? What things would make it different? Why?

6. How do you think particulate matter could be reduced in your community? What would you be willing to do?

What's the Point?

Particulate matter is created by combustion. It also comes from other sources. Too much particulate matter in the air is dangerous to the lungs of people and animals. But the amount of particulate matter in the air can be reduced. That requires identifying where it is coming from. You will spend time later in the Unit reading about how different communities have worked to reduce particulate matter in the air.

More to Learn

Did You Know That Air Contains Water?

You know water in its liquid state because you see it in rainfall, the bathtub, lakes, rivers, and oceans. Water in its solid state, called *water vapor,* is also a familiar sight in ice cubes, snow, and icicles. But water in its gas state is more difficult to detect because it is invisible. Water vapor is a colorless, odorless, and tasteless gas.

Rain is water in its liquid state.

Snow is water in its solid state.

precipitation: water that falls to Earth's surface.

You know there is water in the air because you have seen it fall as **precipitation**. Precipication is water that falls from clouds to Earth's surface as rain, snow, sleet, or hail.

The water that falls as precipitation not only waters plants, including food crops, but it also forms streams, rivers, and lakes. It eventually flows into the oceans. Precipitation cannot form without water vapor.

The air temperature can feel warmer than it really is when the air is very humid.

The measurement of the amount of water vapor in the air is called **humidity**. It may help to remember that air is a homogeneous mixture, or solution, of gases.

However, air is not an ordinary solution. Because the molecules that make up air are so far apart, they do not interact with each other. Each component behaves independently from all other components. For example, if the amount of nitrogen in air were doubled, this would have no effect on the amount of water vapor in air. At the temperatures found on Earth, water is the only component of air that can exist in all three states—solid, liquid, and gas. An increase in temperature provides more energy to the water molecules and makes them move faster. As the

Water vapor condenses into liquid water when it touches a cold windowpane.

humidity: water vapor in air.

molecules of water move faster, more of them can go into the gas state. They cannot stick together as ice or water at these higher speeds and so they become water vapor. The amount of water in air increases with temperature. As air cools in the evening, the water molecules slow down, begin to stick together, and form water droplets. You see these as dew or rain.

Scientists use a term called *relative humidity* to compare the actual amount of water vapor in the air at a given temperature with the total amount it could possibly hold. When relative humidity is 100 percent, the air holds as much water as it can. The air is said to be saturated. The point at which the air holds as much water as it can at a given temperature is called the *dew point*. Below that temperature, the water will begin to condense.

So how does water vapor get into the air? Water vapor forms when liquid water on Earth's surface evaporates, or changes from a liquid to a gas. Recall from *Learning Set 1* that evaporation occurs when particles of a liquid absorb thermal energy. They move faster and farther apart, and they enter the gas state. In the case of water on Earth's surface, that thermal energy generally comes from the Sun.

Once water vapor enters the air, it rises. As it rises, the water vapor cools. As it cools, it loses energy. Recall that when a gas loses enough energy, it changes back into a liquid in a process known as condensation.

You can probably think of many examples of water condensation. On a cold day, you can see your breath as the water vapor in your lungs becomes a fog of tiny water droplets. Some other examples are dew on a cold surface, such as a car windshield, and in the white clouds from the smokestacks of a power plant.

On a cold day, you can see your breath as the water vapor in your lungs becomes a fog of tiny water droplets.

When water vapor high up in the air condenses, it forms tiny droplets of liquid water around small particles of dust. These tiny droplets can join together until they become larger drops. Many drops together form clouds that you can see in the sky. When the drops become heavy enough, they fall to Earth's surface as precipitation.

Reflect

With your group, answer the following questions:

1. In the winter, your skin may feel dry and itchy. What is happening to make your skin dry? Use condensation or evaporation in your answer.

2. Your body cools itself by producing sweat. The sweat evaporates as it absorbs heat from the skin. Why do you think sweating cools the body more effectively when the air is dry?

3. What would happen to life on Earth if water evaporated and condensed only at temperatures not found on Earth's surface? How would this affect climate?

4. Think back to the things you listed on your air walk as factors that affected air quality. Which of the things you saw could be the result of condensation or evaporation? What would you do to find out?

Learning Set 2

Back to the Big Question

How Can You Improve Air Quality in Your Community?

In *Learning Set 2,* you investigated substances that are found in air. Although air is mostly made up of nitrogen and oxygen, it also contains smaller amounts of argon, water vapor, and carbon dioxide. These are all gases. You also read about one pollutant, soot, which is carried by air as a solid. Before moving on to learn more about air pollution, it is time to once more summarize what you know about air.

Update Your Sketch

What Does Air Look Like?

Look back at the sketch of good-quality air you made earlier, and consider the following questions:

- If your sketch of air can show only 100 molecules, how many molecules of N_2 can you draw? Of O_2? Of Ar? Of H_2O and CO_2? Of soot?

- How many total molecules would you have to draw in order to show just one molecule of CO_2?

Using what you know about air, update your sketch of good-quality air. Sketch your idea of what good-quality air would look like if you could see it through a powerful tool. Sketch your picture using as much detail as you can. Use a new *Air Quality* page for your sketch.

When you redraw your sketch of air, add in the new substances you have investigated—N_2, O_2, Ar, CO_2, and H_2O. It will be impossible to show some

Air Quality	1.1.1/ 1.BBQ.1/2.BBQ.1

Name: _____ Date: _____

Sketch what good-quality air would look like under an extremely powerful magnifying tool.	Sketch what poor-quality air would look like under an extremely powerful magnifying tool.

Describe what you included in your sketch of good-quality air and why you chose to include it.

Describe what you included in your sketch of poor-quality air and why you chose to include it.

© It's About Time

of these in the proportion in which they are found in air. However, you will need to decide how to sketch air so that your sketch somehow shows all of the components you know about. For soot in your sketch, simply use the letter C. Be prepared to describe what you included in your sketch and why you chose to include those specific things.

Conference

In your group, discuss what you now think good-quality air looks like. Share and discuss your sketch and the descriptions of what you included in your sketch. Compare your new sketch with the first one you made earlier in the Unit. How do they differ? What things does your new sketch include that your first sketch did not include?

Communicate

Share Your Ideas

Now that you and your group members have redrawn the sketches of good-quality air, discuss them and compare them with the rest of the class. Come to an agreement about what good-quality air should look like based upon the information you have so far.

Revise Your Explanation

At the end of *Learning Set 1*, your class agreed on a claim about what air is. Work with your group to revise the class claim using what you now know about atoms and molecules. Use a new *Create Your Explanation* page to record your claim. Your previous claim was a claim about air as matter. Your new claim should be specific about the types of matter that make up air. In the Evidence and Science Knowledge boxes of your page, record evidence and science knowledge that support your claim. Then write a statement that connects evidence and science knowledge to your claim. This is your explanation.

Create Your Explanation	1.3.2/2.BBQ.2/3.5.2 4.2.2/4.6.7/4.7.1/ABQ.2

Name: _____ Date: _____

Use this page to explain the lesson of your recent investigations.

Write a brief summary of the results from your investigation. You will use this summary to help you write your Explanation.

Claim – a statement of what you understand or a conclusion that you have reached from an investigation or a set of investigations.

Evidence – data collected during investigations and trends in that data.

Science knowledge – knowledge about how things work. You may have learned this through reading, talking to an expert, discussion, or other experiences.

Write your Explanation using the *Claim*, *Evidence*, and *Science knowledge*.

Communicate

Share Your Explanations

When everyone is finished, you will share your explanations with the class. As each group shares theirs, record the explanation. You might also create a poster for the classroom that has a full set of explanations on it.

Revise Your Explanation

As a class, develop a class claim. Be sure to identify the supporting evidence and science knowledge. The results from investigations and demonstrations and your class discussions are your evidence. Then develop an explanation statement that connects the evidence and science knowledge to the claim in a way that convinces others that the claim is correct.

Reflect

Work with your group to answer the following questions. Be prepared to share your answers with the class.

1. Look back at the pictures at the beginning of the Unit. Now that you know that air is composed of different substances, how have your decisions about which pictures represent sources of good air quality changed? Support your answer with evidence.

2. Again, looking at the pictures, how have your decisions about which pictures represent sources of poor air quality changed? Support your answer with evidence.

3. Which of the pictures remind you of scenes in your community? Describe where you have seen a place that is similar to the pictures.

4. What new questions do you have about air now that you know that it consists of different substances?

5. What new questions do you have about pollution and how pollution forms?

6. What new questions do you have about managing pollution in your community?

Update the *Project Board*

In this *Learning Set,* you investigated some of the gases and solids that make up air. You looked at oxygen, nitrogen, argon, carbon dioxide, water, and particulate matter. You built models of the major molecules found in air and read about argon gas and soot. You learned about the role of each in air quality. Now it is time to update the *Project Board.* Add to the *What are we learning?* column what you have learned about the composition of air. Be sure to add your evidence to the *What is our evidence?* column. Record in the *What do we think we know?* column anything you now think you know about how the composition of air affects air pollution and, particularly, air pollution in your community. Record questions you have about other substances, especially pollutants in air, how these pollutants affect air quality in your community, and how you can manage air quality in your community in the *What do we need to investigate?* column.

Learning Set 3

What Are Pollutants, and How Do They Get Into Air?

Good-quality air contains many different particles. Molecules of oxygen and nitrogen make up most of the volume of air. Very small amounts of other molecules make up the rest of air. In the spaces between these molecules can be substances that pollute the air. Particulate matter is one pollutant, but there are many more. Some pollutants are solids, such as soot, and some are gases. As you learn more about these pollutants and how they are formed, you will be able to recognize them in your community and determine how you might use your understanding of them to improve the air quality in your community.

Brush fires release soot, other particulate matter, and gases into the air.

3.1 Understand the Question

What Are the Major Pollutants in Air?

Props

• **2 microphones**

• **2 notebooks**

• **empty spray bottle**

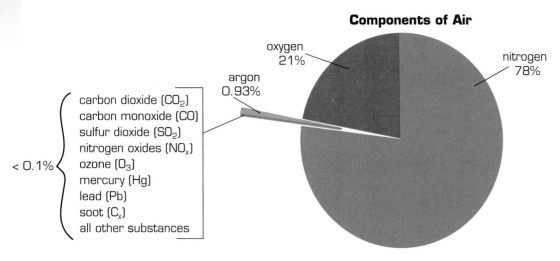

Components of Air

oxygen
21%

argon
0.93%

nitrogen
78%

carbon dioxide (CO_2)
carbon monoxide (CO)
sulfur dioxide (SO_2)
nitrogen oxides (NO_x)
< 0.1% { ozone (O_3)
mercury (Hg)
lead (Pb)
soot (C_x)
all other substances

Pollutants are less than one percent of air, but they can be very dangerous, even deadly.

Sickening Six   3.1.1

Name: _____ Date: _____

Name of Pollutant	Effects on Health	Found in Los Angeles?	Found Elsewhere?	Concentration	Formula

Even though pollutants make up only a tiny amount of the air you breathe, they can be very dangerous, even deadly. Knowing what the pollutants are and how they become part of the air is very important to identifying ways to improve air quality.

Explore

The Sickening Six

To find out what pollutants are commonly found in air, you will be meeting some pollutants in person in a short play. First, listen to the play and pay attention to the pollutants that are mentioned. Then, read the play again, record the information in your *Sickening Six* page, and answer the *Stop and Think* questions at the end.

Cast of Characters:

Susie Lung–reporter SL

Billy Wheezer–reporter BW

Sammy Soot (PM) C

Carbon Monoxide CO

Sulfur Dioxide SO_2

Nitrogen Monoxide NO

Opal Ozone O_3

Mercury Hg

Setting: In front of the **Environmental Protection Agency (EPA)** building in Los Angeles.

The air pollutants are picketing the EPA. Some carry picket signs with phrases such as: "Dirty Air: Let's Keep It That Way!" "Down with the **Clean Air Act**," and so on. TV reporters Susie Lung and Billy Wheezer are at center stage, each holding a microphone and a notebook. In turn, each pollutant comes over to be interviewed. Meanwhile, the other pollutants continue to picket in the background.

> **Environmental Protection Agency (EPA):** the government agency that protects, restores, and improves the environment to guarantee public health and environmental quality.

AIR QUALITY

Clean Air Act: the law that defines the Environmental Protection Agency's responsibilities for protecting and improving the nation's air quality.

SL   Susie: Hi! I'm Susie Lung.

BW   Billy: And I'm Billy Wheezer. We're here in Los Angeles at the Environmental Protection Agency building to cover a late-breaking story. Six of the world's worst air polluters have gathered here to picket the EPA. They're protesting the Clean Air Act.

SL   Susie: In tonight's special report, we'll give you the scoop on who these pollutants are, where they come from, and the ways they can harm people, plants, and animals.

BW   Billy: Our first interview is with Sammy Soot, also known as Particulate Matter.

C   Sammy Soot (chanting): Dust, soot, and grime. Pollution's not a crime. Soot, grime, and dust. The EPA's unjust!

SL   Susie (coughing): So—you're a part of the Matter family, Particulate Matter.

C   Sammy Soot: Yeah, that's me.

BW   Billy: You're one of those tiny bits of pollution that make air look really dirty?

C   Sammy Soot: Yeah. Most of us get into the air when stuff is burned—such as gasoline in cars and trucks, or coal in a power plant, and even wood in a wood-burning stove! And we just love to get into your eyes and make them itch and into your lungs and make you cough, and…(turns to look at picketers, who are now sitting down). Hey! Get up and march! (turns to reporters) I gotta get back to the picket line.

(Sammy Soot returns to the picket line and scolds the slackers. Meanwhile, Carbon Monoxide sneaks up behind Billy.)

BW   Billy: Let's introduce the folks back home to our next pollutant, Carbon Monoxide. Hey! Where did he go? Oh, there you are! Pretty sneaky, Carbon Monoxide.

CO Carbon Monoxide: Yeah, sneaking up on people is what I do best. I get into the air when cars and trucks burn fuel—but you can't see me because I'm a gas, AND I don't even have a smell. You might confuse me with oxygen and nitrogen, but it takes only a few of me to make you really sick.

SL Susie (rubbing her temples): Then how can we tell when you're around?

CO Carbon Monoxide (chuckles): Oh, you'll find out when you breathe me in! I can give you a bad headache and make you really tired. Really tired (gives an evil laugh).

BW Billy (yawning): Oh—I see what you mean. Thanks for talking with us, Carbon Monoxide. (Billy yawns again.)

(Carbon Monoxide returns to the picket line.)

SL Susie (turns to face Sulfur Dioxide): Next we'd like you to meet Sulfur Dioxide. I understand you just blew in from the Midwest.

SO₂ Sulfur Dioxide: Hey, I wouldn't miss this for all the pollution in Los Angeles!

BW Billy: I'm sure the folks at home would like to know how you get into our air.

SO₂ Sulfur Dioxide: Well, heck, don't they read the newspapers? I've been making the headlines for years! Most of the time, I just shoot out of the smokestacks of power plants when they burn coal to make electricity. I start as part of the coal and then hook up with my friend, oxygen, and we move through the air as a gas. Very little of me in the air can make really big changes in air quality.

SL Susie: And what kind of nasty things do you do?

SO₂ Sulfur Dioxide: Nasty, that's me (snickers). I hang out with oxygen and nitrogen, but there aren't many of me compared to them. I can be a big problem, though. I think it's cool to make it hard for people to breathe. And I can hurt trees and other plants, too. You think these other pollutants are tough? I can even dissolve rocks. But here's the most rotten thing I do. When I get way up in the atmosphere, I mix with water in the sky, and presto! I become part of acid rain! (pretends to spray water from a water bottle at the reporters).

BW Billy (brushing at his clothing): Watch that stuff! It will ruin my suit! Acid rain is a big problem. It can kill fish and hurt other animals that live in lakes and rivers. Most scientists think it makes trees sick. Acid rain can even eat away at statues and buildings.

SO₂ Sulfur Dioxide (proudly): That's right. Hey, I can even travel a long way to do my dirty work. If I get pumped out of a smokestack in Ohio, I can ride the wind for hundreds of miles and turn up as acid rain in New York!

SL Susie: It is sure nice saying good-bye to you, Sulfur Dioxide. (Susie coughs.)

BW Billy (to the audience): She's really rotten!

NO Nitrogen Monoxide: You think Sulfur Dioxide is rotten? You haven't met me!

SL Susie: You must be one of the Nitrogen Oxides, aren't you? How do you get into the air?

NO Nitrogen Monoxide: Easy. I get airborne when cars, trucks, and airplanes burn fuel. Right out the old tailpipe.

BW Billy: And what happens once you're in the air?

NO Nitrogen Monoxide: Sulfur Dioxide thinks she's such a big shot. But I can make people's lungs hurt, too—especially people who already have asthma. And, like Sulfur Dioxide, I'm formed in power plants, mix with water in the air, and form acid rain. But I can do one more trick that Sulfur Dioxide can't.

SL Susie: Oh, please tell us! (She sticks her microphone in Nitrogen Monoxide's face.)

NO Nitrogen Monoxide (taking the microphone): Better than that, I'll introduce her to you. Meet my daughter, Opal Ozone!

BW Billy (astonished): Opal Ozone! Here, in LA?

O₃ Opal Ozone: Where else?

BW Billy (stammering): B-b-b-b-b-but, I thought all the **ozone** was way up in the stratosphere and was doing good things for us.

O₃ Opal Ozone: Oh, you mean my do-gooder twin sister. Yeah, she's all gas, way up in the atmosphere, absorbing ultraviolet rays from the Sun. But I find it more interesting down here—at ground level. You know, down and dirty.

SL Susie: So, how do you get made, Opal?

O₃ Opal Ozone: It's fun. My mother and her gassy friends, the nitrogen oxides, come over, and we have a smog party. You know, we have a few **VOC's**, turn up the heat, and the next thing you know, I'm there. And when I'm there, smog is not far behind.

BW Billy (to audience): I'm sure Opal Ozone is a lot of fun, but she's a little shy about her effects on people and other living things. When ozone is on the ground, it is quite dangerous and poisonous. It attacks lung tissue. It also damages crops, trees, and other matter—even breaking down rubber compounds.

SL Susie: Well, that about wraps it up, Billy. It will be a happy day when we see the last of the Sickening…(counting her fingers) Billy, that's only five.

BW Billy (whispering): Are you sure? (looking around)

Hg Mercury (sitting off to the side, talks in a smooth, flowing voice): I'm over here. People always forget about me. Which is sort of funny, since I make people forgetful.

SL Susie: Oh, sorry, Mercury, we didn't see you behind all the other pollutants. (Reads notes.) My notes say that you're from the Midwest, like Sulfur Dioxide.

Hg Mercury: That's correct, Ms. Lung. I'm from the Midwest. I know Sulfur Dioxide, but we don't mix. In fact, I don't mix with any of the other pollutants. You see, I'm not a gas like the others, and I'm not a molecule. I'm much more special than that. I'm a liquid element.

ozone: a molecule made up of three oxygen atoms.

VOC (volatile organic compound): a pollutant that reacts with nitrogen oxides to make smog.

BW Billy: Well, Mercury, how do you get into the air, then? In some special way?

Hg Mercury (dramatically): Trapped in coal at an early age, I'm purified by fire and released into the air through the smokestacks of power plants. Though I'm a heavy element, I can travel hundred of miles before landing gently in forests and fields, and in rivers and streams.

SL Susie: And how do you do your damage?

Hg Mercury (with a sinister look): Slowly. Quietly. I react slowly to form mercury molecules that get into the food chain. I get into the bodies of small animals such as fish. Then, as predators eat prey, I move up the food chain. My effects are seen in the nervous system, especially of young, fast-growing animals—including children! Good day. You're boring me.

BW Billy: That Mercury guy makes me nervous.

SL Susie: Definitely creepy. (to audience) And that wraps it up for tonight. The bottom line? These pollutants are a pretty tough bunch—but people create them, and people can reduce the amounts that are in our air.

BW Billy: Thank you and good night.

Stop and Think

1. Which of the six pollutants are gases? The other pollutants are which state of matter?

2. Which of the pollutants are caused by combustion?

3. Which of the pollutants are elements? Which of the pollutants are compounds?

4. How does the concentration of the pollutants in air compare to the concentration of nitrogen and oxygen?

5. Which of the six pollutants would you expect to find in the air of a big city? Describe why you think each would be in a big city.

6. Which of the six pollutants would you expect to find in your community? Describe why you think each would be in your community.

7. What else do you need to know about pollutants and how they form to understand how they get into the air and cause harm?

Communicate

Compare and discuss your answers to the *Stop and Think* questions with the rest of the class. Add what you think you know about pollutants to the *What do we think we know?* column of the *Project Board*. Add the questions you generated to the *What do we need to investigate?* column of the *Project Board*.

Be a Scientist

How Do Scientists Measure the Amounts of Pollutants?

In the play, *The Sickening Six*, you explored six dangerous pollutants. None of these pollutants are present in air at even 0.1 percent. The concentration of each of these pollutants in air is very, very small, and yet each can cause serious health effects.

Recall from *Learning Set 2* that concentration describes the amount of a solute in a solvent. The concentration of nitrogen in air, for example, is about 78 percent. The concentrations of the pollutants in *The Sickening Six*, however, are much too small to describe in percentages.

To describe the concentration of some pollutants in air, scientists use **parts per million (ppm)**. For example, the amount of carbon dioxide in the air is about 385 ppm. This means that every one million (the m in ppm) particles of air include 385 molecules of carbon dioxide. This is the same as saying that 0.0385 percent of the air is carbon dioxide, but it is easier for most people to think about the concentration as 385 ppm.

When the concentration of some gas in the air is smaller than 1 ppm, scientists use smaller units to describe concentration—**parts per billion (ppb)**. A concentration of 1 ppb is 1000 times less than a concentration of 1 ppm. If a gas has a concentration of 37 ppb in air, then every billion particles of air (the b in ppb) contain 37 particles of the gas.

part per million (ppm): the number of particles of one substance in one million particles of a mixture. One out of a million.

part per billion (ppb): the number of particles of one substance in one billion particles of a mixture. One out of a billion.

AIR QUALITY

Scientists use another unit to describe the concentrations of solids and liquids—micrograms per cubic meter ($\mu g/m^3$). One microgram is 0.000001 g. To understand just how small that is, consider that a penny has a mass of about 3 g, and a pen cap has a mass of about 1 g. One microgram is one millionth of one gram. One cubic meter is the space that is one meter by one meter by one meter.

Look at the table. It lists the allowable concentration of each pollutant in the air and the dangerous concentration of that pollutant. The allowable concentration is the permissible concentration at which the pollutant can exist in air, based on human health standards. The dangerous concentration is the concentration at which the pollutant begins to cause serious harm to living things.

Allowable and Dangerous Levels of Some Air Pollutants

Pollutant	Allowable Level	Dangerous Level
carbon monoxide	35 ppm	50 ppm
nitrogen oxides	0.053 ppm	2 ppm
ozone	0.08 ppm	0.4 ppm
small particulate matter (PM)	65 $\mu g/m^3$*	1000 $\mu g/m^3$
large particulate matter (PM)	150 $\mu g/m^3$	1000 $\mu g/m^3$
sulfur dioxide	0.14 ppm	1 ppm
mercury	none	0.12 $\mu g/m^3$
lead	none	1.5 $\mu g/m^3$
volatile organic compounds (VOC)	none	0.01–2 $\mu g/m^3$

* Some pollutants are not measured in ppm. Instead, they are measured in micrograms/cubic meter ($\mu g/m^3$)

Understanding Concentration

A million or a billion particles is a lot of particles. There are so many that it can be difficult to imagine what the number of particles means. It may also be hard for you to imagine how little of air is actually made up of pollutants. This investigation will help you imagine this concept. In this investigation, you will observe a solution as the concentration of particles gets smaller and smaller. In other words, the solution becomes more dilute. Because gas is hard to see, and gas particles are hard to imagine, you will model concentrations of pollutants using water and food coloring. The food coloring will represent a pollutant, and the water will represent air. You will pay attention to how the color of the water changes as the concentration of food coloring (pollutant) changes.

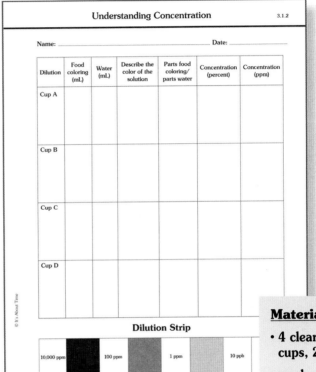

Procedure

1. With a marker, label each cup with a letter: A, B, C, or D.

2. Use a pipette to place 1.0 mL of food coloring into Cup A.

3. Carefully measure 99 mL of water in the graduated cylinder. Add the water to the food coloring and stir with a spoon until you have a homogeneous mixture. Recall that in a homogenous mixture, the particles of solute are spread evenly throughout the solvent.

4. Record the color of the solution on your *Understanding Concentration* page.

5. Compare the color of the solution in Cup A with the dilution strip to determine its concentration.

Materials
- **4 clear plastic cups, 275 mL**
- **marker**
- **blue food coloring**
- **4 plastic pipettes, graduated to 1.0 mL**
- **100-mL graduated cylinder**
- **spoon**
- **water**
- **pen**
- ***Understanding Concentration page***

AIR QUALITY

Analyze Your Data

1. On your *Understanding Concentration* page, record your comparison of the solution in Cup A with the dilution strip. Adding 1.0 mL of food coloring to 99 mL of water makes this a 1 percent solution. The concentration is 10,000 parts of food coloring to 990,000 parts of water (10,000 ppm).

2. What do you think will happen if part of the solution in Cup A were mixed with more water? How will the concentration change?

Dilute the 1 Percent Concentration

To dilute means to decrease the concentration of some substance in a solution. Cup A is a 1 percent (10,000 ppm) solution of food coloring in water. You will decrease the concentration of food coloring in the water by adding some of the 1 percent solution to more water. Follow the instructions below.

Procedure

1. Use a clean pipette to measure 1.0 mL of the solution in Cup A. Add it to Cup B.

2. Measure 99 mL of water in the graduated cylinder. Add the water to Cup B and stir with a spoon.

3. Record the color of the solution on your *Understanding Concentration* page.

4. Compare the color of the solution in Cup B with the dilution strip to determine its concentration.

Analyze Your Data

1. On your *Understanding Concentration* page, record your comparison of the solution in Cup B with the dilution strip. The concentration of food coloring in the water in Cup B is 100 times less than the concentration of food coloring in Cup A. This is because you added 99 mL of water to 1.0 mL of the solution in Cup A. The concentration of food coloring in Cup A is 1 percent, or 10,000 ppm. The concentration of food coloring in Cup B is 100 ppm.

2. Compare the color of the solution in Cup A with the color in Cup B. Describe the difference.

3. If you had a very powerful tool and could see the particles of water and food coloring, how would the solution in Cup B look different from the solution in Cup A?

4. Next you will make another solution in Cup C by taking 1.0 mL of Cup B and diluting it with another 99 mL of water. What do you expect will be the color of the water in Cup C? Why will this happen?

Dilute the Solution in Cup B

Procedure

1. Use a clean pipette to measure 1.0 mL of the solution in Cup B. Add it to Cup C.

2. Measure 99 mL of water in the graduated cylinder. Add the water to Cup C and stir with a spoon.

3. Record the color of the solution on your *Understanding Concentration* page.

4. Compare the color of the solution in Cup C with the dilution strip to determine its concentration.

Analyze Your Data

1. On your *Understanding Concentration* page, record your comparison of the solution in Cup C with the dilution strip. The concentration of food coloring in the water in Cup C is 100 times less than the concentration of food coloring in Cup B. This is because you added 99 mL of water to 1.0 mL of the solution in Cup B. The concentration of food coloring in Cup B is 100 ppm. The concentration of food coloring in Cup C is 1 ppm.

2. Compare the color of the solution in Cup B with the color in Cup C. Describe the difference.

3. If you had a very powerful tool and could see the particles of water and food coloring, how would the solution in Cup C look different from the solution in Cup B?

4. Next you will make another solution in Cup D by taking 1.0 mL of Cup C and diluting it with another 99 mL of water. What do you expect will be the color of the water in Cup D? Why will this happen?

Dilution to a Concentration of Parts per Billion (ppb)

Procedure

1. Use a clean pipette to measure 1.0 mL of the solution in Cup C. Add it to Cup D.

2. Measure 99 mL of water in the graduated cylinder. Add the water to Cup D and stir with a spoon.

3. Record the color of the solution on your *Understanding Concentration* page.

4. Compare the color of the solution in Cup D with the dilution strip to determine its concentration.

Analyze Your Data

1. On your *Understanding Concentration* page, record your comparison of the solution in Cup D with the dilution strip. The concentration of food coloring in the water in Cup D is 100 times less than the concentration of food coloring in Cup C. This is because you added 99 mL of water to 1.0 mL of the solution in Cup C. The concentration of food coloring in Cup C is 1 ppm (1000 ppb). The concentration of food coloring in Cup D is 10 ppb.

2. Compare the color of the solution in Cup C with the color in Cup D. Describe the difference.

3. If you had a very powerful tool and could see the particles of water and food coloring, how would the solution in Cup D look different from the solution in Cup C?

Reflect

1. At which concentration could you no longer see any color? How much food coloring was still in the water?

2. Even though you may not be able to see the food coloring in Cups C and D, how do you know it is still there?

3. Imagine that the food coloring is a dangerous pollutant. How could you decide if the solution in Cup C or Cup D is safe to drink? Justify your answer with evidence.

4. Imagine that the water is air. How does this investigation help you understand the danger of even small amounts of pollution in air?

5. What else do you still need to know to determine how good or bad the quality of the air is in your community?

Update the *Project Board*

In the *What do we think we know?* column of the *Project Board*, record what you think you know about the major pollutants in your community. You may have some ideas about what you need to investigate to identify the pollutants in your community. Record these ideas in the second column, *What do we need to investigate?*

What's the Point?

Six major types of pollutants affect air quality. Five of these pollutants can be produced by combustion in engines and power plants. These are soot (particulate matter, PM), carbon monoxide, the nitrogen oxides, mercury, and sulfur dioxide. Particulate matter is inhaled and affects the breathing of people and animals, particularly infants, older people, and people who already have asthma. Carbon monoxide is a poison that interferes with the uptake of oxygen in the lungs. In extreme cases, it can even kill living things. The nitrogen oxides also cause impaired breathing. When nitrogen oxides react with volatile organic compounds (VOC's), the sixth pollutant, ozone, is formed. Ozone is extremely reactive.

The nitrogen oxides, sulfur dioxide, and mercury get into the air through the burning of coal in power plants. Acid rain forms when nitrogen oxides and sulfur dioxide mix with water vapor. Acid rain can return to the land many hundreds of miles away from the power plants that put the pollutants into the air.

All of the pollutants are gases, except for particulate matter and mercury. Particulate matter is small enough to be carried long distances by the wind. Mercury is a heavy element, but it can be changed into a gas in power plants and carried long distances by the wind.

Air pollutants are present in very small amounts. Scientists need to measure these amounts. For the pollutants that are gases, they use calculations of parts per million (ppm) and parts per billion (ppb).

3.2 Read

Case Study: Pollution in Los Angeles

L.A. COURIER

Los Angeles, California   May 1, 2008

The Most Polluted City in America

Los Angeles under a heavy layer of smog.

When Los Angeles has better air quality, the mountains can be seen in the distance, and people can breathe much easier.

Once again, Los Angeles has topped the American Lung Association's Bad Air list of most polluted cities in America. The association found that the Los Angeles city area had the worst air in the United States.

"Nobody is surprised that LA has an air-pollution problem," said Janice Nolen of the American Lung Association. "The problems there are one of the reasons we have the Clean Air Act. But it is important for folks to know that there has been some improvement."

The news wasn't all bad for Los Angeles. Despite its poor ranking compared to other cities, the number of days residents breathed the nation's worst air was fewer than in previous years. The association based the rankings on pollution levels when heat and sunlight come into contact with pollutants from power plants, cars and trucks, refineries, and other sources. The pollution released from these sources is made up of a mixture of tiny solid, liquid, and gas particles in the air.

Understanding how pollution gets into the air in Los Angeles can help you understand how pollution might get into the air in your community. Los Angeles is a big city that has a big problem with air quality. It has the worst air quality of any United States city. The Los Angeles area is home to over 9 million people. It has the world's largest marine port, one of the largest international airports, and almost 80,467 km (50,000 mi) of highways for car and truck traffic.

Los Angeles highways stretch for almost 90,000 km.

Stop and Think

1. Think about what you know about the activities that produce the six big pollutants. Which of these activities do you think are common in Los Angeles? Look back at the article on the previous page and at the paragraph above to help you answer this question.

2. What do you think might cause the air-pollution problem in Los Angeles? What do you think might make the problem so much greater in Los Angeles than in other large cities?

Conference

Share with your group your ideas about what affects the air quality in Los Angeles. Discuss which sources of pollution you are sure about and which sources of pollution you are still unsure about. It is important for all the members of your group to discuss their ideas. As a group, use a *Sources and Effects of Air Quality* chart to create a list of possible sources and effects of air quality in Los Angeles. This chart should be similar to those you made earlier in the Unit when discussing your community.

Sources and Effects of Air Quality		
Sources	**Effects**	**How to improve the air**

Communicate

Share your sources and effects with the class. If there is disagreement about the sources or effects, record those disagreements.

Factors That Affect the Air in Los Angeles

Your class has determined several of the sources of pollution in Los Angeles. These might be the same sources you thought affected your own community. For example, you probably identified that cars on the road emit soot, carbon monoxide, and nitrogen oxides into the air.

Air pollution from vehicles is a particularly bad problem in Los Angeles. The city of Los Angeles grew very quickly. In 1870, only 5000 people lived in Los Angeles. After 30 years, that number grew to more than 170,000. In another 30 years, by 1930, the population was 1.2 million. Today, it has over 9 million people. Los Angeles has grown faster than almost any other city in the United States. As the city grew, the roads became more crowded with cars. Los Angeles built a very large network of roads and freeways to manage the traffic. That made the roads easier to drive on. This also made it easier for people to live far away from the center of the city and still drive to work in the city.

As more people moved to the Los Angeles area and more houses were built far from the center of the city, the roads became more crowded again. Most people who live in the Los Angeles area need to drive long distances to get from place to place. The large population and the long distances people drive in Los Angeles has resulted in a huge number of cars on the road. All these cars burn fuel. All of this combustion produces many of the pollutants that trouble Los Angeles.

As the population grew in Los Angeles, more power plants were needed to supply electricity to all the houses and other buildings. The combustion in power plants adds more pollutants to the air in Los Angeles.

The geography and weather of Los Angeles also affect its air quality. Los Angeles is situated between the ocean and a mountain range. Combustion produces many air pollutants, and then the mountains trap these pollutants near the city.

The weather in Los Angeles keeps pollutants in the air. Los Angeles is very warm with very little rain. Rain washes pollutants out of the air. After a rain, the air is usually clearer than it was before the rain. However, because there is so little rain in Los Angeles, pollutants stay in the air for longer periods of time than they do in other places.

Stop and Think

1. How did population growth affect the air quality of Los Angeles?

2. How does geography affect the air quality of Los Angeles?

3. How does weather affect the air quality of Los Angeles?

One factor that affects the air quality of Los Angeles is the mountains. They trap the air, keeping the wind from blowing away the polluted air.

What's the Point?

Los Angeles has many of the same pollution problems as other big cities. One factor that contributes to pollution in Los Angeles is the large number of cars, trucks, and buses that emit polluting gases and particulate matter. Another factor that contributes to pollution is its geography. The mountains trap air. The wind cannot easily blow the polluted air over the mountains, so the polluted air stays over the city. Another factor is the weather. Los Angeles generally has warm air with very little rain to wash the pollutants out of the air. The next few sections will help you better understand the impact of these factors. Then you will be able to determine how these factors may or may not also impact the air in your community.

The Los Angeles area has grown to over 9 million people since 1870.

3.3 Explore

How Do Pollutants Form During Combustion?

When you read about Los Angeles, you saw that many of the pollutants came from combustion in cars, trucks, and airplanes. Los Angeles has a lot of people, and a lot of people means a lot of vehicles that burn fuel. Combustion is a major cause of pollution in almost all communities. The pollution from combustion comes from the burning of gasoline in cars, diesel fuel in trucks, and jet fuel in airplanes. Combustion of fuel in vehicles produces nitrogen oxides, carbon monoxide, and particulate matter as waste products. These pollutants are all characters you met in *The Sickening Six* play. You already know that vehicles produce pollution, but you may not know how car engines work to create pollutants.

Observe

Combustion in a Car Engine

You read about combustion in *Learning Set 2*. Combustion is burning, and during combustion, fuel burns in the presence of air to produce water, carbon dioxide, and other molecules. Cars use what is called an *internal-combustion engine* to burn fuel. Combustion takes place inside cylinders. A cylinder is a confined space. It does not easily let heat out. Because a cylinder is a confined space, heat and pressure build up inside it. Watch the video about internal combustion and notice how the pistons move up and down.

The internal-combustion engine used in cars keeps the fuel and air inside a set of cylinders.

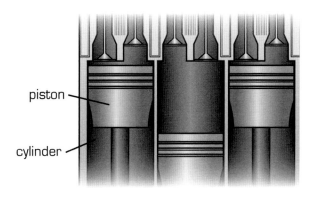

piston

cylinder

The engine uses the heat and pressure that are produced to make the car work. But, as you will see in the video, the great amount of heat and pressure in the cylinder also causes some interesting chemical reactions. Recall that a chemical reaction is a process that changes one or more substances into other substances. After you watch the video about internal combustion, answer the questions below.

Stop and Think

1. What is the fuel in an internal-combustion engine?

2. Where does combustion happen in an internal-combustion engine?

3. Why is there so much heat and pressure in the cylinder of an internal-combustion engine?

4. What substances go into an internal-combustion engine? What substances are produced by an internal-combustion engine?

Chemical Reactions in an Internal-Combustion Engine

All of the products of combustion—NO, NO_2, CO_2, and H_2O—pass through a vehicle's exhaust system and into the atmosphere. NO and NO_2 are the polluting nitrogen oxides you explored in *The Sickening Six* play. Neither CO_2 nor H_2O are pollutants, but they do contribute to global climate change. You will read about that later.

You might wonder why nitrogen monoxide and nitrogen dioxide are produced when combustion takes place in an internal-combustion engine but not during other types of combustion. To understand what is happening in an internal-combustion engine, you need to remember what you read about stable molecules in *Learning Set 2*. Remember that atoms form bonds with other atoms in order to obtain a complete set of outer electrons. Molecules formed in this way are more stable than the atoms themselves.

Remember that atoms form bonds with other atoms to create molecules. When you used your atomic-molecule kits, you used gray bars to form bonds between atoms and create molecules. Some molecules you formed were stable. In these molecules, all of the holes were filled, and all of the gray bars were attached on both sides. In stable molecules, atoms share their outer electrons in a way that allows all of the atoms in the molecule to have a complete set of outer electrons. The atoms in stable molecules remain connected together in a mixture.

Some molecules you created, however, had open holes. Or maybe a gray rod was connected only on one side. Molecules in which all the holes are not filled are unstable. Their atoms do not all have a complete set of outer electrons. These molecules are more reactive. Their atoms are likely to disconnect from the molecule and form bonds with other molecules to obtain a complete set of outer electrons. The atoms in unstable molecules react more easily with other atoms in a mixture than do atoms in stable molecules.

Under everyday conditions, nitrogen molecules and oxygen molecules are stable. The bonds in a nitrogen molecule allow the two nitrogen atoms to share electrons in a way that gives both nitrogen atoms a complete set of outer electrons. The bonds in an oxygen molecule allow the two oxygen atoms to share electrons in a way that gives both oxygen atoms a complete set of outer electrons. This means that under everyday conditions, nitrogen and oxygen molecules do not easily react, even when mixed with other gases. Under everyday conditions, oxygen and nitrogen molecules stay together. Their bonds do not come apart and will not combine with any other atoms to make new substances.

Everything changes, however, with more heat and pressure. When heat and pressure are applied to molecules, the bonds in molecules break apart more easily than when there is less heat or pressure. When the bonds in molecules break apart, the atoms in those molecules become available to form new substances with other atoms. An internal-combustion engine produces so much heat and pressure that even the bonds of stable molecules come apart, and the atoms in those molecules become very reactive.

This is why nitrogen and oxygen molecules in the air are stable and not reactive and why nitrogen and oxygen molecules in an internal-combustion engine break apart and become reactive. Inside an engine cylinder, these gases are brought together at high temperature and high pressure. The bonds in the nitrogen and oxygen molecules in the cylinder come apart and the atoms react with each other to form the polluting nitrogen oxides, NO and NO_2.

chemical equation: a statement that expresses what is happening in a chemical reaction in a brief, abbreviated way.

Using Chemical Equations

How can you describe the combustion reaction in a car's engine? One way is by describing the reaction in a sentence:

Fuel and air are changed into water, carbon dioxide, nitrogen monoxide, and nitrogen dioxide.

That description is quite long, and many chemical reactions are even more complex. As a result, it can be time-consuming to write out the description of a chemical reaction in words. In addition, not all scientists will use exactly the same words to describe the same chemical reaction. They may select different words within the same language. Or they might speak different languages.

To avoid miscommunication, scientists have developed a shorthand notation for describing chemical reactions. That notation is called a **chemical equation**. A chemical equation uses an arrow to show that the reactants have changed into the products. Recall that the reactants are the substances that enter into a chemical reaction. The products are the substances that are formed.

$$reactants \rightarrow products$$

As an example, consider the chemical reaction in which carbon dioxide is formed from carbon and oxygen.

$$carbon + oxygen \rightarrow carbon\ dioxide$$

The arrow in a chemical equation points from the reactants to the products. Plus signs (+) are used to separate reactants from other reactants and products from other products.

The notation shown is still not a complete chemical equation. Rather than words, a chemical equation uses chemical symbols and molecular formulas to describe each substance involved. So the chemical reaction above would become

$$C + O_2 \rightarrow CO_2$$

This chemical equation would be read as carbon plus oxygen yields carbon dioxide.

Compare the atoms of the reactants with those of the product. Remember that the small numbers written down and to the right of a chemical symbol is called a subscript. It shows how many atoms of the element are present in each molecule.

With this in mind, what do you notice about the number of atoms of each element? There is one carbon atom and two oxygen atoms on each side of the arrow. That means that no new atoms were created and no atoms were destroyed. This phenomenon is known as the **law of conservation of matter**. According to this law, matter is neither created nor destroyed in ordinary processes. The figure below shows how matter is conserved in a chemical reaction.

law of conservation of matter: matter is neither created nor destroyed.

Conservation of matter

carbon
1 atom of
carbon (black)

oxygen
1 molecule
containing 2 atoms
of oxygen (white)

carbon dioxide
1 molecule
of carbon dioxide containing
3 total atoms:
1 atom of carbon
2 atoms of oxygen

At the start of the reaction, there are 3 total atoms:
• 1 carbon atom
• 2 oxygen atoms

At the end of the reaction, there are 3 total atoms:
• 1 carbon atom
• 2 oxygen atoms

During a chemical reaction, the bonds of reactants are broken, the atoms are rearranged, and new bonds are formed to create the products. Both the reactants and products are made up of the same atoms, but in a completely different arrangement.

As far back as 450 B.C.E., some believed that matter was not created or destroyed. But it was only in 1785 that a scientist, Antoine Lavoisier, was able to collect evidence supporting the law of conservation of matter. Lavoisier performed a set of experiments in which he set up chemical reactions inside closed containers. He measured the mass of the matter in each container before he added it to the container, and then he measured the mass of the matter in the container after the chemical reaction. Each time, the mass was the same.

Stop and Think

1. What is the advantage of using chemical equations?

2. How does the law of conservation of matter relate to chemical equations?

Reflect

1. Suppose you place a lighted candle on a balance. If you assume that the law of conservation of matter is accurate, how do you account for the decrease in mass as the candle burns? Where does the mass go?

2. Now suppose you put the same lighted candle inside a closed jar. If you assume that the law of conservation of matter is accurate, how do you account for the mass remaining the same as the candle burns?

3. Think about how the two experiments above can be compared to an internal-combustion engine. If the internal-combustion engine were in an enclosed container, you would be able to measure the mass of the products, and you would find the mass of the products to be the same as the mass of the reactants. But an internal-combustion engine is not a closed system. A closed system is one in which substances from the environment do not enter the system, and substances from the system do not leave to enter the environment. What do you think happens to the products of internal combustion? Where do they go? Which of the above experiments is more like an internal-combustion engine?

Model the Products of Combustion

Materials

• atomic-model kit

In *Section 2.6*, you built two of the products of combustion, CO_2 and H_2O. Now you have read about using chemical equations to represent chemical reactions. Using your atomic-model kit, build the reactants of the equations that produce CO_2 and H_2O. Then build the products of the equations. Using what you know about chemical equations, answer the questions below.

Stop and Think

1. How many oxygen molecules did you need to build the water molecules? How many hydrogen molecules did you need to build the water molecules?

2. Write the chemical equation that represents hydrogen and oxygen reacting to form water. Remember that the number of atoms on both sides of the arrow needs to be the same.

3. Now answer the same questions for carbon dioxide (CO_2).

Be a Scientist

Balancing Chemical Equations

If you used two hydrogen molecules and one oxygen molecule to produce two water molecules, you now know something about chemical equations. Remember that a chemical equation has to have the same number of atoms of each type on each side of the arrow.

In *Learning Set 2,* you bonded one of the oxygen atoms from your oxygen molecule with two hydrogen atoms from your hydrogen molecule to produce one molecule of water. But after you made your first water molecule, you found that you had an extra oxygen atom. To use up all the oxygen from your oxygen molecule (O_2), you had to combine the extra oxygen atom with the two hydrogen atoms from a second hydrogen molecule. One oxygen molecule (O_2) and two hydrogen molecules ($2H_2$) allowed you to produce two water molecules ($2H_2O$).

Scientists would write the equation like this:

$$O_2 + 2H_2 \rightarrow 2H_2O$$

They would say the reaction like this:

One oxygen molecule and two hydrogen molecules react to form two molecules of water.

The 2's you see in front of the molecular formulas for hydrogen and water are called **coefficients**. The coefficient shows the number of each type of molecule or atom. If there is no coefficient shown, you know that it is 1. So H_2O represents one molecule of water, and $2H_2O$ represents two molecules of water.

You use coefficients to count the number of atoms of each element in the reaction. For example, to count the number of hydrogen atoms on the reactant side of the equation,

- multiply the coefficient 2 by the subscript 2: $(2 \times 2 = 4)$. There are 4 hydrogen atoms on the reactant side.

- For oxygen, there is no coefficient shown, so you know that it is 1. The subscript for oxygen is 2: $(1 \times 2 = 2)$. There are 2 oxygen atoms on the reactant side.

Now look at the product.

- Again, multiply the coefficient 2 by the subscript 2 to count the number of hydrogen atoms: $(2 \times 2 = 4)$. There are 4 hydrogen atoms on the product side.

coefficient: a number in front of each chemical formula that shows how many molecules of that compound are used or produced in a chemical reaction.

- Multiply the coefficient 2 by the subscript 1 to count the number of oxygen atoms: $(2 \times 1 = 2)$. There are 2 oxygen atoms.

Now that you know a little about balanced equations and coefficients, take a look at a more complicated equation. The chemical equation below shows the reaction that might take place in an internal-combustion engine that uses propane as its fuel. The chemical formula for propane is C_3H_8.

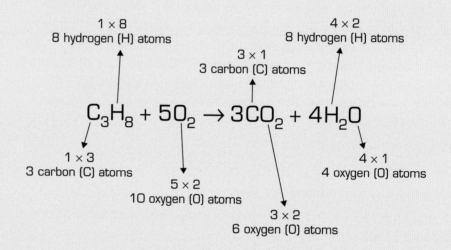

$$C_3H_8 + 5O_2 \rightarrow 3CO_2 + 4H_2O$$

1 × 8
8 hydrogen (H) atoms

3 × 1
3 carbon (C) atoms

4 × 2
8 hydrogen (H) atoms

1 × 3
3 carbon (C) atoms

5 × 2
10 oxygen (O) atoms

3 × 2
6 oxygen (O) atoms

4 × 1
4 oxygen (O) atoms

You can see from the equation that propane combines with oxygen from air to form carbon dioxide and water. Is the equation balanced? Count atoms to find out. Start with the reactants.

- There is no coefficient shown in front of propane, so you know it is 1.

- The subscript 3 tells you that there are 3 carbon atoms.

- The subscript 8 tells you that there are 8 hydrogen atoms.

- Now look at oxygen. It has the coefficient 5 and subscript 2. Multiply 5 by 2 to find 10 oxygen atoms.

Move to the product side of the equation.

- Carbon dioxide has the coefficient 3.

- There is no subscript shown for carbon, so you know it is 1. Multiply 3 by 1 to find 3 carbon atoms.

- The oxygen in carbon dioxide has the subscript 2. Multiply 3 by 2 to find 6 oxygen atoms.

- The water molecule has the coefficient 4. Multiply by the subscript 2 to find 8 hydrogen atoms.

- Multiply the 4 coefficient of water by the subscript 1 to find 4 oxygen atoms.

- Add the oxygen atoms from carbon dioxide and water to find the total.

Each side has 10 oxygen atoms, 3 carbon atoms, and 8 hydrogen atoms. This equation is said to be balanced. A balanced equation shows that the number and type of atoms on the left side of the equation equals the number and type of atoms on the right side of the equation.

Model Other Products of Combustion

Now you will use the same process to model a combustion reaction. This equation is more complicated than the equation for water. You will begin by building the reactant side of the equation, and then you will build the product side of the equation. Remember that the equation must be balanced.

In this reaction, the fuel is a gas named methane. It is the main component of natural gas. The word equation for the combustion of methane is this: Methane (CH_4) and oxygen (O_2) react to form carbon dioxide (CO_2) and water (H_2O).

The word equation tells you that the reactants are methane and oxygen. It tells you that the products of the reaction are carbon dioxide and water.

Materials

• **atomic-model kit**

Procedure

1. Build models of the reactants: methane (CH_4) and oxygen (O_2).

   a) To build a methane molecule, select enough hydrogen atoms (white) to fill all the empty holes on your carbon atom (black).

   b) Build a molecule of oxygen from oxygen atoms (red).

2. Now use the atoms in the reactants to build models of the products of combustion, carbon dioxide (CO_2) and water (H_2O).

   a) Take all the reactant molecules apart.

   b) Build as many carbon dioxide molecules as you can.

   c) Use the remaining atoms to build water molecules. You might have to add some oxygen atoms to use up all the hydrogen atoms and make them into water molecules.

3. How many molecules of carbon dioxide did you make? How many water molecules did you make?

4. Write your equation like this:

$$\underline{\quad} CH_4 + \underline{\quad} O_2 \rightarrow \underline{\quad} CO_2 + \underline{\quad} H_2O$$

   Record the number of molecules of carbon dioxide and water on the product side of the equation.

5. Take apart the carbon dioxide and water molecules. Use the carbon atom to remake the methane molecule. Use the oxygen atoms to make oxygen molecules.

6. Count the number of methane and oxygen molecules you built. Record the number of molecules of each on the reactant side of the equation as coefficients.

Model Nitrogen Monoxide and Nitrogen Dioxide

Materials
- atomic-model kit
- *Model Molecules* page

Carbon dioxide, water, and soot are only three of the products of combustion reactions. Carbon dioxide and water are not air pollutants, but soot is. Combustion in internal-combustion engines also produces other air pollutants. The internal-combustion engine produces nitrogen monoxide (NO), and nitrogen dioxide (NO_2). Using what you know about chemical equations and building molecules, you will use your atomic-model kit to build molecules of NO and NO_2.

Procedure

1. Build a molecule of nitrogen and a molecule of oxygen. If you need help, look back at *Section 2.3*.

2. Take apart your molecules of nitrogen and oxygen, and build as many molecules of nitrogen monoxide (NO) as you can.

3. When you complete your molecules, sketch a diagram on a new *Model Molecules* page. Label the atoms in the molecules so you know which molecules you used. Record the balanced chemical equation that makes nitrogen monoxide.

4. Now build a molecule of nitrogen dioxide (NO_2). Set your molecule aside.

5. Build the reactants of the equation that makes nitrogen dioxide. Set your molecules aside.

6. Look at your reactants and your products of your nitrogen dioxide reaction. How many nitrogen atoms do you have on each side? If the numbers are different, add enough nitrogen atoms so the numbers are equal. How many oxygen atoms do you have on each side? If the numbers are different, add enough oxygen atoms so the numbers are equal.

7. When you complete your molecules, sketch a diagram on a new *Model Molecules* page. Label the atoms in the molecules so you know which molecules you used. Record the balanced equation.

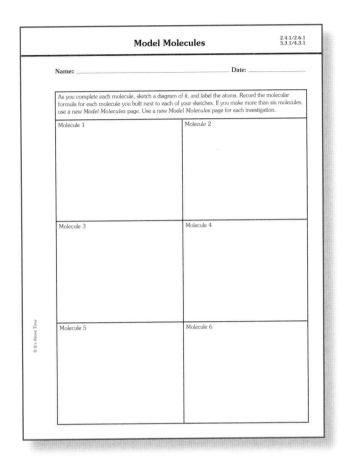

Reflect

Answer the following questions. Be prepared to discuss your answers with the class.

1. For each equation, how did the number of atoms on the reactant side of each equation compare to the number of atoms on the product side?

2. In terms of stability, how would you describe all of the molecules that you made?

3. Write a general rule for determining if an equation is balanced.

Update the *Project Board*

In the *What are we learning?* column of the *Project Board*, record what you now know about how pollutants are formed during the combustion of fuels, the role of the law of conservation of matter, and balancing equations. Include what you know about chemical equations. Be sure to record your evidence in the *What is our evidence?* column. You may have identified additional questions you need to investigate to answer the *Big Question*. Record those questions in the second column, *What do we need to investigate?*

What's the Point?

Many of the pollutants in air form during the combustion of fuels in internal-combustion engines. Because of high temperatures and high pressures inside engines, nitrogen and oxygen react with one another. As a result, the nitrogen oxides, NO and NO_2, are formed and find their way into the atmosphere through the exhaust pipe of the vehicle. In some cases, the pollutants carbon monoxide (CO) and particulate matter (soot) form in addition to CO_2 and H_2O. The pollutants cause problems with breathing, especially for people who have asthma. This is true even though the pollutants are found at low levels, in parts per million (ppm) and even parts per billion (ppb).

The law of conservation of matter states that matter cannot be created or destroyed. Therefore, chemical equations must always be balanced. A balanced equation has the same number of atoms and the same type of atoms on each side of the equation.

Exhaust fumes pollute the air.

3.4 Read

What Causes the Smog in Los Angeles?

If you were to take a walk in Los Angeles on a hot, sunny day, you might notice that the air looks orange. You might also have heard people use the word **smog** and talk about smog alerts. But you may not know exactly what smog is, where it comes from, and how it affects air quality.

Smog is a big problem for Los Angeles. Smog is also one of the few air pollutants you can see. In Los Angeles, it makes the air look orange.

smog: an air pollutant formed from nitrogen oxides and VOC's and activated by sunlight energy.

photochemical: a chemical reaction that requires energy from the Sun.

UV light: ultraviolet rays; very short, high-energy rays from the Sun.

hydrocarbon: a compound that contains only hydrogen and carbon atoms.

How Does Smog Form?

The term smog was first used to describe a combination of smoke and fog that occurred in London in the 1900s. The smog in London was caused by soot and other air pollutants that form during combustion of fuels, such as coal. In Los Angeles, smog is caused by a set of chemical reactions that require sunlight. When the Sun plays a role in chemical reactions, the reactions are called **photochemical** reactions. Smog formed in this way is known as photochemical smog.

This type of smog has four main requirements: oxygen (O_2), nitrogen oxides (NO_x), hydrocarbons, and **ultraviolet light (UV)**. You already know about oxygen and nitrogen oxides. A **hydrocarbon** is a compound containing only hydrogen and carbon atoms. Hydrocarbons can be simple molecules made up of just a few atoms, or they can be much more complicated with many atoms.

Many hydrocarbons are volatile organic compounds (VOC's). You were introduced to VOC's in *The Sickening Six* play. A VOC is a compound that evaporates at room temperature. Its vapors rise into the air. Gasoline is a VOC, as are solvents in paints, glues, and inks.

The other requirement, ultraviolet light, is part of the energy that comes from the Sun. The energy that travels to Earth from the Sun is carried by waves. There are different types of waves, including the visible light you can see, X-rays a doctor might use to see broken bones, and microwaves that are used to cook food and carry information. These waves are described by their lengths, known as wavelength, and the amount of energy they carry. When compared with other types of waves, ultraviolet light has short wavelengths and carries a lot of energy.

Smog forms through a cycle of reactions. In this cycle, sunlight hits nitrogen dioxide molecules in the atmosphere. When sunlight strikes the molecules, they split into nitrogen monoxide and single oxygen atoms. Then those oxygen atoms bond with oxygen molecules (O_2), making ozone molecules (O_3). Ozone is a particularly dangerous component of smog. The other chemicals needed for smog to form are nitrogen monoxide, nitrogen dioxide, and hydrocarbons. All these chemicals are products of combustion.

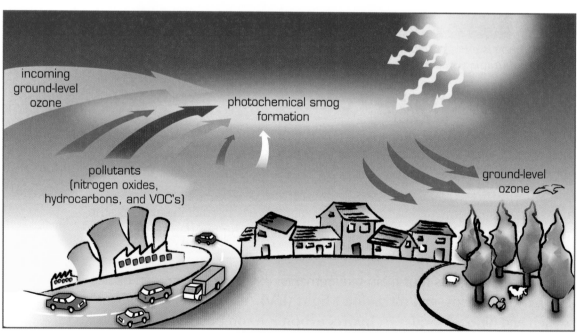

incoming ground-level ozone

photochemical smog formation

pollutants (nitrogen oxides, hydrocarbons, and VOC's)

ground-level ozone

For smog to form, four main ingredients are needed: oxygen (O_2), nitrogen oxides (NO_x), hydrocarbons, and UV light from the Sun.

Ozone: Good up High, Bad Nearby

You may have heard about something called the ozone hole where ozone high in the atmosphere is getting thinner and even disappearing. The ozone hole is caused by chemicals, such as CFC's (chlorofluorocarbons) in aerosol spray cans. These chemicals break down ozone into oxygen molecules and oxygen atoms. The ozone hole is a big problem. If you have heard that, then you will be wondering why ozone is a dangerous component of smog. The reason is that ozone high in the atmosphere is very different than ozone close to Earth's surface.

Normally, molecular oxygen is found as O_2 in the atmosphere. However, under the intense heat of the Sun, O_2 molecules can be broken into highly reactive oxygen atoms that then bond with other oxygen molecules, forming ozone, O_3. Ozone has very different properties than molecular oxygen.

In order to understand the role of ozone, you first need a brief description of the atmosphere. Earth's atmosphere consists of the gases that surround the planet—air. The atmosphere is described as five basic layers. Air becomes thinner and thinner as height, or altitude, increases within the layers.

Cars, trucks, power plants, and factories emit air pollution that forms ground-level ozone, a primary component of smog.

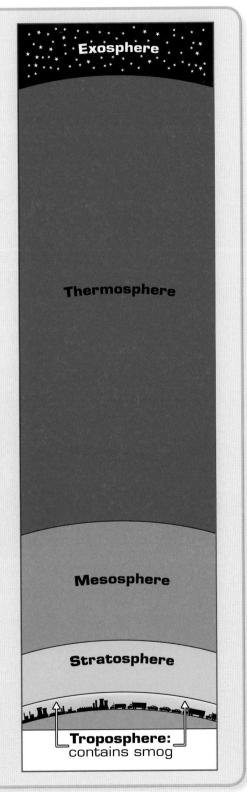

Exosphere

Thermosphere

Mesosphere

Stratosphere

Troposphere: contains smog

AIR QUALITY

troposphere: Earth's atmosphere from the ground to about 10 km (6 mi) up.

stratosphere: the atmosphere from about 10–48 km (6–30 mi) above Earth's surface.

mesosphere: the atmosphere from about 48 km to 85 km (30 to 53 mi) above Earth's surface.

thermosphere: the atmosphere that extends from about 85 km to between 500 and 1000 km (53 mi to between 311 and 621 mi) above Earth's surface.

exosphere: the highest level of the atmosphere; from the edge of the thermosphere, gradually becoming outer space.

ground ozone: ozone found in the troposphere; also known as bad ozone.

The first layer, which is closest to Earth's surface, is known as the **troposphere**. Extending from the ground to about 10 km (6 mi), the troposphere is where weather occurs.

The next layer of the atmosphere is the **stratosphere**, which extends from about 10 km to 48 km (6 mi to 30 mi). Air in the stratosphere is about 1000 times thinner than it is at sea level. As a result, the highest altitudes that can be reached by jet aircrafts and weather balloons are found in this layer.

Above the stratosphere is the **mesosphere**. It extends to 85 km (53 mi) above Earth's surface. Air in this layer is so thin that particles in air rarely collide with one another.

On top of the mesosphere is the **thermosphere**, which extends to between 500 and 1000 km (311 to 621 mi). The space shuttle orbits Earth in the thermosphere.

The highest layer of the atmosphere is called the **exosphere**. In this layer, the atmosphere gradually becomes outer space.

The space shuttle orbits Earth in the thermosphere.

Ozone found up high in the stratosphere protects life on Earth from the Sun's harmful ultraviolet (UV) rays. This ozone is known as "good ozone." It occurs in very tiny amounts, about one to ten ozone molecules for every one million molecules of other gases (1–10 ppm). This ozone, often known as the ozone layer, was formed over 600 million years ago, before the first humans appeared.

Ozone that is closer to Earth, in the troposphere, however, is "bad ozone." This ozone, called **ground ozone**, is formed from photochemical reactions that produce smog. This type of ozone can be found in the air you breathe and can do damage to your lungs and respiratory system. High levels of ground-level ozone can cause chest pain, coughing, sore throat, head congestion, and diseases of the lungs. Bad ozone also damages vegetation and ecosystems.

Stop and Think

1. The oxygen molecule (O_2) is a stable molecule because all the holes are filled and there are no bare bonds. Is ozone (O_3) a stable molecule? It might be helpful to use your atomic-model kit to build an ozone molecule.

2. Identify how good ozone and bad ozone are the same. Describe how they are different.

Primary and Secondary Pollutants

Smog is formed when pollutants already in the air react to form other pollutants. Scientists call the pollutants that are emitted directly into the air **primary pollutants**. Some primary pollutants you have studied include sulfur dioxide (SO_2), carbon monoxide (CO), and nitrogen monoxide (NO). They are emitted directly into the air from combustion engines.

Pollutants that are formed when primary pollutants react with each other are called **secondary pollutants**. Ground-level ozone is a secondary pollutant. So is nitrogen dioxide, the reddish gas that gives smog its reddish-orange color. The chart below shows some primary and secondary pollutants. Some you have already read about. Others you will read about later in the Unit.

primary pollutant: pollutants formed directly from natural activities and human activities.

secondary pollutant: pollutants formed from primary pollutants.

Primary Pollutants	Secondary Pollutants
Sulfur dioxide (SO_2) ⟶	Sulfur trioxide (SO_3) and Acid rain
Nitrogen oxides (NO_x) ⟶	Nitrogen dioxide (NO_2), Ground-level ozone (O_3), and Acid rain
Carbon monoxide (CO)	
Particulate matter, soot	
Volatile organic compounds (VOC's)	
Toxic metals (mercury)	

Update the *Project Board*

Add what you now know about ozone and smog formation to the *What are we learning?* column of the *Project Board*. Include what you know about primary and secondary pollutants. Record your evidence in the *What is our evidence?* column. You may have identified some questions you need to answer to better understand the pollution in Los Angeles or to answer the *Big Question*. Add those to the *What do we need to investigate?* column.

What's the Point?

Most of the atmospheric pollutants in Los Angeles are primary pollutants caused by combustion of fuels in cars, trucks, and other vehicles. A primary pollutant is a pollutant formed as a direct result of human or other activities. However, ozone (O_3) and nitrogen dioxide (NO_2), the major components of smog, are secondary pollutants. Secondary pollutants form in the air from primary pollutants. Ozone high up in the stratosphere protects life on Earth from the Sun's UV radiation. However, ground ozone in the air is very harmful. It can cause chest pain, coughing, sore throat, head congestion, and diseases of the lungs. Bad ozone also damages vegetation and ecosystems.

Ozone is one harmful component of smog. It is generated in dangerous quantities when the nitrogen oxides (NO and NO_2) react with volatile organic compounds (VOC's) in sunlight. The nitrogen oxides are products of combustion. VOC's result from the evaporation of fuel and chemical solvents. The chemical reactions that cause smog are photochemical reactions. This means they require sunlight. A greater amount of smog is produced when the weather is sunnier.

Groud ozone can make asthma worse.

3.5 Explore

What Other Factors Contribute to the Air Quality in Los Angeles?

Los Angeles is a large city with about 9 million people. New York City and its surrounding region have about the same size population. Both cities have lots of cars, are seaports, and have airports. But the pollution in Los Angeles is much worse than in New York City. You will look at maps of Los Angeles and New York City to help you identify the geographic factors that are contributing to the poor air quality in Los Angeles. Then you will think about how the **climate** might affect air quality. Finally, you will observe models showing how the climate and geographic features of Los Angeles contribute to its pollution.

climate: the normal weather conditions of a region, throughout the year, averaged over a series of years.

Observe

Every area in the United States has geographic and geologic features that affect its air quality. If a city is located on the ocean, winds might carry its pollution out to sea. Or, winds blowing in from the sea might carry the pollution in the opposite direction. In flat areas, the wind usually blows pollution away from cities. Mountains might keep polluted air inside an area.

Look at the maps on the next page of the Los Angeles area and New York City to see what you can figure out about how the geography of Los Angeles might affect its air quality.

1. Compare the geography that is west of Los Angeles with the geography that is west of New York City. What is the same? What is different?

2. Prevailing winds in the United States generally blow from the west or southwest. With this in mind, compare the geography east of Los Angeles with the geography east of New York City. Where will pollutants go in each case?

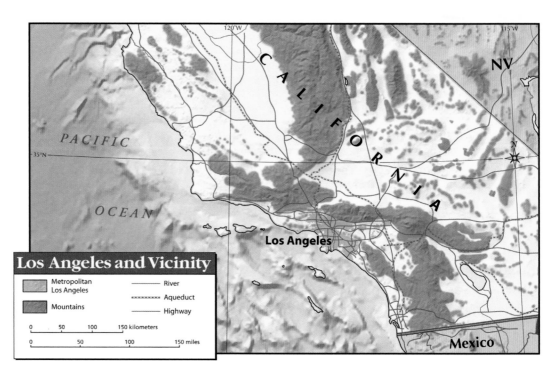

Los Angeles and Vicinity

Metropolitan Los Angeles	——— River
Mountains	·········· Aqueduct
	——— Highway

0   50   100   150 kilometers

0   50   100   150 miles

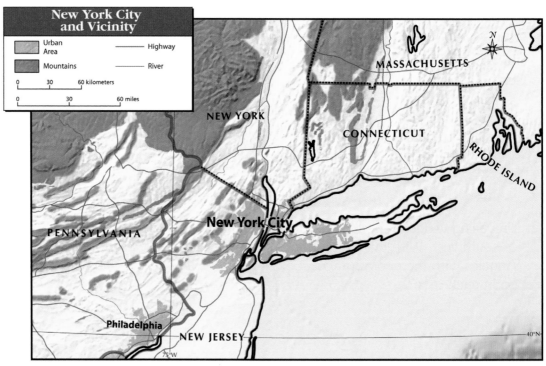

New York City and Vicinity

Urban Area	——— Highway
Mountains	——— River

0   30   60 kilometers

0   30   60 miles

The climate of an area can also affect air quality. Many areas in the Western United States receive more sunshine and are drier than areas along the East Coast. In drier areas, the wind may lift more dust particles into the air. In areas with more sunshine, more smog may form from ground-level ozone. Many areas in the south are warmer and more humid than areas in the north. In areas with a lot of rain, the rain may wash some types of pollution out of the air. Look at the charts showing the climate in Los Angeles and New York to see what you can figure out about how the climate of Los Angeles might affect its air quality.

Los Angeles, CA Climate Data

Average Temperature

	For the Year	Jan.	Feb.	Mar.	Apr.	May	Jun.	Jul.	Aug.	Sep.	Oct.	Nov.	Dec.
°C	18.3	13.8	14.4	15	16.6	17.7	19.4	22.2	22.7	22.2	19.4	17.7	15
°F	65	57	58	59	62	64	67	72	73	72	67	64	59

Average High Temperature

	For the Year	Jan.	Feb.	Mar.	Apr.	May	Jun.	Jul.	Aug.	Sep.	Oct.	Nov.	Dec.
°C	22.7	18.3	18.8	20	21.1	22.7	24.4	27.7	27.7	27.2	25	22.7	20
°F	73	65	66	68	70	73	76	82	82	81	77	73	68

Average Low Temperature

	For the Year	Jan.	Feb.	Mar.	Apr.	May	Jun.	Jul.	Aug.	Sep.	Oct.	Nov.	Dec.
°C	12.7	8.8	9.4	10	11.6	13.3	14.4	16.6	17.2	16.1	14.4	11.6	10
°F	55	48	49	50	53	56	58	62	63	61	58	53	50

Average Precipitation

	For the Year	Jan.	Feb.	Mar.	Apr.	May	Jun.	Jul.	Aug.	Sep.	Oct.	Nov.	Dec.
cm	35.6	6.9	7.9	5.6	3.3	0.8	0.3	0	0	0.5	1.0	2.8	6.4
in.	14	2.7	3.1	2.2	1.3	0.3	0.1	0	0	0.2	0.4	1.1	2.5

Average number of days above 32°C (90°F)

	For the Year	Jan.	Feb.	Mar.	Apr.	May	Jun.	Jul.	Aug.	Sep.	Oct.	Nov.	Dec.
Days	16	0	0	0	1	1	1	3	3	5	3	1	0

3. Look at the data for average daily temperatures for Los Angeles and New York City. During what time of year do you see the highest temperatures? These are the most likely times for ozone and smog.

What difference do you see in the average daily temperatures of Los Angeles and New York City?

4. Look at the data for average rainfall. You already know that rain cleans the air. How do you think the average rainfall in Los Angeles contributes to its pollution?

New York, NY Climate Data

Average Temperature

	For the Year	Jan.	Feb.	Mar.	Apr.	May	Jun.	Jul.	Aug.	Sep.	Oct.	Nov.	Dec.
°C	12.7	0	1	6.1	12	17.2	22.2	25	24	20	15	8.8	3
°F	55	32	34	43	53	63	72	77	76	68	58	48	37

Average High Temperature

	For the Year	Jan.	Feb.	Mar.	Apr.	May	Jun.	Jul.	Aug.	Sep.	Oct.	Nov.	Dec.
°C	17.2	3.3	4.4	10	16.1	22.2	26.6	29.4	28.8	24	18.3	12.2	6.1
°F	63	38	40	50	61	72	80	85	84	76	65	54	43

Average Low Temperature

	For the Year	Jan.	Feb.	Mar.	Apr.	May	Jun.	Jul.	Aug.	Sep.	Oct.	Nov.	Dec.
°C	8.3	-3.3	-2.7	1.7	7	12.2	17.2	20.5	19	15.5	10	5	-0.5
°F	47	26	27	35	44	54	63	69	67	60	50	41	31

Average Precipitation

	For the Year	Jan.	Feb.	Mar.	Apr.	May	Jun.	Jul.	Aug.	Sep.	Oct.	Nov.	Dec.
cm	188.6	8.8	7.9	10.2	9.7	11.2	9.1	11.2	10.4	10.2	8.6	11.2	9.7
in.	46.7	3.5	3.1	4.0	3.8	4.4	3.6	4.4	4.1	4.0	3.4	4.4	3.8

Average Number of Days Above 32°C (90°F)

	For the Year	Jan.	Feb.	Mar.	Apr.	May	Jun.	Jul.	Aug.	Sep.	Oct.	Nov.	Dec.
Days	19	0	0	0	0	1	3	8	5	1	0	0	0

Reflect

Why do you think the air in Los Angeles is so much more polluted than the air in New York City? Use your observations to justify your answer. Discuss your answers with the class. Later, you will observe models that will allow you to better understand the answer to this question, and you will have a chance to answer it again.

Observe

Convection, Part 1

The air near Los Angeles is much warmer than the air near New York City. The air warms up and stays warm. This warmed air moves in a **convection** current.

You will be watching a video of the convection model. The water in the model represents air. Liquid water and gaseous air are both fluids. A fluid is matter that can flow. Even though they are different states of matter, the flow of water can be used to represent the flow of air. As you watch, notice how the warm water moves and how the cold water moves. After you have observed the model two times, you will match the parts of the model to the features around Los Angeles.

convection: the transfer of heat in a fluid through a current made up of warm, rising fluid and cool, sinking fluid.

Analyze Your Data

1. Describe what you saw in the convection model. On a *Convection and Inversion* page, sketch what you saw, and label the parts of the model. Indicate the direction in which the water (representing air) moves. Indicate where the warmer water and the cooler water are in the model.

2. What do you think is the source of energy that heats the air in Los Angeles?

3. Imagine that the convection model was Los Angeles in the summer. What happens to the polluted air?

4. What would be different in New York City? Why?

Convection and Inversion	3.5.1

Name: _____ Date: _____

Circle One: Convection   Inversion

Describe what you saw in the model. Sketch the model and label the parts of the model. Sketch the direction the water (air) moves. Indicate where the warmer water (air) and the cooler water (air) are in the model.

© It's About Time

Observe

Convection, Part 2

You have seen the process of convection. As the water moves in the model, the warmer water moves to the top. The process of convection happens in the Los Angeles area and has a large impact on the air quality in the area.

Watch the convection video again. This time, the parts of the model in the video are labeled.

Analyze Your Data

1. How did the parts in your original sketch compare with the parts labeled on the second video?

2. Examine your answers to the questions you answered after watching the first video. Answer each question again.

> ### How Does the Convection Video Model the Air in Los Angeles?
> When air near Earth's surface is warmed, its particles spread out, and the air rises. The particles of the cooler air above the warm air are packed more tightly together. This air then sinks. As the warm air rises, it cools, while the cool air close to the ground warms. Again, the warm air rises, and the cooler air sinks. The continuous process of rising and sinking air forms a pattern known as a convection current. The process of convection transfers heat through a fluid by the movement of particles.

Observe

Inversion, Part 1

thermal inversion: a weather condition where an overlaying mass of heated air prevents the circulation of air beneath it, stopping convection.

The convection process you observed in the earlier video is the air pattern that occurs under normal circumstances. It shows how air moves when it is free to move anywhere. All over the world, convection currents move air from one area to another. In some places, however, geography prevents air from flowing freely. In Los Angeles, mountains tower high over the region to the north, east, and south. These mountains affect how the air can move.

You will now watch a video that models an atmospheric condition called **thermal inversion**. In an inversion, the position, or arrangement, of something is changed. The video will show you what a thermal inversion is. Thermal inversion is common in Los Angeles. As in the other model, the water in this model represents air. Watch what happens to the warmer water and the cooler water in the model. Remember that this model is similar to Los Angeles. Cool water moves in and bumps against an obstacle. It cannot move freely. Watch what happens to the cool water, and watch what happens to the warm water. You will watch the video two times.

Analyze Your Data

1. On a new *Convection and Inversion* page, sketch the path of the water that you observed, and label the parts of the model.

2. Compare the water movement in this video to the water movement in the convection video.

3. Imagine that the cool water in this model represents cool air coming in to Los Angeles from the ocean, and the obstacles represent the mountains to the north, east, and south of Los Angeles. How do you think these air movements affect the air quality in Los Angeles?

4. Do you think it would be different in New York City? Why or why not?

Observe

Inversion, Part 2

Watch the video again. This time, the parts of the model are labeled.

Analyze Your Data

1. How did the parts in your original sketch compare with the parts labeled on the second video?

2. Examine your answers to the questions you answered after watching the first video. Answer each question again.

Reflect

1. Which parts of the inversion model match the geographic features of the Los Angeles region? For example, which features represent the mountains?

2. Think about the models you observed. If these models are accurate, what happens to the air of Los Angeles as it moves from west to east and bumps into the mountain range?

3. Why do you think the number of sunny days in Los Angeles affects its air pollution?

Why Do Thermal Inversions Happen?

Thermal inversions are common to Los Angeles because of its unique combination of geography, climate, and population. In normal convection, warm air near the ground rises into cooler air higher up. As warm air mixes with cooler air, the pollution breaks up. The rising air helps carry pollutants up and away from the ground.

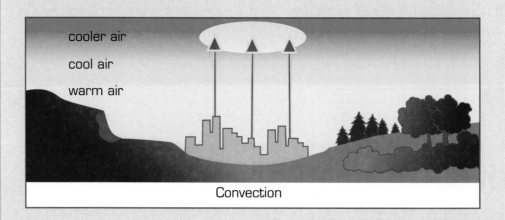

Convection

However, in a thermal inversion, warm air sits on top of cold air and acts like a lid. This is the situation you observed in the second video. When this happens, the warm air and cool air cannot mix, and the pollutants are not broken up and carried away.

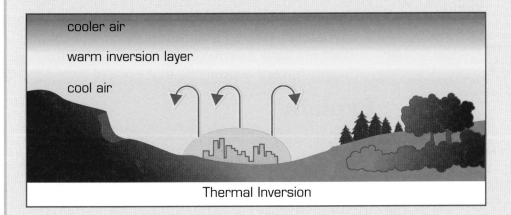

cooler air

warm inversion layer

cool air

Thermal Inversion

In California, cool air from the ocean blows in at ground level during the night, especially in the winter. Normally, when the Sun rises, this air heats up, rises, and convection begins. But when the air above the cool air is warmer than normal, the cool air mass cannot rise. It gets "stuck" against the mountains and might stay there for several days.

Meanwhile, car exhausts continuously emit nitrogen oxides, carbon monoxide, and VOC's. The longer the thermal inversion lasts, the more pollution builds up in the air. The increased pollutants, combined with heat from the Sun, cause ozone levels to exceed safe health levels. A cloud of smog covers the city. It blocks vision and causes eye irritation and lung distress. During these "smog alert" days, people are cautioned to remain inside as much as possible. Thermal inversions in Los Angeles are serious health hazards, causing lung problems, asthma, and even death for people who are already ill.

Reflect

Answer the following questions with your group. Be prepared to share your answers with the class.

1. Why do you think warm air rises? To answer, use what you know about gases, mass, behavior of molecules, and temperature.

2. Geography and frequent thermal inversions cause Los Angeles to have the worst air quality in the United States. What factors cause Los Angeles to have frequent thermal inversions?

3. What do you think a community can do to decrease air pollution during thermal inversions?

4. Do you think your community experiences thermal inversions? Why or why not? If your community does not have thermal inversions, describe the factors in your community that prevent inversions.

Create Your Explanation

1.3.2/2.BBQ.2/3.5.2
4.2.2/4.6.7/4.7.1/ABQ.2

Name: _____ Date: _____

Use this page to explain the lesson of your recent investigations.

Write a brief summary of the results from your investigation. You will use this summary to help you write your Explanation.

Claim – a statement of what you understand or a conclusion that you have reached from an investigation or a set of investigations.

Evidence – data collected during investigations and trends in that data.

Science knowledge – knowledge about how things work. You may have learned this through reading, talking to an expert, discussion, or other experiences.

Write your Explanation using the **Claim**, **Evidence**, and **Science knowledge**.

© It's About Time

Explain

Now that you know about Los Angeles and the factors that affect its air quality, you will explain the causes of its poor air quality. Begin by developing a claim about factors that affect air quality in Los Angeles. Record your claim on a *Create Your Explanation* page. Use as evidence what you know about the pollutants, and the geography, population, and climate of Los Angeles. Record science knowledge that supports your claim from your experiences. It may also come from readings. Then write a statement that connects your claim to the evidence and science knowledge. This is your explanation. A good explanation statement will describe how the geography, pollutants, and climate of Los Angeles act together to cause Los Angeles's air pollution.

Communicate

Share Your Revised Explanation

Share your group's claim and explanation with the class. Tell the class what makes your claim accurate based on your evidence and science knowledge. Pay special attention to how the other groups have supported their claims with science knowledge and to other groups' explanation statements. Ask questions or make suggestions if you think a group's claim is not as accurate as it could be, if the group has not supported their claim well enough with evidence and science knowledge, or if you think a group's explanation statement is not complete or accurate.

Revise Your Explanation

As a class, develop a claim and explanation statement that the entire class agrees with. Notice any disagreements class members have. Develop questions for the *Project Board* that can be answered to settle any disagreements.

Update the *Project Board*

Use the *Project Board* to record what you have learned about convection and inversion in the *What are we learning?* column. Include what you know about thermal inversion and the effect of inversions on air pollution, especially in Los Angeles. Record your evidence in the *What is our evidence?* column. Add any questions the class has developed to the *What do we need to investigate?* column.

What's the Point?

The pollution problems in Los Angeles are due to a combination of climate, combustion products, and geography. The large population in Los Angeles results in a large number of cars and other sources of combustion. The cars, in turn, produce nitrogen oxides, carbon monoxide, and VOC's. The nitrogen oxides and VOC's, combined with sunlight, lead to the formation of ozone and smog.

The geography of Los Angeles adds to its pollution. Los Angeles has the Pacific Ocean to the west. Mountains surround it on the other three sides. These mountains trap the air, making Los Angeles likely to have thermal inversions, often for several days at a time.

In the normal situation of convection, warm air close to land rises and mixes with colder air in the upper atmosphere. Convection moves pollution away from the land and dilutes it in the upper atmosphere. In thermal inversion, warm air sits on top of colder air, holding it in place. Pollutants stay trapped in the colder air, close to the ground. The mountains east of Los Angeles keep the cold air from escaping out from under the "lid" of warm air.

dense: having a high mass per unit volume.

density: the relationship between the mass and volume of a substance. Density is calculated by dividing the mass by the volume.

metal: a substance, usually a solid that is hard, shiny, can conduct electricity, and can be made into a wire. Metals are found on the left side and center of the Periodic Table of the Elements.

Materials

• **aluminum cube**

• **copper cube**

• **balance**

• **metric ruler**

• *Density of Solids* **page**

• **Periodic Table of the Elements chart**

More to Learn

Density and States of Matter

You may wonder why warm air rises and cool air sinks during convection. The reason is that warm air is less **dense** than cool air. **Density** has to do with how much mass fits into a certain volume.

You learned earlier that anything that has mass and volume is matter. Mass and volume are two physical properties of matter. The relationship between the mass and volume of a sample of matter is density. In a series of explorations, you will calculate density and compare densities of solids, liquids, and gases.

You will learn more about what density means as you do this activity.

Density of Two Solids

You will soon examine two solid objects that are the same size. One is made of the element aluminum (Al). This means that all of its atoms are aluminum atoms. The other is made of the element copper (Cu). All of its atoms are copper atoms. These elements both have special properties that make them **metals**. You will examine both metals and calculate their densities.

Procedure: Calculating the Densty of two Solids

1. Record descriptions of the two metals on your *Density of Solids* page. How are they similar? How are they different? Which do you think has more mass? Why?

Cubes of aluminum (left) and copper (right).

2. Using a balance, measure the mass of each cube. Record the masses and circle the greater mass.

3. Measure the length of one side of each cube. The volume of a cube is found by multiplying the length by the width by the height. For a cube, the length, width, and height are all the same length, s.

$$V_{cube} = side \times side \times side = s^3$$

If the length of each side is measured in centimeters, the volume is measured in cubic centimeters, cm³. Calculate the volume of each cube in cubic centimeters.

4. Determine the density of each cube.

$$density = \frac{mass}{volume}$$

For each cube, divide the mass of the cube by the volume of that cube.

Analyze Your Data

1. Which cube has a larger mass? Which is more dense?

2. Find the symbol for aluminum (Al) on the Periodic Table. What is the atomic mass of aluminum? Now find copper. What is the atomic mass of copper? Compare the atomic masses. Which element has the greater atomic mass?

3. Even though the cubes have the same volume, they have different densities. Why is this?

4. Both cubes are matter, and they have mass and volume. They are also made up of atoms. How would you describe the number of atoms in each cube to a friend?

5. Think about the atoms in matter. Why would two cubes, equal in volume, have different masses?

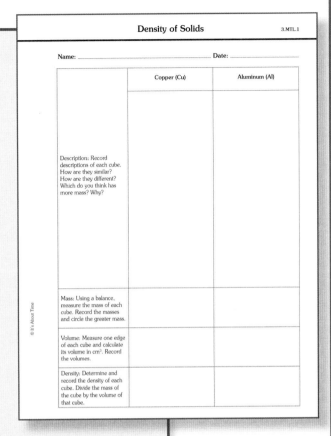

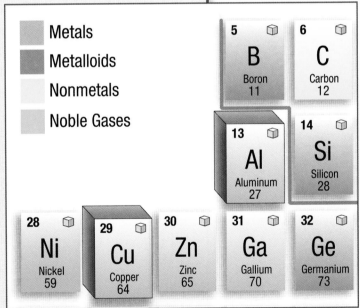

PBIS

ratio: one number divided by another.

How Is Density Measured?

Density is the **ratio** of mass of a substance to its volume. If you know the mass and volume of a sample of matter, you can use an equation to calculate its density.

$$\text{density} = \frac{\text{mass}}{\text{volume}}$$

When mass is measured in grams (g) and volume is measured in cubic centimeters (cm³), the unit for density is grams per cubic centimeter (g/cm³). Sometimes mass is measured in kilograms (kg) and volume in cubic meters (m³). In this case, the unit for density would be kilograms per cubic meter (kg/m³). For liquids and gases, density might be measured in grams per milliliter (g/mL).

When you looked at the atomic mass of copper, you found it was about 64, compared to 27 for aluminum. Yet the atoms are approximately the same size. This means that identical cubes of each element contain about the same number of atoms. So each atom of copper is about 2.4 times as dense as each atom of aluminum. The large difference in density is caused by a large difference in the mass of the nuclei. Remember that the nucleus of an atom is very small compared to the size of the atom, yet it contains essentially all of the mass of the atom. The copper nucleus contains 29 protons and 35 neutrons. Each aluminum nucleus has 13 protons and 14 neutrons.

A more familiar example might help you understand density better. If you measured the mass of a 1 m³ box of feathers and an identical box filled with rocks, which would you expect to have the greater mass?

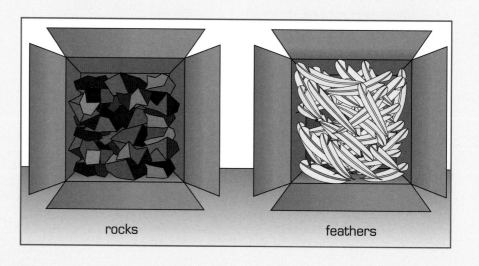

rocks   feathers

The box of rocks would have the greater mass. Since both boxes have the same volume, the box of rocks would have the greater density. This is because each rock is more dense than each feather. This is similar to what you measured with the cubes.

Stop and Think

1. What do you think would happen to the density of the cube of copper if you cut the cube in half? Think about how this would change the mass and the volume of the cube. Compare the changes in mass and volume to each other.

2. What is the relationship among density, mass, and volume?

Density of Three Liquids

In this exploration, you will explore the densities of three different liquids. The liquids are water, vegetable oil, and glycerin (a substance in hand lotion). All the liquids are colorless. Therefore, food coloring has been added to the water and glycerin so you can tell them apart. Record all of your observations and data on your *Density of Liquids* page.

Procedure: Finding the Density of Your Liquids

1. Describe each liquid and record your descriptions on your *Density of Liquids* page.

2. Measure and record the mass of the graduated cylinder.

3. Begin with one of the liquids. Using the graduated pipette, measure 2.0 mL of the liquid. Record the volume of the liquid on the *Density of Liquids* page.

4. Place the liquid you selected in a graduated cylinder by slowly running it down the inside wall of the cylinder.

5. Measure the total mass of the graduated cylinder and the liquid. Record this mass. Subtract the mass of the graduated cylinder from the mass of the combined cylinder and liquid to find the mass of the liquid alone. Record this mass on your *Density of Liquids* page.

Density of Liquids   3.MTL.2

Name: _____ Date: _____

Record the mass of the graduated cylinder: _____

	Water	Glycerin	Vegetable oil
Description of liquid			
Volume of liquid			
Mass of liquid			
Density of liquid			

	Record prediction or results. Sketch prediction or results.
Your prediction of how the liquids will stack	
Group prediction of how the liquids will stack	
Results of how the liquids stacked	

© It's About Time

Materials

- **4 test tubes**
- **test tube rack**
- **colored markers**
- **graduated cylinders, 10-mL**
- **vegetable oil**
- **water with red food coloring**
- **glycerin with blue food coloring**
- **3 graduated pipettes**
- **balance**
- **safety goggles**
- ***Density of Liquids* page**

6. Calculate the density of the liquid by dividing its mass by its volume. Record the density for this liquid on your *Density of Liquids* page. Be sure you record this number in the correct space.

7. Pour the liquid into a test tube, and set it aside in the test tube rack. Clean the graduated cylinder and dry it before measuring the mass of the next liquid.

8. Follow this same procedure for the other two liquids. Remember to record the masses and volumes in the correct places on your *Density of Liquids* page.

Predict

In the next part of this investigation, you will build a density column using your three different liquids. A density column is an arrangement of substances in order of density. It does not matter in what order you pour the liquids into the column. They will always settle the same way. You will begin by using what you know about density to predict their order.

1. You will use the samples of each of the three liquids to build your density column: vegetable oil, water, and glycerin.

2. Working by yourself, list the liquids from most dense to least dense. What characteristics do you think will affect where in the column each liquid will stack?

3. Still working by yourself, sketch the way you think the liquids will stack on your *Density of Liquids* page. Where do you think each liquid will end up in the column? Use colors and labels so that your diagram is clear to someone else.

Conference

Before you actually place the liquids in the clean test tube, share your prediction with your group. Describe why you think the liquids will stack according to your prediction. Listen carefully as your group members describe their ideas. Compare your predictions. Look for differences in how others ordered the liquids. Ask your group members why they made their predictions. Make a group prediction. Record the group prediction on your *Density of Liquids* page.

Procedure: Layering Your Liquids

To make your column, use the clean test tube and a separate pipette for each liquid, following the order your group predicted.

1. Use a pipette to place each liquid in the test tube, starting with the bottom layer. Drop the liquids in the order your group predicted. Try to drip each liquid down the center without touching the sides of the test tube. It is all right if the liquids mix a little.

2. Place your density column in the test tube rack. Observe your density column until the liquids have settled. They may move after you have layered them.

3. Next to your prediction on your *Density of Liquids* page, draw the ordering of the liquids as you observed in your results. Use colors and labels to make sure you sketch an accurate density column showing how each of the liquids is layered.

Conference

Discuss with your group how your prediction compared to your results. How did your prediction differ from your results? What would you do differently if you could layer the liquids again?

Communicate Your Results

Investigation Expo

Display your density column for the class in an *Investigation Expo*. Make a small poster that shows the density layers that you made. On the poster, make sure you include

- information on the order in which you added your liquids;

- the mass, volume, and density of each liquid; and

- sketches of how your column looked after you added each liquid.

Walk around the room and examine all of the posters and density columns. When you look at the other density columns and the other groups' analyses, pay attention to the similarities and differences among them. Ask questions if you do not understand what they found or how they analyzed their data.

Reflect

1. How different were the columns in your class? Why do you think they were similar or different?

2. If you were given another liquid, with a density of 1.5 g/mL, where would it form a layer in the density column? Sketch a new density column with the three liquids you used and the fourth liquid.

3. Solids vary in density, as do liquids. What do you think about gases? How do you think the density of gases might vary?

The Density of Two Gases

You have seen that solids and liquids vary in density, and that the density of these states of matter does not change based on the amount, or the volume, of the substance. The question now is whether gases can be more or less dense than each other or than solids or liquids. To answer that question, you will explore two familiar examples.

The Helium Balloon

Imagine you have two identical balloons. You fill each balloon with the same volume of gas. The first balloon you fill with helium gas. The second balloon you fill with oxygen gas.

Predict

If you let the two balloons go, what will happen to the balloon filled with helium? What will happen to the balloon filled with oxygen? Sketch what you think will happen.

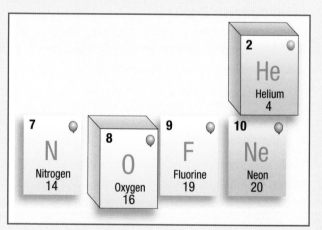

Reflect

1. How do you think helium gas differs from oxygen gas?

2. Find the symbol for helium (He) on the Periodic Table. What is the atomic mass of helium? Now find the symbol for oxygen (O) on the Periodic Table. What is the atomic mass of oxygen? Compare the atomic masses. Which element has the lower atomic mass?

3. How do you think the atomic mass of each element relates to the way the balloons act when you release them?

The Hot Air Balloon

You may not be as familiar with hot air balloons as with helium balloons. In a hot air balloon, the balloon rises as the air inside the balloon is heated. Look at these balloons. Both balloons hold the same volume of air. One balloon is filled with hot air, and the other balloon is filled with cold air.

Predict

If you cut the ropes, the hot air balloon will rise, but the balloon filled with cold air will not. Do your best to describe why.

Reflect

Reread the box in *Learning Set 1* about phase changes. Use what you read there to imagine the differences between molecules of cool air and molecules of warm air. Answer these questions. Be prepared to share your answers with the class.

1. Using what you read in *Section 1.4*, answer these questions.

   a) What do you think happens to the molecules in air as the air heats up?

   b) What do you think happens to the molecules in air as the air cools down?

2. Describe how the movement of the molecules differs in the two balloons.

3. Describe how you would determine which gas is more dense.

4. Sketch a picture of the air molecules in the balloon filled with cold air.

5. Sketch a picture of the air molecules in the hot air balloon.

6. Using what you read in *Section 1.4*, answer these questions.

    a) How do you think what happens to the air molecules affects what happens to the balloons when you cut the ropes?

    b) How does cooling and heating create normal convection? How does cooling and heating play a role in thermal inversion?

    c) Discuss in class how the temperature of the air can affect air quality, particularly in a city such as Los Angeles.

A hot air balloon fair in Iowa.

Properties of Matter

Some properties of matter, known as **extensive properties**, depend on the amount of matter present in a sample. For example, if you remove half of a sample of salt, the mass of the sample will change. It will decrease by one half. Mass, volume, length, and weight are examples of extensive properties.

Other properties of matter, known as **intensive properties**, do not depend on the amount of matter present in a sample. You may have discovered that density is an intensive property. No matter how much pure gold you have, the density will always be the same. Color, odor, boiling point, melting point, and the ability to conduct electricity are other intensive properties.

extensive property: property of matter that depends on the amount of matter present in a sample, for example, the mass of the matter.

intensive property: property of matter that do not depend on the amount of matter present in a sample, for example, the density of the matter.

Learning Set 3

Back to the Big Question

How Can You Improve Air Quality in Your Community?

Los Angeles has some serious air-quality issues. Its air quality is affected by the number of people who live in the area, the climate, and the geography. All these factors work together to create a situation that is very complicated.

There are many other big cities in the United States. Some have air-quality issues, too. Others have much better air quality. To complete this *Learning Set*, you will think about all the factors you learned about in the Los Angeles case study and apply those ideas to a new city, Denver, Colorado, to try to determine what causes air-quality issues in Denver. Then you will use what you have learned to think about the air quality in your community.

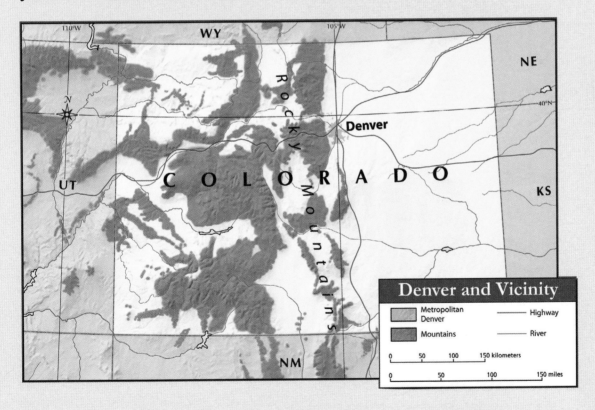

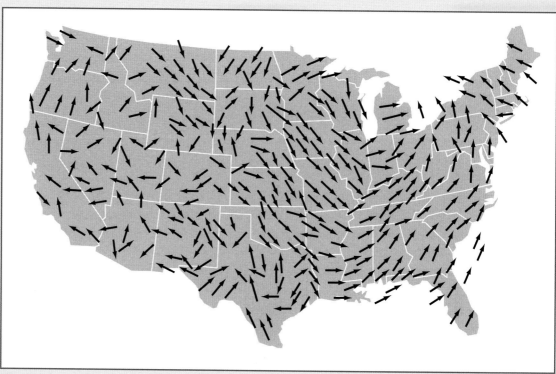

Wind patterns across the United States.

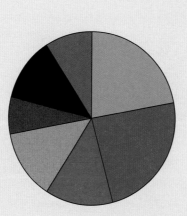

■ Vehicle exhaust - 22%

■ Wood burning - 24%

■ Geologic natural
sources - 13%

■ Nitrates
(agriculture) - 13%

■ Sulfates
(power plants) - 7%

■ Nitrogen dioxide
(power plants and
factories) - 12%

■ Other
(dust and
construction) - 9%

Sources of air pollution in Denver, Colorado.

Conference

You know that population, climate, and geography all play a role in the air quality in Los Angeles. Look at the relief map of Colorado, the wind currents, pollution sources, and the table of climate data to identify factors that you think might affect air quality in Denver. Then answer the questions.

Denver, Colorado Climate Data

Average Temperature

	For the Year	Jan.	Feb.	Mar.	Apr.	May	Jun.	Jul.	Aug.	Sep.	Oct.	Nov.	Dec.
°C	10.5	1.1	1.1	3.8	8.8	14.4	20	22.7	22.2	17.2	11.1	3.8	0
°F	51	30	34	39	48	58	68	73	72	63	52	39	32

Average High Temperature

	For the Year	Jan.	Feb.	Mar.	Apr.	May	Jun.	Jul.	Aug.	Sep.	Oct.	Nov.	Dec.
°C	17.7	6.1	8.3	11.1	16.6	21.6	27.7	31.1	30	25	18.8	11.1	7.2
°F	64	43	47	52	62	71	82	88	86	77	66	52	45

Average Low Temperature

	For the Year	Jan.	Feb.	Mar.	Apr.	May	Jun.	Jul.	Aug.	Sep.	Oct.	Nov.	Dec.
°C	2.8	-8.9	-6.7	-3.3	1.7	6.7	11.6	15	13.9	8.8	2.8	3.9	-7.8
°F	37	16	20	26	35	44	53	59	57	48	37	25	18

Average Precipitation

	For the Year	Jan.	Feb.	Mar.	Apr.	May	Jun.	Jul.	Aug.	Sep.	Oct.	Nov.	Dec.
cm	39.1	1.3	15	3.3	4.6	6.4	4.3	4.8	3.8	2.8	2.5	2.3	1.5
in.	15.4	0.5	0.6	1.3	1.8	2.5	1.7	1.9	1.5	1.1	1.0	0.9	0.6

Average Number of Days Above 32°C (90°F)

	For the Year	Jan.	Feb.	Mar.	Apr.	May	Jun.	Jul.	Aug.	Sep.	Oct.	Nov.	Dec.
Days	34	0	0	0	0	0	7	14	10	3	0	0	0

1. Which factors do you think affect Denver's air quality? Why?

2. How do you think each factor you listed affects Denver's air quality?

3. Do you think there are thermal inversions in Denver? Why or why not?

4. How often will you expect thermal inversions in Denver? Will they be frequent, as they are in Los Angeles, or more rare? Why?

5. What time of year do you expect to see thermal inversions in Denver? Why?

Pull all of your answers together to make a prediction about the air quality in Denver.

Communicate Your Results

Investigation Expo

Share your predictions about Denver with the class in an *Investigation Expo*. Make a poster or other visual aid that includes the following information:

- the specific factors (population, climate, geography, pollution sources, etc.) that led to your prediction. Describe how you think these factors affect Denver's air quality.

- sketches or other depictions of how convection and thermal inversion would occur in Denver.

- a short paragraph describing your ideas about what affects air quality in Denver. You might compare and contrast to Los Angeles's air quality to help everyone understand your thinking.

When it is your group's turn to present, each member of your group should present one part of your prediction. Make sure you identify the impact of each factor that played an important role in Denver.

When you listen to other presentations, pay attention to the similarities and differences among them. Ask questions if you do not understand what evidence other groups used or how they interpreted that evidence.

Air Quality in Your Community

The *Big Question* for this Unit is *How can you improve air quality in your community?* To answer this question, you have to think carefully about the air quality in your community and the factors that affect it. You know several factors that affect the air quality in Los Angeles, and you have predicted how those factors may affect another big city. Now using what you know about these factors, you will think about how these factors might affect the air quality in your community. Answer the questions below. You may already know the answers, or you may have to look them up.

- Population: What is the population of your community, and how might the population impact the air quality in your area?

- Climate: In Los Angeles, sunlight and heat created a situation of increasingly bad air quality. How might the climate of your community affect the air quality where you live?

- Geography: Geography affects the possibility of thermal inversions. How might geography affect the air quality of your community?

- Sources of pollution: Your air walk may have introduced you to some of the sources of pollution in your area. What other sources do you now know about? How might those sources affect the air quality in your community?

Communicate

Share with the class your answers to the questions above. Pay attention to the other groups' answers and how they differ from your answers.

Reflect

You have heard how other groups applied factors that affect air pollution to your community. You might have heard ideas that you did not think about. Discuss with your group how you might now answer the same questions. Identify what else you need to learn about your community and about improving air quality to answer the *Big Question*.

Update the *Project Board*

In this *Learning Set*, you investigated pollutants and how those pollutants get into the air. You explored density and how density relates to air quality. You observed how temperature and density affect convection and thermal inversions in air. Then you read about how these factors, combined with geography and climate, affect one city—Los Angeles, California. Finally, you applied your knowledge to make a prediction about thermal inversions in Denver, Colorado. You began to collect data about factors that might affect the air quality in your community.

Now it is time to update the *Project Board*. Add to the *What are we learning?* column what you have learned about air pollutants, density, convection, and inversion. Add what you learned about the geography, climate, and other factors that contribute to air pollution. Record your evidence in the *What is our evidence?* column. Record in the *What do we think we know?* column anything you now think you know about how density, climate, and geography affect air pollution and, particularly, air pollution in your community. Record questions you have about other pollutants you want to know more about and how you can manage air quality in your community, in the *What do we need to investigate?* column.

The air in Denver looks clean, but Denver has some of the same air-quality problems as Los Angeles.

Learning Set 4

How Does Air Pollution Affect Other Regions?

The picture below shows a beautiful scene from the Adirondack Mountains of New York State. The green trees, mountains, streams, and wildlife you see are just a small part of a huge preserve dedicated as the Adirondack Park with the words "...the lands here or hereafter constituting the Forest preserve shall be forever kept as wild forest lands..." The Adirondack Park is the largest park in the adjoining United States and the largest area protected by any state. It is located in the northeastern part of New York.

The Adirondack Mountains is a mostly unpopulated region.

At first glance, the region generally known as the Adirondacks looks clean and beautiful. Unfortunately, things are not always as they seem. The air in the Adirondacks is not as clean as it looks.

The downward trend in the quality of the air in the Adirondacks has affected the entire environment. For example, one of the lakes of the region, Big Moose Lake, shows an example of the change. Back in 1951, the lake was filled with trout, crayfish, frogs, and other aquatic organisms. Living things that make their homes in a water environment are known as aquatic organisms. Today, nearly all the aquatic organisms are gone from Big Moose Lake. The animals that depend on the aquatic organisms for food, such as otters, are also gone. Big Moose Lake is not alone. The changes that have occurred at Big Moose Lake can be observed in lakes throughout the Adirondacks.

Big Moose Lake was once home to all kinds of fish and other aquatic organisms, as well as the animals that depended on them for food. Today, nearly all of this wildlife is gone.

Scientists have studied the changes in the environment of the Adirondack area for over 40 years. They have collected data on sources and effects of air quality. In this *Learning Set*, you will consider some of these data and learn why the air-quality issues in this area exist. Understanding the sources and effects of air pollution in the Adirondacks will help you answer the *Big Question, How can you improve air quality in your community?*

4.1 Understand the Question

Think About How Air Pollution Affects Other Regions

When scientists study some problems, such as air quality, they consider several different cases to identify what is similar and what is different. This method helps them explain what processes are occurring and how to solve the problems. You are using this same procedure to help you answer the *Big Question*. You saw that in Los Angeles, air-quality problems have resulted from rapid growth and a large population of people, vehicles, trains, airplanes, and industry. Unique geography, geology, and climate add to the problem. Understanding changes in conditions in the Adirondacks will provide other clues about what causes poor air quality.

As you read about the Adirondack area and investigate the sources and effects of its air pollution, think about how this area compares to the areas you know something about: Los Angeles and your community. Think about how the factors that affect those regions might affect air quality in the Adirondack Mountains. Also, pay attention to the other factors that affect the air quality in the Adirondacks. You may need to consider all of the different factors that affect air quality to make recommendations about how to improve the air quality in your community.

Adirondack Park—A Case Study

The Adirondack Park is a very different type of place than the city of Los Angeles. For one thing, it is huge in size. The park covers more than 6 million acres, which is about the size of the entire state of Vermont. Perhaps you have heard of some other parks, such as Yellowstone, Yosemite, Grand Canyon, Glacier, and Great Smoky Mountains National Park. Adirondack Park is larger than all of these parks put together!

In addition to its many lakes, streams, and rivers, Adirondack Park contains the Adirondack Mountains. This mountain range consists of more than 100 different peaks.

Nearly half of Adirondack Park belongs to the people of New York State and is protected so that it remains a "forever wild" forest preserve. The other half of the park is private land. It includes farms, homes, businesses, and camps, along with land for growing trees to be used for wood.

In the Adirondacks, you can find camps and stands of timber.

There are no large cities in the Adirondacks. In the 2000 census, the Adirondack Park had only 132,000 residents. Although the area around the park has grown in population, the population has grown very slowly and is still small. People value the park as a recreational and wilderness area that deserves to be protected. The park has no industry and only a small number of paved roads. There are no large airports and only about 250 km (150 mi) of railway. The Adirondack climate is cool and cloudy with an average of 7.6 cm (3 in.) of precipitation each month of the year.

Although the population, industry, and climate of the Adirondacks is quite different from those of Los Angeles, the Adirondacks region also suffers from air-quality problems. As you read earlier, wildlife has all but disappeared from many of the lakes and the areas around them. In addition, many types of trees have died. Scientists know that many of these changes have resulted from air pollution. Unlike in the city of Los Angeles, the pollution in the Adirondacks is not coming from cars and other vehicles. It must have a different source.

Stop and Think

1. You have examined the sources and effects of air quality in two places: your community and Los Angeles. Use the case study of the Adirondacks to predict sources and effects of air quality in the Adirondacks. Record your sources and effects on a new *Sources and Effects of Air Quality* chart. Remember that effects are what happen as a result of pollution, and sources are where the pollutants come from.

2. Look back at the *Sources and Effects of Air Quality* charts you recorded earlier in the Unit.

   a) What do you think the Adirondacks have in common with your community or with Los Angeles?

   b) Which sources and effects of air quality in the Adirondacks might be similar to the ones you identified? On your chart for the Adirondacks, make a light circle around the sources and effects that you think are similar to those you have seen previously.

   c) Which sources and effects of air quality in the Adirondacks might be different from the ones you identified? On your chart for the Adirondacks, underline the sources and effects that are different from those you have seen previously.

Sources and Effects of Air Quality		
Sources	Effects	How to improve the air

Conference

How do you think pollutants get into the air in the Adirondacks? To find out, begin by finding the Adirondack region on the map below. As a group, use the map to answer these questions.

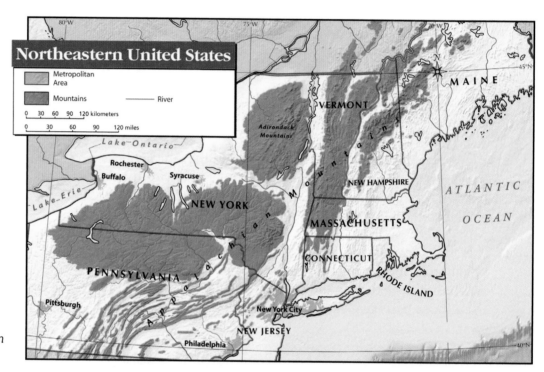

The Northeastern United States.

1. Approximately how much of New York State do the Adirondacks take up?

2. What other geographic features do you notice in the map?

3. What major geographic features are near the Adirondack Mountains? How far away is the largest body of water? In what direction is the water?

4. Large populations, such as those in Los Angeles, produce pollution that affects air quality. Use the map to determine the number of large cities in the Adirondack Mountains.

5. Look at the nighttime map of the Eastern United States on the next page.

   a) Where do you think the Adirondacks are on the map?

   b) What did you use to determine its location?

Continue by sharing with your group the sources you think affect the Adirondacks and the effects they have on air quality. Discuss how you chose the sources you did and how you determined the effects of each source. Identify anything missing in your chart. For example, you may have identified some effect of pollution without identifying its source.

You may agree with your group members on some of their choices. You may also have disagreements. It is important for each member of your group to present why they made their choices and how they determined the effects of each source. Come to a decision, as a group, on a list of sources and effects on air quality you might find in the Adirondacks. Note, too, what you think you still need to know more about and any disagreements you have.

Then look at the climate table of the Adirondacks on the following page, and answer these questions as a group.

National Oceanic and Atmospheric Administration (NOAA) satellite image of the city lights at night over the Eastern United States.

1. What is different about the climate of the Adirondacks and the climate of Los Angeles?

2. How do you think these differences in climate might make the air quality different?

Lake George, NY (Adirondacks) Climate Data

Average Temperature

	For the Year	Jan.	Feb.	Mar.	Apr.	May	Jun.	Jul.	Aug.	Sep.	Oct.	Nov.	Dec.
°C	7	-8	-6	0	7	13	18	21	19	15	9	3	-4
°F	45	17	20	32	45	56	65	70	67	59	48	37	24

Average High Temperature

	For the Year	Jan.	Feb.	Mar.	Apr.	May	Jun.	Jul.	Aug.	Sep.	Oct.	Nov.	Dec.
°C	13	-2	-1	6	13	20	24	28	26	21	14	8	1
°F	56	28	31	42	56	68	76	82	79	70	57	46	33

Average Low Temperature

	For the Year	Jan.	Feb.	Mar.	Apr.	May	Jun.	Jul.	Aug.	Sep.	Oct.	Nov.	Dec.
°C	1	-14	-13	-6	1	7	12	15	13	9	3	2	-9
°F	34	6	9	22	33	44	53	58	56	48	37	29	15

Average Precipitation

	For the Year	Jan.	Feb.	Mar.	Apr.	May	Jun.	Jul.	Aug.	Sep.	Oct.	Nov.	Dec.
cm	91	6.6	5.8	7.4	7.6	9.1	8.1	7.6	9.4	7.9	7.4	7.9	7.6
in.	36	2.6	2.3	2.9	3.0	3.6	3.2	3.0	3.7	3.1	2.9	3.1	3.0

Average Number of Days Above 32°C (90°F)

	For the Year	Jan.	Feb.	Mar.	Apr.	May	Jun.	Jul.	Aug.	Sep.	Oct.	Nov.	Dec.
Days	1.1	0	0	0	0	0	0.2	0.4	0.4	0	0	0	0

Communicate

Share Your Ideas

Your charts contain a lot of information about sources and their effects of air quality in the Adirondacks. Share your sources and effects with the class, and identify any effects for which you cannot identify the source. Also, share with the class the similarities and differences you identified between the Adirondacks and Los Angeles.

As you are listening to others, keep track of what you agree with and what you disagree with. Identify what you need to know more about to resolve your disagreements. After all of the presentations, discuss what you know from earlier in the Unit that might help you identify the sources of pollution in the Adirondacks and what might be going on in the Adirondacks that you have not seen before.

Reflect

1. If you had to make a claim right now about what is causing air pollution in the Adirondacks, what would you claim? Why?

2. Suppose you had to explain what is causing the poor air quality in the Adirondacks. What do you know from earlier in this Unit that might help you make that explanation?

3. What else do you need to know to explain what is causing the poor air quality in the Adirondack Park? Think back to disagreements you had with your classmates about sources and their effects on air quality. These may help you identify what you need to investigate.

Update the *Project Board*

You may have some ideas about what kinds of pollution are affecting air quality in the Adirondacks. Update the *Project Board* with your ideas about what is affecting the air quality in the Adirondacks. Record your ideas in the *What do we think we know?* column. Your class probably did not all agree about what is causing air pollution in the Adirondacks. Identify what you need to learn more about to resolve your disagreements about what is causing air-quality problems in the Adirondacks. Record your questions and ideas for investigations in the *What do we need to investigate?* column.

How can you improve air quality in your community?				
What do we think we know?	What do we need to investigate?	What are we learning?	What is our evidence?	What does it mean for the challenge or question?

AIR QUALITY

What's the Point?

Scientists often look at several different examples when trying to solve a problem. Poor air quality is a problem shared by many different places. The sources and effects may be similar, or they may be different. The New York Adirondacks are a very different type of place than Los Angeles. Because of this, the Adirondacks may have problems that are much different than those in a large city. You may need to understand the air-quality problems in both types of places to identify how to solve air-quality problems in your community.

Many people use the Adirondacks for outdoor activities.

The Adirondacks look very peaceful and beautiful, but plants and animals in the Adirondacks have been damaged by air pollution. You know there is pollution in the air, but you do not know how it got there, and you do not know which pollutants are in the air. In the rest of this *Learning Set,* you will be examining how the pollutants got in the air, what they are, and how air pollution can harm plants and animals.

4.2 Explore

What Causes the Air Pollution in the Adirondacks?

In your case study of Los Angeles, you saw how geography, climate, and human activity caused air pollution. As you examine the Adirondacks, you will continue to see that this area is different from Los Angeles in important ways.

Los Angeles has thousands of businesses, factories, power plants, a major airport, and a marine port. The Adirondacks have none of these.

Comparison of Los Angeles and the Adirondacks		
	Los Angeles	**Adirondacks**
Population	9 million	132,000
Area	1290 km² (498 mi²)	24,700 km² (9537 mi²)
Highway system	80,467 km (50,000 mi)	11,217 km (6970 mi)

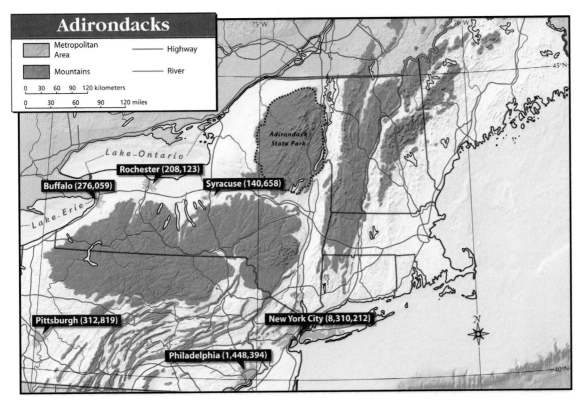

The Adirondack region. The park is the green area at the center top of the map.

Now it is time to answer the question: How did the pollutants get into the air, and which pollutants are in the air in the Adirondacks?

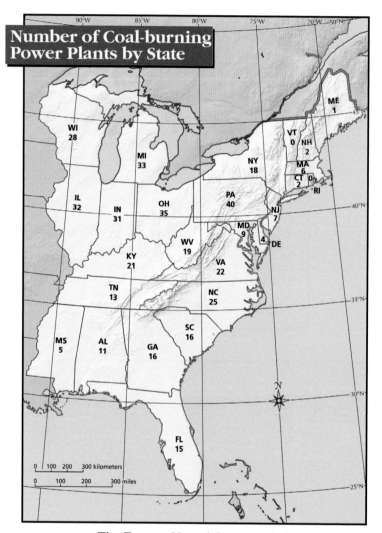

Number of Coal-burning Power Plants by State

The Eastern United States and the number of coal-burning power plants in each state.

Conference

Look at the map of the Adirondack region on the previous page, and look at the map of the eastern half of the United States on this page. The map on this page shows the number of coal-burning power plants by state. Find the chart you made while reading *The Sickening Six* play. Examine what you recorded about air pollutants, and see if you can find sources of any of those pollutants on the maps.

With your group, answer these questions.

1. What causes of air pollution outside of the Adirondacks did you find?

2. How might those causes affect the air quality in the Adirondacks?

Communicate

Share your ideas with the class. Make a class list of possible causes of air pollution in the Adirondacks.

How Might the Wind Affect Air Quality in the Adirondacks?

Most of the time, air-quality issues are local. Air pollutants are released in an area, and they lower the air quality in that area. In the Adirondacks, there is little to actually cause the air pollution, but air quality is still a problem. You have noticed that there are many coal-burning power plants to the west and south of the Adirondacks. In this investigation, you will examine a map you examined once before. This map shows the wind patterns over the United States. You will use this map to determine if it is possible for the air-quality issues in the Adirondacks to be caused by these coal-burning power plants.

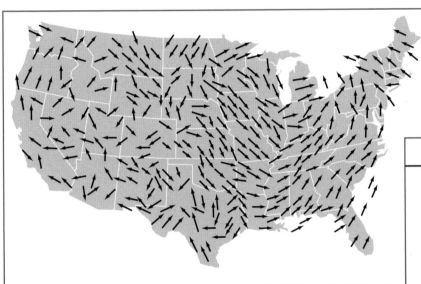

Procedure

1. Find and mark the location of the Adirondacks on your *Adirondacks* page.

2. Put an X on the map on your *Adirondacks* page for every state with coal-burning power plants that might affect the air quality in the Adirondack Mountains. Using the map of wind patterns, identify how the wind might blow pollutants from coal-burning power plants to the Adirondacks. Sketch in the paths of pollutants on your map.

Analyze Your Data

Answer the following questions in your group. Be prepared to discuss your answers with the class.

1. From which direction do the winds blow over the Adirondacks? What region of the country do you think the pollution in the Adirondacks might be coming from?

2. In which direction are the emissions from the greatest concentration of coal-burning power plants carried?

Communicate

Share Your Results

Share your maps and discuss your answers to the questions with your class. As a class, look back at the relief map of the Eastern United States that shows the coal-burning power plants. Discuss how the geography of the area between the states with the most power plants and the Adirondacks might affect how the air moves.

What Are the Products of Combustion From Coal-burning Power Plants?

fossil fuel: a nonrenewable resource formed from the remains of living things over millions of years.

Along with petroleum and natural gas, coal is a **fossil fuel**. Fossil fuels are natural resources burned for energy. They are given their name because they

Over time, heat and pressure change plant remains into coal.

were formed from the remains of plants and animals that lived millions of years ago. For example, coal was formed when ancient plants died and became buried under layers of mud and sediment. Over time, heat and high pressure changed the plant remains into coal. The substances stored in the plants became stored in the coal. These substances include carbon and hydrogen, along with the energy in the bonds that hold matter together. When coal is burned, the released energy can be used to produce electricity. The carbon and hydrogen are released into the environment as CO_2 and H_2O. Coal is considered nonrenewable because it exists in a limited supply and will eventually be used up.

Because coal contains carbon and hydrogen atoms like gasoline does, some of the products from the combustion of coal are the same as the products from the combustion of gasoline. Coal also contains some elements that are not found in gasoline, so the combustion of coal results in some additional products as well. Knowing the products formed during the combustion of coal in coal-burning power plants will help you determine the effects of these products blowing toward the Adirondacks.

Observe

Take a virtual tour of a coal-burning power plant.

As you investigate the coal-burning power plant through this virtual tour, observe the matter that is burned and the products of that burning.

Procedure

1. Open the Coal Power Plant virtual tour.

2. Move your mouse over the colored buttons in the upper left corner of the screen to observe the power plant in action.

3. Navigate through each system. As you pass your mouse over the colored buttons, read the details about what is happening in the power plant.

4. Before you end your tour, make sure you can identify the products of the coal-burning process.

Analyze Your Data

You may need to look at the virtual tour again to answer these questions. Be prepared to discuss the answers with the class.

1. Where does combustion take place in a coal-burning power plant?

2. What fuel is used in combustion?

3. What process prepares the fuel for combustion?

4. What products of combustion did you see in the virtual tour? Which of these are characters in the *Sickening Six* play?

5. What causes the turbine to spin?

6. What happens in the precipitator? What happens in the scrubber? Why are the precipitator and scrubber needed?

7. What pollutants from coal-burning power plants could be causing the air-quality problems in the Adirondacks? Justify your answer with evidence.

What Kind of Pollutants Come From Burning Coal?

Many regions of the United States, and other parts of the world for that matter, are dependent upon the combustion of coal to generate electricity. The advantage of using coal is that it is currently one of the least expensive fuels to mine and burn. The disadvantages are not only that coal is a nonrenewable resource, but also that the combustion of coal produces pollutants.

Like the combustion of gasoline, the combustion of coal produces particulate matter consisting of carbon. Some of this particulate matter is soot, which you saw in *Learning Set 3*. Some of this particulate matter is ash. Soot is carried by air, whereas ash remains in the bottom of the structures of the coal-burning power plant.

As in the case of the combustion of gasoline, the temperatures involved in the combustion of coal are so high that nitrogen reacts with oxygen to produce NO and NO_2.

Nitrogen plus oxygen yields nitrogen monoxide.

$$N_2 + O_2 \rightarrow 2NO$$

Nitrogen plus oxygen yields nitrogen dioxide.

$$N_2 + 2O_2 \rightarrow 2NO_2$$

Coal also contains sulfur. During combustion in a power plant, the sulfur reacts with oxygen to produce sulfur dioxide (SO_2), a toxic, choking gas.

Sulfur plus oxygen yields sulfur dioxide.

$$S + O_2 \rightarrow SO_2$$

Sulfur dioxide can then combine with oxygen to produce sulfur trioxide (SO_3), an even more dangerous gas than sulfur dioxide.

Sulfur dioxide plus oxygen yields sulfur trioxide.

$$2SO_2 + O_2 \rightarrow 2SO_3$$

Another component of coal is mercury (Hg), a very poisonous metal. During the combustion of coal, mercury is released into the air through the smokestacks of the power plant.

Finally, you already know that carbon dioxide (CO_2) is a natural product of combustion. The carbon in the fuel reacts with oxygen in the air to produce carbon dioxide.

Carbon plus oxygen yields carbon dioxide.

$$C + O_2 \rightarrow CO_2$$

In low concentrations, carbon dioxide is not actually poisonous to breathe. However, large amounts of carbon dioxide can have negative effects on natural processes in the atmosphere. You will learn more about these processes later in this Unit.

Stop and Think

The wind direction and products of combustion suggest ways that coal-burning power plants in the Midwest and South might lead to poor air quality in the Adirondacks. Discuss the answers to the following questions in your group, and justify your answers with evidence from your readings and investigations. Be prepared to share your answers in class.

1. What kinds of pollutants do coal-burning power plants produce?

2. How can power plants in the Midwest and South affect air-quality problems in the East?

3. How might pollutants carried by the winds affect air quality in the Adirondacks?

Demonstration

1. Examine a piece of chalk and record your observations.

2. Watch as the piece of chalk is placed into a cup of soda.

3. Examine the chalk again after 24 hours and record your observations.

4. As you complete this *Learning Set*, examine the chalk several more times. Record your observations each time.

Acids in the Air

You now know that pollutants are carried by wind from coal-burning power plants in the Midwestern and Southern United States to the Adirondacks. You also know some of the pollutants produced by those power plants. One more thing you need to know is that some pollutants in the air can react with other molecules to produce *acids*. You will learn more about acids throughout this *Learning Set*. For now you need to know that acids are sour liquids.

You are probably already familiar with some acids. Acetic acid gives vinegar its sour taste, and citric acid gives lemons their sour taste. Hydrochloric acid helps your body to digest food. Carbonic acid is in soft drinks, such as the soda in which the chalk was placed.

Do not get the idea that all acids are safe to eat or drink. Acids can be corrosive, which means they can burn your skin. The acid in a car battery, for example, is extremely corrosive. To be safe, never eat or drink anything in the science laboratory unless your teacher specifically instructs you to do so.

In the environment, acids can cause damage to plants and trees. They can harm animals, and they can cause damage to structures, such as statues and buildings.

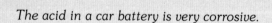

The acid in a car battery is very corrosive.

Explain

Based on what you now know, work with your group to create your best explanation of the sources of air pollution in the Adirondacks. Begin by using what you know to make a claim about the sources of air pollution in the Adirondacks. Record it in the *claim* section of a *Create Your Explanation* page. Then use evidence from the maps of power plants and wind patterns and your tour of the coal-burning power plant to support your claim. Record science knowledge from your readings, investigations, and explorations.

Using what you have recorded, write an explanation statement that pulls together your evidence and science knowledge to support your claim. Make sure your claim, evidence, science knowledge, and explanation statement all match each other. If they do not match each other, revise them until they match each other well. Do your best using what you know right now. As you learn more, you will get a chance to revise your claim and explanation.

Create Your Explanation	1.3.2/2.BBQ.2/3.5.2 4.2.2/4.6.7/4.7.1/ABQ.2

Name: _____ Date: _____

Use this page to explain the lesson of your recent investigations.

Write a brief summary of the results from your investigation. You will use this summary to help you write your Explanation.

Claim – a statement of what you understand or a conclusion that you have reached from an investigation or a set of investigations.

Evidence – data collected during investigations and trends in that data.

Science knowledge – knowledge about how things work. You may have learned this through reading, talking to an expert, discussion, or other experiences.

Write your Explanation using the *Claim*, *Evidence*, and *Science knowledge*.

© It's About Time

Communicate

Share Your Explanation

Share your group's claim and explanation with the class. Tell the class what makes your claim accurate based on the *evidence* you have and your science knowledge. Pay special attention to how other groups have supported their claims with science knowledge. Ask questions or make suggestions if you think a group's claim is not as accurate as it could be or if the group has not supported their claim well enough with *evidence* and science knowledge.

Revise Your Explanation

As a class, come up with your best explanation so far of the sources of air pollution in the Adirondacks. As you work, keep track of what you still do not know and what you still disagree about. Identify what you would need to know more about to make your explanation more complete and to settle your disagreements.

Update the *Project Board*

You now know a lot about what is causing the air pollution in the Adirondacks. Add what you know and your evidence to the *What are we learning?* and *What is our evidence?* columns of the *Project Board*. In the *What do we need to investigate?* column, record questions you need to answer to make a more complete explanation and to resolve disagreements among class members.

What's the Point?

The major type of industry affecting the air in the Adirondacks is electricity production in coal-burning power plants. Coal-burning power plants produce pollutants, including nitrogen monoxide, nitrogen dioxide, sulfur dioxide, sulfur trioxide, and carbon dioxide.

When you examined a map of the coal-burning power plants in the United States, you observed that the majority of coal-burning power plants are concentrated in the Midwest and South. When you examined a map of the wind currents in the United States, you found that the direction of winds makes it possible for pollutants produced by coal-burning power plants in the Midwest and the South to be carried all the way to the Adirondacks. As they travel, some of these pollutants mix with other molecules in the air to produce acids. These acids can harm the environment.

4.3 Explore

What Happens to Pollutants When They Get Into Air?

The pollutants produced by combustion are known as primary pollutants because they are formed directly by the chemical reaction in which a fuel burns in air. These pollutants can then be carried to high altitudes and over long distances in the atmosphere. Some of the pollutants, such as sulfur dioxide (SO_2) and nitrogen dioxide (NO_2), can then react with water in the air to form acids. The acids are called secondary pollutants because they are formed from the primary pollutants rather than directly by combustion. When acids fall back to Earth, usually in rain or snow, the precipitation is known as acid rain. You will model the formation of one of these secondary pollutants so you can begin to understand how acids form in the atmosphere.

Model Sulfur Dioxide

When coal burns, it forms carbon dioxide (CO_2), sulfur dioxide (SO_2) and the nitrogen oxides (NO and NO_2). You have modeled all of these gases before except those made from sulfur. You will now use your atomic-model kit to model SO_2 and SO_3.

Materials

- **atomic-model kit**
- *Model Molecules* **page**

Sulfur atoms from your atomic-model kit.

1. Select 1 sulfur atom (yellow) and 2 oxygen atoms (red) from your atomic-model kit. Also take some gray rods (bonds). Arrange the oxygen atoms into an oxygen molecule.

2. Use the sulfur atom and oxygen molecule to assemble a sulfur dioxide (SO_2) molecule that has as few empty holes as possible. You may use single bonds and double bonds.

3. Sketch the molecule on a new *Model Molecules* page.

4. Do you think the sulfur dioxide molecule is stable or unstable? Why? Record your answer on your *Model Molecules* page.

5. You formed sulfur dioxide from sulfur and oxygen. What are the reactants of this reaction? What are the products? Record the balanced equation. Remember that it has to have equal numbers of atoms of each type on both sides of the arrow.

6. Remember that sulfur dioxide can also combine with oxygen to produce sulfur trioxide (SO_3). Use one more oxygen atom to change your sulfur dioxide (SO_2) molecule into a sulfur trioxide (SO_3) molecule. It should have as few empty holes as possible. You may use single bonds and double bonds.

7. What are the reactants of this reaction? What are the products? Record the balanced equation.

Sometimes a Model Is Just a Model

In the atmosphere, sulfur dioxide can react with oxygen to make sulfur trioxide. Because you are trying to build stable molecules, you may have connected the three oxygens to sulfur with three double bonds. This is correct. However, since all the "holes" are filled, sulfur trioxide will appear to be a stable molecule. However, sulfur trioxide is very reactive and corrosive. This is one example where your model is no longer valid.

A model can be used to help to understand a concept. In this Unit, plastic atoms with holes were used to introduce bonding, stability, and reactivity. Many atoms need more electrons to be stable. They bond with other atoms to meet their electron needs. For example, in sulfur trioxide, oxygen and sulfur share electrons. Although sulfur trioxide appears to have all its "holes" filled, it is a highly reactive compound.

Reflect

In your atomic-model kit, stable molecules have filled holes or no rods with empty places for atoms. All of the pollutants you have explored have been unstable molecules.

1. SO_2 and SO_3 are unstable molecules. Provide evidence from the models you built and your reading to support this statement.

2. Why is an understanding of unstable molecules important to understanding pollution?

3. How do you know each of your equations is correct?

Formation of Acids and Acid Rain

Remember that many of the products of coal-burning power plants are unstable molecules. This means that once they get into the air, they can continue to react with other molecules in the air. In Los Angeles, where there is a lot of sunlight, nitrogen oxides (NO_x) react with oxygen in the air to form ozone and polluting smog. In the Adirondacks, there is not as much sunlight, so very little smog forms. Instead, as the products of coal-burning power plants float through the air, they react with water in the air to form compounds called acids.

Look at the model of sulfur dioxide (SO_2) you built. You can see that this molecule is unstable. It has holes without bonds. Sulfur trioxide (SO_3) is unstable for other reasons. Look at nitrogen dioxide (NO_2) on your *Model Molecules* page. Notice that this molecule, too, is unstable. It has holes without bonds. When these molecules react with water (H_2O) in the atmosphere, they form acids. The two major acids they form are called sulfuric acid (H_2SO_4) and nitric acid (HNO_3). Look at the equations that show how these acids are formed.

Sulfur trioxide plus water yields sulfuric acid.

$$SO_3 + H_2O \rightarrow H_2SO_4$$

Model Molecules

2.4.1/2.6.1
3.3.1/4.3.1

Name: _____ Date: _____

As you complete each molecule, sketch a diagram of it, and label the atoms. Record the molecular formula for each molecule you built next to each of your sketches. If you make more than six molecules, use a new *Model Molecules* page. Use a new *Model Molecules* page for each investigation.

Molecule 1	Molecule 2
Molecule 3	Molecule 4
Molecule 5	Molecule 6

© It's About Time

Nitrogen dioxide plus water yields nitric acid plus nitrous acid.

$$2NO_2 + H_2O \rightarrow HNO_3 + HNO_2$$

All rainwater also includes one more acid—carbonic acid (H_2CO_3). This is a weak acid and does not make a significant contribution to the acid-rain problems of the Adirondacks. Carbon dioxide, which is found in all air, is slightly soluble in water. A small part of the dissolved CO_2 will react with water to form carbonic acid. The equation for formation of carbonic acid is shown below.

Carbon dioxide plus water yields carbonic acid.

$$CO_2 + H_2O \rightarrow H_2CO_3$$

You can build the acids in acid rain with your atomic-model kit, and you will find that some of them form stable compounds (with no "holes"). Therefore, they do not follow the rules for stability that you have been using. You would also find that, in acids, a hydrogen atom is attached to an oxygen atom. This is what makes them acids. In water, the hydrogen leaves the acid molecule as a proton, leaving its electron behind with the oxygen atom. You will learn more about what acids are and how acids react with other substances later in this Unit.

Acid rain forms when products of coal-burning power plants react with water in the air. Acid particles and gases are known as acid rain dry deposition. You will learn about dry deposition in Section 4.4.

Update the *Project Board*

Record what you now know about the formation of pollutants in the Adirondacks in the *What are we learning?* column. Record your evidence in the *What is our evidence?* column. You also now know some new things about the relationship between unstable molecules and pollution. Record what you know about that in the *What are we learning?* column also. Do not forget to record your evidence.

You probably still have questions about what is affecting the environment in the Adirondacks. For example, you still do not know exactly how acids harm the environment. Record your questions and any ideas for investigations in the *What do we need to investigate?* column.

How can you improve air quality in your community?				
What do we think we know?	What do we need to investigate?	What are we learning?	What is our evidence?	What does it mean for the challenge or question?

What's the Point?

You saw that sulfur dioxide, a product of coal-burning power plants, is an unstable molecule that reacts with oxygen in the atmosphere to form sulfur trioxide. Sulfur trioxide, too, is an unstable molecule. So are other products of combustion. The nitrogen dioxide formed in power plants and the sulfur trioxide formed in the atmosphere combine with water in the atmosphere to form the acids that fall to the ground in acid rain.

Acid rain forms as a secondary pollutant from the sulfur and nitrogen compounds released from coal-burning power plants. Sulfur combines with oxygen to form unstable molecules. These molecules then combine with water in the air to form sulfuric acid, a component of acid rain. Nitrogen oxides from combustion can form nitric acid. Both these acids are components of acid rain.

Acid rain, ozone, and nitrogen oxides can damage or kill trees.

Acid rain can eat away at stone and other building materials.

4.4 Read

What Is an Acid, and How Do Acids Cause Damage?

Harmful Effects of Air Pollution Are Far-Flung, a Study Finds

NEW YORK, NEW YORK—Air pollution in the Northeast is not just about lakes without fish. It is also about forests losing their trees and soils that store up acid before releasing it back out to pollute local waters all over again, according to a scientific study of upstate New York and New England.

Many lakes in the Adirondacks are "dead." Acid rain has killed the fish and other organisms that used to live in the lakes.

In short, the acid-rain problem is more connected to the ecosystems it affects than scientists had previously believed, the report says—and thus harder to fight than it had appeared.

"It's a lot more complicated," said Charles T. Driscoll, a professor of environmental engineering at Syracuse University and the lead author of the study, which was published in the journal *BioScience*.

The study confirmed that although new deposits of airborne acid compounds, such as sulfur dioxide and nitrogen oxides,

have declined, decades of acid buildup in the forest soils is still being washed into waterways by erosion and **spring runoff**, the water that comes from melting snow and runs into lakes and other bodies of water.

The two-year study concluded that red spruce and sugar maple trees in the Adirondacks have been hurt in different ways by acid soils. Many tree deaths that had been attributed to things like insect infestation or drought, the study said, had in fact been accelerated by acidic soil that made the trees more vulnerable.

Red spruce trees (top) and sugar maple trees (bottom) are especially affected by acid rain.

spring runoff: the water that comes from melting snow and runs into lakes and other bodies of water.

Acid rain can contain a mixture of acids formed from sulfur trioxide (SO_3) and nitrogen dioxide (NO_2). You have learned that acid rain forms when these gases react with water in the atmosphere. But what exactly are acids, and how do they harm the environment?

What Is an Acid?

More than 2000 years ago, the ancient Greeks began to sort substances into categories. One criterion people used was how substances tasted. They recognized that some substances taste sweet, others taste salty, some are sour, and others are bitter. Another criterion was how substances felt. People noticed that some substances stung the skin, especially in open wounds. Based on these observations, the Greeks classified sour substances that sting the skin as *oxein*, which became the Latin word *acidus*, or *acid*. Some sour foods you know about are lemon juice and vinegar. The Greeks knew that these sour substances were very useful.

Lemon juice is a source of acid.

ion: an atom, or group of atoms, that has more electrons than protons and an overall negative charge; or fewer electrons than protons and an overall positive charge.

Recall that atoms are more unstable if they do not have a complete set of outer electrons. Some atoms form a complete set of outer electrons by sharing electrons with other atoms. This was true for the molecules you modeled with your atomic-model kit. In some cases, atoms do not share electrons. Instead, atoms take electrons from other atoms or give electrons away. An atom, or group of atoms, that has gained or lost electrons is called an **ion**.

You might also remember that electrons and protons carry electric charges. Protons carry a positive charge and electrons carry a negative charge. An atom does not have an overall charge because the number of protons (positive charges) is equal to the number of electrons (negative charges). As a result, the charges cancel out.

If an atom gains electrons, it has more negative charges (electrons) than positive charges (protons), so it has an overall negative charge. In other words, an atom that gains electrons becomes a **negative ion**. If an atom loses electrons, it has more positive charges (protons) than negative charges (electrons), so it has an overall positive charge. An atom that loses electrons becomes a **positive ion**.

negative ion: an atom, or group of atoms, that has gained electrons.

positive ion: an atom, or group of atoms, that has lost electrons.

As an example, consider a hydrogen atom. It has one electron. If it loses that electron, it becomes a positive hydrogen ion. In the equation below, the positive hydrogen ion is represented as H^+. The plus sign is written upward to the right of the chemical symbol as a superscript. The superscript gives the charge of the particle. The electron that the hydrogen atom lost is written as e^-. In this case, the minus sign indicates the charge of the electron.

A hydrogen atom can lose its electron. This yields a positively charged hydrogen ion plus a negatively charged electron.

$$H \rightarrow H^+ + e^-$$

What do ions have to do with acids? Scientists define an acid as a chemical compound that breaks apart in water to form hydrogen ions plus negative ions. That means that if you put an acidic compound in water, it will produce positive hydrogen ions and an equal number of negative ions.

acidic: solutions that have more hydrogen ions than pure water.

acidity: the concentration of hydrogen ions in a solution.

A solution is described as **acidic** if it has more hydrogen ions than pure water.

The concentration of hydrogen ions in a solution is called the solution's **acidity**. Solutions that are more acidic have a greater concentration of hydrogen ions than solutions that are less acidic.

Since you know that acid rain is harmful to plants, animals, and structures, you can probably guess that the more acidic a solution is, the more damage it can do. Small amounts of acid may not be harmful and, in some instances, may be beneficial. But very few life forms can survive a strongly acidic environment.

Just as matter cannot be created or destroyed by ordinary means, unbalanced charges cannot be created or destroyed. When an acid is dissolved in water, it becomes ionized. This means that it forms a hydrogen ion, which is positive, and a second ion, which is negative. Nitric acid, HNO_3, provides a good example.

Nitric acid, in water, yields hydrogen ions and nitrate ions.

$$HNO_3 \text{(in water)} \rightarrow H^+ + NO_3^-$$

This reaction happens because water molecules surround the positive and negative ions, making them more stable.

Stop and Think

1. How is a positive ion different from a negative ion?

2. What happens when acidic compounds are mixed with water?

3. Now that you know a little about how acid rain forms, how do you think acid rain causes damage?

How Does Acid Rain Cause Damage?

To understand what **acid rain** can do, you should first recognize that acid rain is a broad term. It applies to more than just rain. The term acid rain describes any of several ways that acid falls out of the atmosphere. The term acid deposition is a more precise term. Deposition is the process through which materials are dropped in a new location. Acid deposition can be wet or dry. Wet deposition applies to acid rain, snow, or fog. This acidic water can flow over the ground, seep into the soil, or flow into lakes, ponds, and rivers. Dry deposition applies to acidic gases and acidic particulate matter. Acidic gases and particles can be blown by winds onto trees, buildings, cars, and other surfaces. It can also be washed off those surfaces by acidic rain, making the rain even more acidic.

Acid rain can affect the environment in many ways. One way is by changing the natural acidity of soils and water in lakes and ponds. Living things can survive only within a certain range of acidity. If acid rain increases the acidity, many organisms are not able to survive. Two ways acids enter the cells of living organisms are osmosis and diffusion. You will learn more about these processes in another Unit. In addition, acid rain dissolves some building materials by reacting with substances in the materials.

acid rain: any of several ways that acid falls out of the atmosphere.

Acid deposition can be present in snow or fog, as well as in rain.

What's the Point?

Acid rain forms when pollutants formed through combustion combine with water in the atmosphere. Acids are substances that taste sour and sting the skin. Acids are compounds that, added to water, produce solutions that have more hydrogen ions than pure water alone. A hydrogen ion is a hydrogen atom that has lost an electron and has therefore become positively charged.

Acid rain describes several ways that acids fall from the atmosphere to Earth's surface. Wet acidic deposition is acidic rain, snow, or fog. Dry acidic deposition includes acidic gases and particulate matter. Acids can change the acidity of water and soils on which living things depend. They can also react with substances in building materials.

4.5 Investigate

How Do Scientists Measure Acidity?

pH scale: a measure of the concentration of hydrogen ions in a substance.

neutral: a solution with a pH of 7. pH 7 has an equal number of hydrogen ions and hydroxide ions.

acid: a solution that tastes sour, has more hydrogen ions than pure water, and has a pH of less than 7.

base: a solution with a bitter taste, a slippery feel, and a pH more than 7.

hydroxide ion: one oxygen atom, one hydrogen atom, and an extra electron.

You know that the more acidic the solution is, the higher the concentration of hydrogen ions. Scientists communicate how acidic a solution is using numbers on a **pH scale**. The pH scale tells you the concentration of hydrogen ions in a solution. The name of this scale, pH, stands for "power of hydrogen." The scale ranges from 0 to 14. In the middle of the scale is 7. Solutions with a pH of 7 are called **neutral**. Pure water, or distilled water, is neutral and has a pH of 7. Keep in mind that water from a faucet and rainwater are not pure water. They have substances dissolved in them, so their pH is not 7. **Acids** are solutions that have a pH less than 7. The lower the pH, the more acidic a solution is. This may sound confusing, but it is important to remember. When pH is lower, a solution is more acidic. Normal rainwater is slightly acidic, with a pH of about 5.6. The pH of acid rain is closer to 4.3.

You might wonder about the numbers that are higher than 7 on the pH scale. Solutions with a pH higher than 7 are called **bases**. Bases have a bitter taste, and they tend to feel slimy or slippery. When placed in water, a base produces **hydroxide ions** (OH^-). A hydroxide ion consists of one oxygen atom, one hydrogen atom, and an extra electron. The minus sign (–) shows that the ion that has gained an electron and has a negative charge.

Pure water has fewer hydrogen ions than acids, and bases have fewer hydrogen ions than pure water.

If a solution has a pH less than 7, then it has a higher concentration of hydrogen ions than pure water. If it has a pH greater than 7, then it has fewer hydrogen ions than pure water.

The pH scale ranges from 0 to 14. Pure water is neutral and has a pH of 7. The pH of an acid is less than 7, whereas the pH of a base is greater than 7.

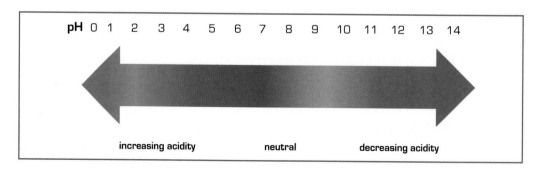

The interval between numbers on the pH scale is different from the interval on a number line. On a number line, the interval between each number is one. On the pH scale, each number indicates a change of ten times. For example, a solution with a pH of 4 is ten times more acidic than a solution with a pH of 5 and one hundred times more acidic than a solution with a pH of 6.

Car battery acid is a strong acid. It measures 1 on the pH scale. The acid in oranges is a weaker acid. It measures 4 on the pH scale.

Be a Scientist

Acid-base Indicators

You know that pH measures the acidity of a solution, but how do you measure pH? After all, you cannot directly measure the concentration of hydrogen ions. Scientists have found many different **indicators** for measuring pH. An indicator is a tool that can be used to determine the condition of something that cannot be measured directly.

indicator: a tool that can be observed to determine the condition of something.

Red Cabbage Juice

Boiled red cabbage juice has been used as an acid indicator for thousands of years. People who dyed cloth in ancient times often used the juice from boiled red cabbage leaves to produce a pale bluish-purple dye. They noticed that when sour-tasting substances (acids) were added to the cabbage juice, the dye turned red. When bitter-tasting substances (bases) were added to the cabbage juice, the dye turned green. Red cabbage juice became one of the first pH indicators. But it can determine only whether a solution is an acid or a base. It cannot measure exactly how acidic or basic a solution is.

Red cabbage juice was one of the first pH indicators.

Acids turn red cabbage juice red. Bases turn red cabbage juice green.

lichen: two distinct organisms, a fungus and an alga, living as one.

litmus paper: a paper made from wood, lichen, and other compounds that is used to determine whether a solution is acidic or basic.

universal indicator: a test used to measure a range of pH's.

pH paper: a universal indicator that determines how acidic a solution is.

Litmus Paper

Ancient people also observed that sour substances changed the color of a substance called litmus. Litmus is a dye extracted from **lichen**. Lichen is an odd kind of organism. It is both a fungus and an alga, living as one. Lichen was often called "dyer's weed," and people used it to dye cloth. Early scientists also used litmus to indicate if a solution was acidic or basic. They knew that litmus changed color according to the acidity of a substance. In the 1800s, a scientist developed litmus paper made from wood, lichens, and other compounds. An acid turns blue litmus paper red. A base turns red litmus paper blue. **Litmus paper** is still used today to determine whether a solution is acidic or basic.

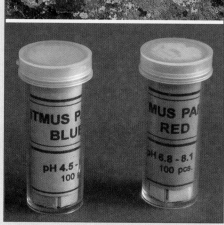

Lichen, a fungus and an alga living as one, are used to make litmus paper.

pH Paper: A Universal Indicator

Litmus paper and red cabbage juice can indicate whether a solution is an acid, but they cannot measure the strength of the acid. A different type of test is needed for that. Modern scientists have developed what they call **universal indicators**. A universal indicator is a mixture of substances that each changes color at different pH values. You test how acidic a solution is by dipping the universal indicator in the solution and observing what color it turns. An indicator for pH can be a liquid or a solid. The most commonly used universal indicator for pH is called **pH paper**. When you dip pH paper

pH paper turns different colors to indicate the pH of a solution.

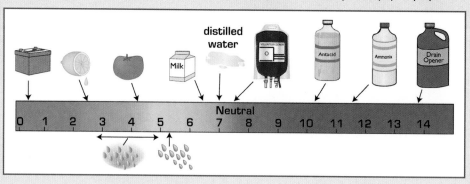

into a solution, it changes color to indicate the pH of the solution.

pH Meters

pH meters can also test the strength of an acid or a base. A pH meter measures hydrogen ions in the solution tested. On most pH meters, the pH of the solution is displayed on a digital readout. This makes pH meters the most accurate way to measure pH.

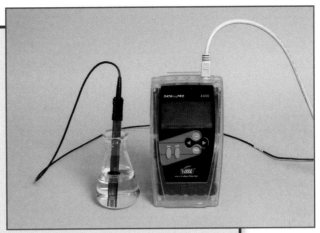

A pH meter is the most accurate way to measure the pH of a solution.

How Acidic Is Each Solution?

Each group in the class will measure the pH of distilled water and 5 different liquids. You will use pH paper or a pH meter to measure the pH of each of the liquids. Then you will report to the class.

Predict

Record the names of the 5 solutions you will be testing in the first column of your *Acids and Bases* page. You are familiar with some of these solutions. For each of your solutions you are familiar with, predict where it will fall on the pH scale. Use information you know about the pH scale and about each solution to make your decision. Keep in mind the characteristics of acids and bases while you are making your predictions. Record your predictions on your *Acids and Bases* page.

Acids and Bases			4.5.1

Name: _____   Date: _____

Solution	Predicted pH	Actual pH	Tape pH strip
Distilled water			

© It's About Time

Materials

- well plate
- pH paper
- tape
- water in a dropper bottle
- tea in dropper bottle
- coffee in dropper bottle
- baking powder (dissolved in water) in dropper bottle
- milk in dropper bottle
- power drink in dropper bottle
- pickle juice in dropper bottle
- window cleaner in dropper bottle
- stain remover (liquid) in dropper bottle
- liquid antacid in dropper bottle

Materials

- aspirin (dissolved in water) in dropper bottle
- buffered aspirin (dissolved in water) in dropper bottle
- clear carbonated beverage in dropper bottle
- household bleach in dropper bottle
- vinegar in dropper bottle
- mineral water in dropper bottle
- liquid soap in dropper bottle
- rubbing alcohol in dropper bottle
- hydrogen peroxide in dropper bottle
- liquid shampoo in dropper bottle
- mouthwash in dropper bottle
- safety glasses
- *Acids and Bases* page

Some of these solutions can burn your eyes or skin. Some are poisonous. Be sure to wear safety glasses. Do not taste any of the solutions. When you are finished, allow your teacher to dispose of the solutions.

Procedure

1. One member of your group should take the well plate to the solution station. Place 4–5 drops of water in well A1. Place 4–5 drops of each of your solutions into wells A2 through A6 in Row A of your well plate.

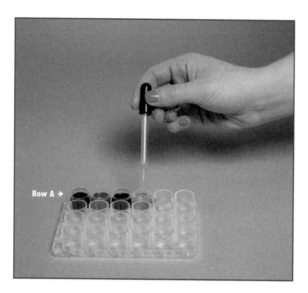

2. Each member of your group should have 6 pieces of pH paper. Take turns testing the pH of each of the solutions in your well plate. Use a fresh strip of pH paper for each solution. After you see the color the paper turns, match its color to the colors on the pH scale, and record the pH of each solution on your *Acids and Bases* page.

3. Allow your test strips to dry, and then tape them on your *Acids and Bases* page.

Analyze Your Data

Work with your group to analyze your data, and make sure you all agree on the pH of each solution. If group members determined a different pH for any of the solutions, measure the pH of those solutions again. Retest the liquids until you are satisfied that you have accurately determined their pH.

1. Which of your solutions were neutral? How do you know?

2. Which of your solutions were acidic? How do you know? Which was most acidic? How do you know?

3. Which of your solutions were basic? How do you know? Which was most basic? How do you know?

4. Compare your predictions with your results. Which solutions were you able to predict accurately? Which solutions were difficult to predict? Why?

Communicate

Share Your Results

As a class, arrange all the solutions in order from most acidic to most basic. Each group measured the pH of different solutions. Each member of the group measured the pH of each of the group's solutions. As you are arranging the solutions in order, compare the results of those measurements. For each liquid for which members of the group recorded different pH results for the same solution, retest the liquid until you are satisfied that you have accurately determined the pH.

Earlier in the Unit, you saw that, when you diluted colored water, you produced solutions that had fewer parts per million of the dye. Dilution is also a way to change the acidity of a solution. Choose one of your solutions, and predict what would happen to its pH if you added water to the solution.

What Is the pH of Acid Rain?

You cannot directly measure the acidity of acid rain, because you most likely do not have a sample of acid rain in front of you. You can, however, model acid rain and measure the acidity of the water in your model. You can model acid rain by capturing smoke from combustion and dissolving it in water. It will not have all of the products of combustion from a coal-burning power plant, but it will have some of them. Your teacher has burned some paper, captured the smoke, and then dissolved the smoke in water. You will measure the pH of the resulting solution.

Procedure

Slowly open your bag containing the solution of smoke dissolved in water, and pour the solution into the cup. Dip a strip of pH paper in the water. Record your observations.

Analyze Your Data

1. What was the color of the pH paper after it was dipped in the smoke/water solution? Use the pH scale to determine the pH of the smoke/water solution.

2. How did the pH of the smoke/water solution differ from the pH of the distilled water you tested in the previous investigation? What does that tell you about the smoke/water solution?

Materials
- **pH paper**
- **clear plastic cup**
- **bag with smoke/ water solution**

AIR QUALITY

Reflect

1. Compare the acidity of the smoke/water solution to the acidity of the household liquids you tested earlier. Which liquid is closest in acidity to the smoke/water solution?

2. Normal rainwater is slightly acidic (pH = 5.6). How much more acidic is the smoke/water solution? Why do you think rainwater that contains the products of combustion is more of a problem for the environment than normal rainwater?

3. Your smoke/water solution had only some of the products of combustion dissolved in it. How do you think the pH of the smoke/water solution compares to the pH of acid rain? Why?

4. Earlier in the Unit, you learned about measuring concentration using parts per million (ppm) and parts per billion (ppb). pH is also a measure of concentration. How do you think the concentration of hydrogen ions in ppm or ppb is different when pH is higher than when it is lower?

Update the *Project Board*

Acid in the air is a big problem in the Adirondacks. As air pollutants mix with water, acid rain is formed. Add your understanding of acids and acid rain to the *Project Board* in the *What are we learning?* column. Be sure to include evidence from your reading and from your investigations that help you to support your learning. You may also have some new questions to add to the *Project Board*. For example, you still do not know exactly how it causes damage to the plants and animals.

What's the Point?

All substances can be classified as acids, bases, or neutral. Acids produce hydrogen ions when placed in water. The concentration of hydrogen ions in a solution is a measure of its acidity. Hydrogen ions cannot be measured directly, so indicators are used to determine whether a solution is an acid, a base, or neutral. Acid-base indicators include red cabbage juice, litmus paper, and pH paper. A color change in the indicator shows the presence of an acid or a base. No color change indicates a neutral substance. The pH of a substance is a measurement of the concentration of hydrogen ions in a solution. The pH scale has a range of 0-14 and indicates the strength of an acid or a base. When the pH changes by one number on the scale, the level of acidity changes by a factor of ten.

4.6 Explore

How Is Air Pollution Harming the Adirondacks?

The Adirondack region has almost 3000 ponds and lakes. Many different types of animals live in this region and depend on the water in the ponds and lakes. To grow and thrive, the diverse plant life needs both the **surface water** found in ponds, lakes, and streams, and the **groundwater** in and under the soil. If acid rain affects surface and groundwater, it affects the animals and plants that depend on that water.

As you read earlier, acid rain also affects structures in the region, both natural structures and ones made by people.

To find out how acid rain affects the environment, your class will view videos of different explorations. The videos will show the effects of acid on water, plant life, and structures over time.

- Some of you will observe how acid rain falling in or running off into lakes with different kinds of rock on the bottom affects the acidity of the water.

- Some of you will observe how acid rain affects the way plants grow.

- Some of you will observe how acid rain can affect rock structures made by people.

- Some of you will observe how acid rain can affect metal structures.

To understand the possible effects of air pollution in your community, you will need to know how acid rain affects water, organisms, and structures. So when you have completed your observations and analyzed your data, you will share with the class what you have learned in an *Investigation Expo*.

surface water: water found in ponds, lakes, streams, and oceans on the surface of Earth.

groundwater: water found in the soil and beneath the surface of Earth.

AIR QUALITY

Observation A: How Does the Composition of a Lake Bottom Affect the Acidity of the Lake Water?

The rocks and soils in a region can determine how acid rain affects the water in lakes, ponds, and streams. Some types of rock react with the acid rain and keep it from making lake water acidic. Other types of rock cannot do that, and the acid rain makes the lake water acidic. In this video, you will observe the effects of a limestone lake bottom and a granite lake bottom on the acidity of the lake water. Limestone is a soft rock formed from the fossil shells of sea creatures. Granite is one of the oldest, hardest, and strongest rocks on Earth. It formed from volcanoes in the early formation of Earth.

Predict

Limestone is a base. In water, the pH of limestone dust varies from 7.5 to 8.6. As acidic water moves through or over limestone, a chemical reaction occurs. During this chemical reaction, sulfuric acid in acid rain combines with limestone to produce carbonic acid. The pH of carbonic acid averages about 5.6. How do you think the pH of lake water changes when the lake has a limestone bottom and acid rain falls on it? If you think the acidity of the water will change when acid rain falls in a lake with a limestone bottom, record how you think it will change and why. Record your prediction on your *Lake Bottom and Acid* page.

Granite is not an acid, and it is not a base. Granite does not dissolve in solution and does not react with acid. How do you think a granite lake bottom affects the pH of water in the lake when acid rain falls on it? If you think the acidity of the lake water will change when acid rain falls in a lake with a granite bottom, record how you think it will change and why. Record your prediction on your *Lake Bottom and Acid* page.

Lake Bottom and Acid Water 4.6.1

Name: _____ Date: _____

Predict the effect of limestone on acid water	Predict the effect of granite on acid water

Results of limestone on acid water	Results of granite on acid water

© It's About Time

Observe

You will observe a video of a scientific study of the effects of acid on two kinds of rocks, limestone and granite. As you watch the video, remember that the pH scale is not linear. Water at a pH of 4 has 10 times the concentration of hydrogen ions, H^+, as water at a pH of 5. If you compare pH 4 water to neutral water of pH 7, the pH 4 has 1000 times the concentration of H^+.

Procedure

1. The first beaker in the video is labeled *water*, the second beaker is labeled *acid water plus limestone*, and the third beaker is labeled *acid water plus granite*. The pH of the acid water is pH 4.

2. On a *Lake Bottom and Acid Water* page, record on the graphs the pH for each beaker at the beginning of the exploration, *Day 0*. Use an "X" for each data point.

3. For each beaker, record the pH on the graphs for the next data point shown in the video. Enter the day you record your data on the dashes at the bottom of the graphs. Be sure to place each data point on the correct day.

4. Continue to record the day and the pH's of the beakers on your graphs for each day shown in the video.

Analyze Your Data

1. Draw a smooth line through the X's on your graphs. You should have several X's on each graph, one for each day shown on the video. What do the lines look like? Are the graphs the same or different? If they are different, how do they differ?

2. How did the pH of the *acid water plus limestone* change over time?

3. How did the pH of the *acid water plus granite* change over time?

4. Compare your predictions with your results. How do they differ?

5. If acid rain falling on a lake with a limestone bottom reacts like the acid solution over the limestone pictured in the video, how will it affect the acidity of the lake water?

6. If acid rain falling on a lake with a granite bottom reacts like the acid solution over the granite pictured in the video, how will it affect the acidity of the lake water?

PBIS

Explain

Read the information about limestone and granite on the next page. Then develop a claim about the effects of acid rain on the acidity of groundwater and surface water in the Adirondacks. Your claim will be about the effects of acid rain on water in the Adirondacks. You may want to phrase it like this: *When acid rain falls in the Adirondacks, it makes the water in the lakes and soil more/less acidic.* Record evidence from your investigation that supports your claim. Record science knowledge that supports your claim. Some might come from what you have just read. Other science knowledge that supports your claim might come from other readings and investigations in this Unit. Then develop an explanation statement that pulls together your claim and your evidence and science knowledge. Your statement should convince someone that your claim is trustworthy. It should also help someone understand why the acid rain affects the acidity of water the way it does. Be as specific as you can be.

Create Your Explanation
1.3.2/2.BBQ.2/3.5.2
4.2.2/4.6.7/4.7.1/ABQ.2

Name: _____ Date: _____

Use this page to explain the lesson of your recent investigations.

Write a brief summary of the results from your investigation. You will use this summary to help you write your Explanation.

Claim – a statement of what you understand or a conclusion that you have reached from an investigation or a set of investigations.

Evidence – data collected during investigations and trends in that data.

Science knowledge – knowledge about how things work. You may have learned this through reading, talking to an expert, discussion, or other experiences.

Write your Explanation using the **Claim**, **Evidence**, and **Science knowledge**.

© It's About Time

Why Does Limestone Neutralize Acid Rain Better Than Granite?

Acid rain falls in many places in the United States, but many factors determine how much an area suffers from the acid rain. One factor is the total amount of acid deposited. If there is more acid rain, or if the rain is more acidic, the acid rain will do more damage than if there is less rain or the rain is less acidic.

Another factor is how sensitive an area is to acid. The geology of an area often determines its sensitivity to acid. In areas where the bedrock (the rock under the soil) is limestone, acid rain can be **neutralized** to some degree. To neutralize a solution means to bring its pH closer to 7 (neutral).

Limestone, along with other rocks and soils that contain calcium carbonate ($CaCO_3$), are most effective at neutralizing acid. Acids react with calcium carbonate to produce neutral compounds and carbon dioxide.

Sulfuric acid (H_2SO_4) reacts with calcium carbonate to produce calcium sulfate and carbonic acid.

$$CaCO_3 + H_2SO_4 \rightarrow CaSO_4 + H_2CO_3$$

Carbonic acid then forms carbon dioxide gas and water.

$$H_2CO_3 \rightarrow CO_2 + H_2O$$

Because carbonic acid is less acidic than sulfuric acid, limestone helps neutralize the acid in acid rain. This lessens the acid rain's impact on the groundwater and surface water. If the acid rain is neutralized, it will not change the acidity of lakes and groundwater.

In mountainous areas, on the other hand, the bedrock is usually granite. Granite does not react with acid, so it does not neutralize acid. In these areas, acid rain enters surface and groundwater systems unchanged. When the acid water mixes with water in the lakes and soil, it makes that water more acidic.

The ability of forest soils or rock to neutralize acidity is known as its **buffering capacity**. The buffering capacity of a region depends on the composition of the soil, the thickness of the soil, and the bedrock beneath the soil. The buffering capacity of the Adirondacks is low. Most of the lakes in the Adirondacks have granite bottoms. Because granite does not neutralize the acid, the acidity of water in the lakes and soil increases with acid rain and affects sensitive plants and animals.

neutralize: to bring the pH of a solution close to 7 (neutral).

buffering capacity: the ability to neutralize acid.

neutralization: the reaction of an acid and a base to form water.

salt: a compound made of a positive ion and a negative ion.

ionic bond: a chemical bond between a positive ion and a negative ion.

precipitate: a solid substance formed from a liquid solution.

What Does Neutralizing Mean?

In water, an acid releases hydrogen ions, H^+, and a base releases hydroxide ions, OH^-. These two ions will always react to form water. This is called **neutralization** because the low pH of the acid and the high pH of the base counteract each other. The solution approaches the neutral pH of water, about pH 7.

The reaction below shows the reaction of hydrochloric acid and sodium hydroxide in water. Before the reaction, the two compounds are found as a mixture of ions in water. Only H^+ and OH^- react when they collide. The sodium and chloride ions remain in solution without change.

$$H^+ + Cl^- + Na^+ + OH^- \rightarrow H_2O + Na^+ + Cl^-$$

During this neutralization reaction, the negative ion of the acid, Cl^-, and the positive ion of the base, Na^+, are left behind to form a salt if the water is evaporated away. In this case, the salt is sodium chloride, or common table salt. If you tasted the solution formed by this reaction, it would taste like salt water. However, you would not be able to see the salt until the water was removed.

A **salt** is a compound formed from ions, such as the sodium ion and the chloride ion. The force of attraction between ions of opposite charges is called an **ionic bond**. A compound held together by ionic bonds is called an ionic compound. Most, but not all salts, are formed from a positive metal ion and a negative ion made of nonmetal atoms. Another example would be iron oxide, Fe_2O_3, or rust.

If the forces of attraction between the positive and negative ions is strong enough, the ions will stick together and come out of solution, falling to the bottom as a solid **precipitate**. Just as rain and snow are precipitates, chemical precipitates fall to the bottom of the container due to gravity.

You observed a precipitator in the coal-burning power-plant animation. Knowing what you have now learned, what do you think the precipitator does? How does it remove pollutants from the products of combustion? How can you use this information to make recommendations about improving the air quality of your community?

Observation B: How Does Acid Rain Affect Plant Growth?

Plants are an essential component of any environment, and plants require water. Plants can live in water, or they can get their water from groundwater or from the soil. Some of that water may be acidic. Most of this water comes from rain and snow, and some of the rain or snow may be acidic. Acidity can affect plants in many ways. In this observation, you will observe how acidity affects two different types of plants.

Philodendron, begonia, and coleus plants are common plants that grow roots from cuttings, leaves, or pieces of stems. These plants are also particularly sensitive to acid water. You will observe one of the direct effects of acid water on plant growth.

Predict

You read about the effects of acid rain on some of the trees in the Adirondacks. Use what you read to predict the effect of acidic water on the root growth of the plants you will observe in the video. Predict whether you think root growth of a plant growing in acidic water will be greater than, less than, or the same as the root growth of a plant growing in water. Record your prediction and your reasoning on your *Plant and Acid Water* page.

Observe

You will observe a video of a scientific study of the effects of acid on the root of a begonia plant. As you watch the video, remember that the pH scale is not linear. Water at a pH of 4 has 10 times the concentration of hydrogen ions, H^+, as water at a pH of 5. If you compare pH 4 water to neutral water of pH 7, the pH 4 has 1000 times the concentration of H^+.

Procedure

1. The first beaker in the video is labeled *water plus root,* and the second beaker is labeled *acid water plus root.* The pH of the second beaker has been adjusted to pH 4.

2. On a *Plant and Acid Water* page, record the number of roots and the length of the roots for each plant for *Day 0.*

3. For the next measurements shown in the video, record the number of roots and the length of the roots in each beaker. Be sure to record the *Day* shown in the video as well.

AIR QUALITY

Create Your Explanation

1.3.2/2.BBQ.2/3.5.2
4.2.2/4.6.7/4.7.1/ABQ.2

Name: _____ Date: _____

Use this page to explain the lesson of your recent investigations.

Write a brief summary of the results from your investigation. You will use this summary to help you write your Explanation.

Claim – a statement of what you understand or a conclusion that you have reached from an investigation or a set of investigations.

Evidence – data collected during investigations and trends in that data.

Science knowledge – knowledge about how things work. You may have learned this through reading, talking to an expert, discussion, or other experiences.

Write your Explanation using the **Claim**, **Evidence**, and **Science knowledge**.

© It's About Time

---

4. Continue to record the day, the number of roots, and the length of the roots for each beaker on each day shown in the video.

Analyze Your Data

1. What were the differences between the plant grown in tap water and the one grown in acid water?

2. What factors do you think produced these changes?

3. Compare your results to your prediction. How do they differ?

Explain

Read the box about plants growing in water and acidic water. Then develop a claim about the effects of acid rain on plant and tree growth in the Adirondacks. Your claim will be about the effects of acid rain on the growth of plants and trees. Record evidence from your investigation that supports your claim. Record science knowledge that supports your claim. Some might come from what you just read. Other science knowledge that supports your claim might come from other readings and investigations in this Unit. Then develop an explanation statement that pulls together your claim and your evidence and science knowledge. Your statement should convince someone that your claim is trustworthy. It should also help someone understand why acid rain affects plant life and the health of trees the way it does. Be as specific as you can be.

Why Do Plants Grow Better in Tap Water Than in Acidic Water?

Plants require water to live and grow. They take up water and use it for their life processes. Each type of plant is more or less sensitive to acidity in water. If a plant takes in water with a higher concentration of acid than the plant can tolerate, the life processes of the plant slow or even stop. One of these life processes is the ability to grow roots.

Observation C: How Does Acid Rain Affect Stone Structures?

You may have seen a statue in a park or a gravestone in an old cemetery. The face on the statue or the words on the gravestone were no longer easy to recognize. The stone looked like it had been "eaten" away. Acid rain can have a destructive effect on structures constructed by people, such as buildings, statues, gravestones, and monuments. These structures are made of many different materials. Some are made from rock, such as granite, marble, sandstone, or limestone. Others are made from metal, such as iron, steel, or copper. The effects of acid rain are different on different types of materials. In this Observation, you will observe the effect of acid rain on two common building materials: marble and sandstone.

Predict

Predict the effect of acid on the mass and physical appearance of sandstone and marble, two common materials used for buildings and monuments. Marble is a hard stone made of calcium carbonate (or limestone) that has changed into crystals because of heat and pressure. Sandstone is a rock made mostly of the elements silicon and oxygen. Individual grains of sand are hard, but the stone has many holes between the grains, and sandstone breaks down easily. How do you think the mass and/or the physical appearance of each type of stone will change when exposed to acid water? Record your predictions and your reasoning on your *Sandstone and Acid Water* page and your *Marble and Acid Water* page.

Observe

You will observe a video of a scientific study of the effects of acid on two kinds of building materials, sandstone and marble. As you watch the video, remember that the pH scale is not linear. Water at a pH of 4 has 10 times the concentration of hydrogen ions, H^+, as water at a pH of 5. If you compare pH 4 water to neutral water of pH 7, the pH 4 has 1000 times the concentration of H^+.

Sandstone and Acid Water   4.6.3

Name: _____   Date: _____

Predict the effect of acid on sandstone:

Materials in Water			Materials in Acid		
Beginning pH:			Beginning pH:		
Sample description:			Sample description:		
Sample initial mass:			Sample initial mass:		
Sample final mass:			Sample final mass:		

Day	Results in water		Day	Results in acid	
	Sample appearance	Water pH		Sample appearance	Acid pH
0			0		
—			—		
—			—		
—			—		
—			—		
—			—		

Marble and Acid Water   4.6.4

Name: _____   Date: _____

Predict the effect of acid on marble:

Materials in Water			Materials in Acid		
Beginning pH:			Beginning pH:		
Sample description:			Sample description:		
Sample initial mass:			Sample initial mass:		
Sample final mass:			Sample final mass:		

Day	Results in water		Day	Results in acid	
	Sample appearance	Water pH		Sample appearance	Acid pH
0			0		
—			—		
—			—		
—			—		
—			—		
—			—		

Procedure

1. The first beaker in the video is labeled *water plus sandstone*, and this is the control. The second beaker is labeled *acid water plus sandstone.* The pH of the acid water is pH 4.

2. On a *Sandstone and Acid Water* page, record an initial description of each piece of sandstone as well as the initial mass. Also record the beginning pH of the water and acid water.

3. For *Day 0* in your tables, record the appearance of each sample and the pH of the water in each beaker.

4. For each day on the video, record changes in appearance and in pH for both beakers. Be sure to record the *Day* shown in the video as well.

5. At the end of the video, the samples in both beakers are rinsed, dried, and remassed. Record the final appearance and the final mass of each sample.

6. Repeat steps 2–5 for the samples of marble. Record your observations and other data on a *Marble and Acid Water* page.

Analyze Your Data

1. Describe in detail the physical changes in each sample of stone in both tap water and acid water. If the acid water affected one type of stone more than the other, describe why you think you got that result.

2. How much mass did each sample of stone gain or lose over the days of the investigation? Where do you think the mass came from or went to? (Remember what you know about conservation of mass.)

3. How do your results compare with your predictions? How do they differ?

Explain

Read the box at the end of this section about how acid rain affects building materials. Then develop a claim about the effects of acid rain on stone structures. Record evidence from your investigation

---

Create Your Explanation

1.3.2/2.BBQ.2/3.5.2
4.2.2/4.6.7/4.7.1/ABQ.2

Name: _____ Date: _____

Use this page to explain the lesson of your recent investigations.

Write a brief summary of the results from your investigation. You will use this summary to help you write your Explanation.

Claim – a statement of what you understand or a conclusion that you have reached from an investigation or a set of investigations.

Evidence – data collected during investigations and trends in that data.

Science knowledge – knowledge about how things work. You may have learned this through reading, talking to an expert, discussion, or other experiences.

Write your Explanation using the **Claim**, **Evidence**, and **Science knowledge**.

© It's About Time

that supports your claim. Record science knowledge that supports your claim. Some might come from what you just read. Other science knowledge that supports your claim might come from other readings and investigations in this Unit. Then develop an explanation statement that pulls together your claim and your evidence and science knowledge. Your statement should convince someone that your claim is trustworthy. It should also help someone understand why acid rain affects stone structures the way it does. Be as specific as you can be.

Observation D: How Does Acid Rain Affect Metal Structures?

You may have seen a rusty metal bench in a park. The bench may be falling apart. Acid rain can have a destructive effect on metal structures. In this investigation, you will observe the effect of acid water on two common metal building materials: steel and copper.

Predict

Steel is a metal made mostly of the element iron (Fe). It also contains carbon and other elements. These other elements are used to make the iron harder. Steel reacts with air in the presence of water, forming an orange or brown substance on its surface. Copper (Cu) is an element. It is softer than steel and easy to bend. It is a good conductor of heat and electricity. Copper is often used to make pipes that carry water inside buildings, because copper does not react with water. It does react with air and forms a greenish substance on its surface.

Predict the effect of acid water on the mass and physical appearance of steel and copper, two common metals used for buildings and monuments. How do you think the mass and/ or the physical appearance of each type of metal will change when exposed to acid? Record your predictions and your reasoning on your *Steel and Acid Water* page and your *Copper and Acid Water* page.

Steel and Acid Water		4.6.5

Name: _____ Date: _____

Predict the effect of acid on steel:

Materials in Water	Materials in Acid
Beginning pH:	Beginning pH:
Sample description:	Sample description:
Sample initial mass:	Sample initial mass:
Sample final mass:	Sample final mass:

	Results in water			Results in acid	
Day	Sample appearance	Water pH	Day	Sample appearance	Acid pH
0			0		
—			—		
—			—		
—			—		
—			—		
—			—		

© It's About Time

Observe

You will observe a video of a scientific study of the effects of acid on two kinds of building materials, steel and copper. As you watch the video, remember that the pH scale is not linear. Water at a pH of 4 has 10 times the concentration of hydrogen ions, H^+, as water at a pH of 5. If you compare pH 4 water to neutral water of pH 7, the pH 4 has 1000 times the concentration of H^+.

Procedure

1. The first beaker in the video is labeled water plus steel, and this is the control. The second beaker is labeled acid water plus steel. The pH of the acid water is pH 4.

2. On a *Steel and Acid Water* page, record an initial description of each piece of steel wool as well as the initial mass. Also record the beginning pH of the water and acid water.

3. For *Day 0* in your tables, record the appearance of each sample and the pH of the water in each beaker.

4. For each day on the video, record changes in appearance and in pH for both beakers. Be sure to record the *Day* shown in the video as well.

5. At the end of the video, the samples in both beakers are rinsed, dried, and remassed. Record the final appearance and the final mass of each sample.

6. Repeat steps 2–5 for the samples of copper. Record your observations and other data on a *Copper and Acid Water* page.

Copper and Acid Water   4.6.6

Name: _____   Date: _____

Predict the effect of acid on copper:

Materials in Water	Materials in Acid
Beginning pH:	Beginning pH:
Sample description:	Sample description:
Sample initial mass:	Sample initial mass:
Sample final mass:	Sample final mass:

Day	Results in water		Day	Results in acid	
	Sample appearance	Water pH		Sample appearance	Acid pH
0			0		
—			—		
—			—		
—			—		
—			—		
—			—		

© It's About Time

Analyze Your Data

1. Describe in detail the physical changes in each type of metal in both tap water and acid water. If the acid affected one type of metal more than the other, describe why you think you observed that result. What other changes did you observe?

2. How much mass did each sample of metal gain or lose over the days of the investigation? Where do you think the metal went or came from? Use what you know about conservation of mass to answer this question.

3. How did your results compare with your prediction? How did they differ?

Explain

Read the box on the next page about how acid rain affects building materials. Then develop a claim about the effects of acid rain on metal structures. Record evidence from your investigation that supports your claim. Record science knowledge that supports your claim. Some science knowledge might come from what you just read. Other science that supports your claim might come from other readings and investigations in this Unit. Then develop an explanation statement that pulls together your claim and your evidence and science knowledge. Your statement should convince someone that your claim is trustworthy. It should also help someone understand why acid rain affects metal structures the way it does. Be as specific as you can be.

Create Your Explanation 1.3.2/2.BBQ.2/3.5.2 4.2.2/4.6.7/4.7.1/ABQ.2

Name: _____ Date: _____

Use this page to explain the lesson of your recent investigations.

> Write a brief summary of the results from your investigation. You will use this summary to help you write your Explanation.

> **Claim** – a statement of what you understand or a conclusion that you have reached from an investigation or a set of investigations.

> **Evidence** – data collected during investigations and trends in that data.

> **Science knowledge** – knowledge about how things work. You may have learned this through reading, talking to an expert, discussion, or other experiences.

> Write your Explanation using the **Claim**, **Evidence**, and **Science knowledge**.

© It's About Time

Why Do Some Building Materials React Differently to Acid Rain Than Other Building Materials?

In *Learning Set 3*, you read about how the periodic table is used to group elements according to their physical and chemical characteristics. One way the elements differ is in the way they react chemically with acids. Different building materials are made up of different elements. Some elements are metals, and some building materials are nonmetals.

Elements used in building materials.

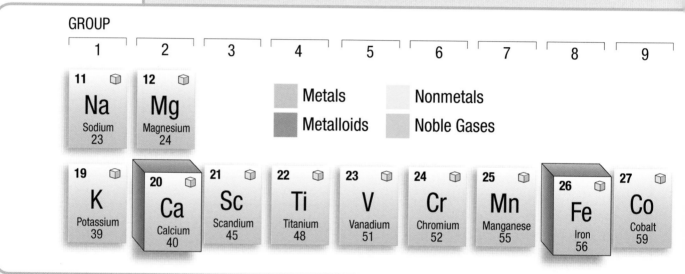

GROUP

| 1 | 2 | 3 | 4 | 5 | 6 | 7 | 8 | 9 |

| 11 Na Sodium 23 | 12 Mg Magnesium 24 |

Metals   Nonmetals

Metalloids   Noble Gases

| 19 K Potassium 39 | 20 Ca Calcium 40 | 21 Sc Scandium 45 | 22 Ti Titanium 48 | 23 V Vanadium 51 | 24 Cr Chromium 52 | 25 Mn Manganese 55 | 26 Fe Iron 56 | 27 Co Cobalt 59 |

rust: a chemical reaction that occurs when certain metals react with oxygen and water and produce a reddish brown or green film as the metal breaks down.

A metal reacts chemically with oxygen to form oxides. (Some oxides you learned about earlier are the nitrogen oxides. These are oxides that do not contain a metal.) One common metal oxide is iron oxide (FeO_3). When a metal oxide is dissolved in water, it forms a basic solution. Copper and steel (which is mostly iron) react with water and oxygen by forming rust. **Rust** results from the movement of electrons from one material to another. When rust forms, you see a reddish-brown or green crust as some of the metal changes into other substaces.

Iron reacts with oxygen and water to form brown or red rust.

Copper reacts with air to form greenish rust known as a patina.

The Effects of Acid Rain on Human History

Acid rain is not a problem found only in the Adirondacks. It is also a worldwide problem. In addition to acid rain affecting the environment, acid rain is also eating away at human history by destroying famous monuments, statues, and landmarks, some of which are thousands of years old.

GROUP

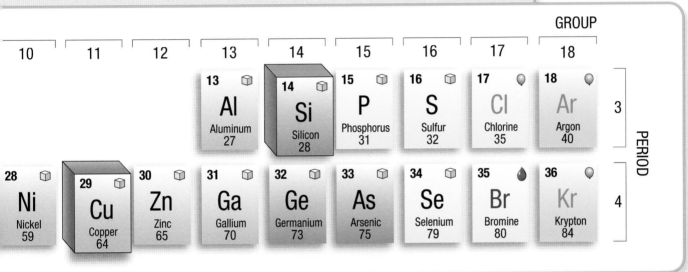

10	11	12	13	14	15	16	17	18	
			13 Al Aluminum 27	**14** Si Silicon 28	**15** P Phosphorus 31	**16** S Sulfur 32	**17** Cl Chlorine 35	**18** Ar Argon 40	3
28 Ni Nickel 59	**29** Cu Copper 64	**30** Zn Zinc 65	**31** Ga Gallium 70	**32** Ge Germanium 73	**33** As Arsenic 75	**34** Se Selenium 79	**35** Br Bromine 80	**36** Kr Krypton 84	4

PERIOD

Many famous historical structures across the world have been damaged by acid rain.

The Great Sphinx of Giza, Egypt.

The Statue of Liberty in New York Harbor, New York City.

The Parthenon in Athens, Greece.

AIR QUALITY

What's the Point?

The geology of an area can affect how much of the acid from acid rain stays in lakes and how much is neutralized. Basic rock, such as limestone, neutralizes more acid than neutral rock, such as granite. Plants are affected in many ways by acidity. Trees and other plants can tolerate a small amount of acid, but when the acid level becomes too high, it can cause slow plant growth, slow root growth, and even death. Building materials, such as stone and metal, can react with the acids in acid rain. Structures made of metal react with oxygen to form oxides. These oxides become rust.

Pine trees need acidic soil to grow. However, too much acid can slow their growth or kill them.

More to Learn

More About the Periodic Table

Throughout this Unit, you have used the periodic table as a tool to learn more about the elements. You have looked at particular elements or small groups of elements. The periodic table is organized so that you can learn much more about the elements it contains.

You know that the elements in the periodic table are arranged in rows and columns. Each element as you travel across a row increases by 1 in atomic number. This means each element has one more proton than the last element. And, in order to maintain its neutral state, each element contains one more electron. For example, the element corresponding to atomic number 13 is aluminum. Aluminum has 13 protons and 13 electrons.

You are already familiar with some of the columns. You learned about the noble gases in group 8A. These gases are stable and do not react with other elements. Most of the elements on the periodic table are metals, and most of these are on the left side of the table. Some of you worked with or read about some of these, such as aluminum, copper, calcium, and iron. Most metals are solids, but you also read about one liquid metal, mercury, which is an air pollutant. Most metals are shiny, bendable, and conduct electricity. When metal oxides combine with water, they form basic solutions.

Materials that are typically gases or soft solids, such as carbon, are classified as **nonmetals**. The nonmetals are at the upper right corner of the periodic table. Solid nonmetals are dull instead of shiny. The solid nonmetals are brittle and do not conduct electricity. When nonmetals react with oxygen, they also produce oxides. Many of these oxides, such as the nitrogen oxides (NO_x) and sulfur dioxide (SO_2), are air pollutants. When nonmetal oxides react with water, they form acidic solutions, such as acid rain.

> **nonmetal:** an element that is a gas or a soft, brittle solid. It does not conduct electricity.

Stop and Think

1. What metals did you investigate or read about in this Unit? Find them on the periodic table. What is the atomic number of each of these metals? What is the atomic mass? Which ones are pollutants or become pollutants when reacting with other elements?

2. What nonmetals did you investigate or read about in this Unit? What is the atomic number of each of these nonmetals? What is the atomic mass? Which ones are pollutants or become pollutants when reacting with other elements? Which ones are essential to life?

3. Why do you think nonmetal oxides are more likely to be air pollutants than metal oxides?

4.7 Communicate

Share the Results of Your Observations

During the past week, you have investigated the effects of acid rain on lakes, organisms, and building materials. You have also read a lot about how atoms combine with each other to form molecules and how molecules react with each other to form new molecules. You have a lot of data to share with the class, and you have done your best to construct explanations of the effects you have observed. It is now time to share with the class what you have learned. Remember that everyone needs the results of everybody else's investigations to successfully achieve the challenge, and everybody needs to understand the science you read to develop your explanations.

Communicate Your Results

Investigation Expo

Each group in the class observed a different video. Each will present its observations, results, and explanations to the class. Then everyone will be able to observe and understand each group's conclusions. To prepare for your presentation, make a poster to share with the class. Include the following on your poster:

- the materials and the environmental factors of your observation

- the data you collected, including any graphs or data sheets

- your answers to the *Analyze Your Data* questions

- your explanation. Make sure to present the science clearly.

- your answers to these questions:

  - How did your investigation relate to acid rain in the Adirondacks?

  - Why do you think acid water had a different effect on different materials or organisms?

  - How did what you observed compare with your predictions?

When it is your turn to present, use your poster to help you organize your presentation. Present in a way that teaches others in the class what you have learned about the effects of acid rain on the environment. Tell the class which video you observed and what your data showed. Then present your claim and explanation, and teach others in the class why acid rain has the effects you observed.

As you listen to each presentation, think about the factors each group observed and how you think each factor might affect the environment as a whole. Pay attention to similarities and differences among the observations. Be sure you understand how each observation was carried out and how each group analyzed their data. If you do not understand something, or another group did not present something clearly enough, ask questions. Remember that you will need to understand the results of each of the observations to achieve the challenge.

Reflect

Work with your group to answer the following questions. Be prepared to share your answers with the class.

Lake Bottom Material and the Effect on Water pH

1. What differences did you observe in the change in acidity between the limestone lake and the granite lake? What do you think was happening to cause that change? Use what you have learned in this Unit to justify your answer.

2. Imagine you take samples of water from two acidic lakes and measure the pH. You graph your data. Examine the two graphs.

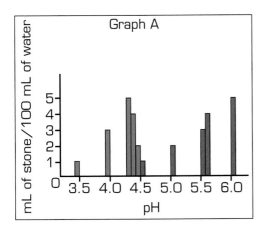

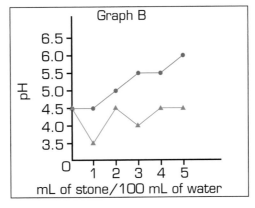

The effect of granite and limestone on acid water (pH 4.5).

a) In Graph A, which color represents granite and which color represents limestone? How do you know?

b) In Graph B, which line (dots or triangles) represents granite? Which line represents limestone? How do you know?

Effect of Acid Water on Plants

1. The observations measured the effects of acid water on plants. What were those effects?

2. Why would the effect of acidic water differ in different plants?

3. Why are these effects important to plants and to the environment?

4. Many lakes in the Adirondacks contain few plants or animals. Other lakes lack organisms of any kind. What kind of geology do you think these lakes have? Support your answer with evidence from the investigations.

5. How could people protect lakes and ponds from the effects of acid rain? What will happen to plant life in these lakes if nothing is done? What will happen to plants near these lakes if nothing is done? Justify your answers with evidence from the investigations.

Effect of Acid on Materials

1. What kinds of building materials would last longer in a city with an acid-rain problem?

Synthesis

1. Based on the results of all the observations, what do you think is the relationship between the environment and acid rain?

Other Pollutants in the Adirondacks

Acids are not the only air-pollution problem in the Adirondacks. The wind carries other harmful substances toward the Adirondacks. Power plants and other industries release toxic metals, such as lead, mercury, zinc, copper, cadmium, and chromium, into the atmosphere. These metals are deposited on the ground or in lakes when it rains, and they accumulate there. More rain washes the metals into lakes and streams, where they are taken up by plants and animals, particularly fish.

Mercury, a highly toxic metal, is a particular problem. Mercury comes from combustion in coal-burning power plants and other types of industries. When fish take in mercury through their gills, the mercury builds up in their bodies. Then, when other animals eat the fish, the mercury passes to their bodies. The flow of energy stored in food from one organism to another is described as a **food chain**. For example, small fish might feed on tiny plants in the water. Larger fish might eat the smaller fish. An eagle or bear might eat the larger fish. As organisms in the food chain increase in size, they need to eat more food to meet their energy needs. The more food they eat in an environment contaminated with mercury, the more mercury they take into their bodies. As a result, the concentration of mercury in the bodies of organisms increases along a food chain.

People are often near the ends of many food chains. If people eat a lot of fish containing mercury, it can affect their health. Mercury can interfere with the normal functioning of the nervous system, which controls movement and the body's responses to changes in the environment. It can also affect the processes through which the body digests food and gets rid of wastes. If a pregnant woman takes in too much mercury, the development of her fetus's brain and nervous system can be affected.

Another problem related to acid rain is known as **leaching**. Trees get their nutrition from positively charged ions of some elements, such as calcium (Ca), magnesium (Mg), and potassium (K). These elements come from rocks that have broken down and dissolved into the soil. They stay in the soil because of attractive forces between the positive metal ions and negative ions in the soil. Acid rain adds hydrogen ions (H^+) to the soil. Leaching is the process through which the hydrogen ions from acid rain displace some of the nutrient ions. The nutrient ions are washed deeper into the soil or washed completely out of the topsoil. If the nutrient ions are leached from the soil, they are no longer available to the roots of the plant. The loss of these ions can cause plants to grow slowly or not at all.

food chain: the flow of energy stored in food from one organism to another.

leaching: the removal of nutrients in the soil by acids.

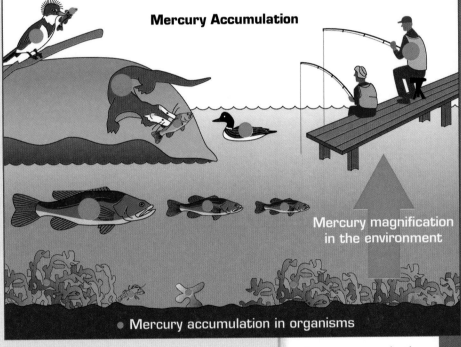

Mercury Accumulation

Mercury magnification in the environment

● Mercury accumulation in organisms

As mercury and other toxic pollutants move up the food chain, their concentration increases.

Acid rain also affects aluminum (Al) in the soil. Aluminum is an element that is not needed by plants and is toxic to humans, plants, and animals. In the forest soil, aluminum exists as a salt in an insoluble form. If acid rain is abundant, as in the Adirondacks, the aluminum ions become soluble and available to the root system of the trees. This can slow the growth of plant life. When the toxic aluminum ions are washed into lakes and streams, they are taken up by fish and other organisms. It can stunt their growth or even kill them. Aluminum, at higher levels, is also toxic to people.

Revise Your Explanation

Earlier in this *Learning Set*, in *Section 4.2*, your class developed an explanation of the sources of air pollution in the Adirondacks. You have learned a lot since then about the effects of this pollution. It is now time to make a new set of claims about air pollution in the Adirondacks. You will make one claim about the sources of air pollution in the Adirondacks and another claim about the effects of air pollution. Then you will support and explain each.

Use a new *Create Your Explanation* page for each of your claims. Begin by updating your claim about the sources of air pollution in the Adirondacks. Use evidence from the investigations to support your claim. Record the science knowledge that supports your claim. Then update your explanation. Remember that your statement should convince somebody that your claim is trustworthy. It should also help someone understand why the sources of pollution are present.

Then make another claim about the *effects* of acid and other sources of air pollution on the Adirondacks. Record this claim on a second *Create Your Explanation* page. Record evidence from the observations about the effects of acidity on bodies of water, organisms,

Create Your Explanation

1.3.2/2.BBQ.2/3.5.2
4.2.2/4.6.7/4.7.1/ABQ.2

Name: _____ Date: _____

Use this page to explain the lesson of your recent investigations.

Write a brief summary of the results from your investigation. You will use this summary to help you write your Explanation.

Claim – a statement of what you understand or a conclusion that you have reached from an investigation or a set of investigations.

Evidence – data collected during investigations and trends in that data.

Science knowledge – knowledge about how things work. You may have learned this through reading, talking to an expert, discussion, or other experiences.

Write your Explanation using the **Claim**, **Evidence**, and **Science knowledge**.

© It's About Time

and structures. Record the science knowledge from your previous readings, investigations, and explorations that helped you develop your claim. Then write a statement that pulls together your evidence and science knowledge to support your claim. This statement is your explanation. Remember that your explanation statement should convince someone that your claim is trustworthy. This explanation statement should also report how the sources of pollution in the Adirondacks cause the effects. Be as specific as you can. If you want to write separate claims and explanations for each effect of air pollution in the Adirondacks, you may do that.

Communicate

Share Your Explanation

Share your group's claims and explanations with the class. Tell the class what makes your claim accurate based on your evidence and science knowledge. As you listen to the claims and explanations of others, pay special attention to how other groups have supported their claims with science knowledge. Ask questions or make suggestions if you think a group's claim is not as accurate as it could be or if the group has not supported their claim well enough with evidence and science knowledge.

Revise Your Explanations

As a class, develop a set of claims and explanations that the entire class agrees with. Make each claim and explanation as specific as possible. Use all of the science you have been reading and everything you understand from the investigations you have done.

Identify what else you need to know to make your claims and explanations more complete and to answer the *Big Question*.

Update the *Project Board*

Acid rain is a problem in the Adirondacks, but it is also a problem in cities and in all parts of the world. Update the *What are we learning?* column with conclusions from the investigations and your discussions. Record your evidence in the *What is our evidence?* column. You might want to add the class's claims to this column and put the evidence and explanations for those claims in the *What is our evidence?* column.

You may also have ideas about what else you need to know to answer the *Big Question*. Record these ideas in the *What do we need to investigate?* column. You may now know enough about air quality so that you can begin to think about how to improve air quality in your community. Record your ideas in the *What does it mean for the challenge or question?* column. You will add to this column as you finish the Unit.

What's the Point?

Acid rain can interact with the environment in many ways. Acid rain can cause lakes to become more acidic, affecting organisms that live in the lakes. The geology of an area can have a great effect on the ability of lakes to respond to acid rain. In some parts of the country, limestone may line the bottom of a lake. In other areas, the bottom material may be granite or another type of hard stone. The composition of a lake bottom can determine how much the water is affected by acid rain. Limestone lakes are less affected by acid rain than granite lakes because the limestone neutralizes some of the acid in acid rain. The Adirondack region has mostly granite lakes.

Plants exposed to acid rain can grow slowly or not at all. Some plants can even die from acid rain. However, the effect of acid rain on plants depends on the type of plant and the concentration of the acid. Some plants are more sensitive to acid rain than other plants.

All parts of an ecosystem are interconnected. When acid rain affects one part of the ecosystem, the result is felt throughout the system. Acid rain affects bodies of water, organisms, and structures built by people. Some parts of the environment are affected more than other parts of the environment. The organisms in lakes are particularly sensitive to acid rain. The other organisms in the ecosystem often rely on the aquatic organisms in lakes and ponds that are at the bottom of food chains.

Products from the emissions of smokestacks also carry dangerous metals, such as mercury. When toxic metals get into the ecosystem, they can become concentrated as they move up through the food chain. At the top level, they can cause illness or even death in humans and other organisms.

More to Learn

How Does Air Pollution Lead to Global Climate Change?

Before learning about the Adirondacks, you may have thought that air pollution affects only the air you take into your lungs. You now know that polluted air can cause changes to trees and even to fish that live underwater. In fact, air pollution is responsible for some of the most dramatic changes in life on Earth. One of those changes causes the **greenhouse effect**.

Have you ever seen a greenhouse? Most greenhouses look like glass houses. Greenhouses are used to grow plants, especially in the winter. They work by trapping heat from the Sun. The glass panels of the greenhouse let in light but keep heat from escaping. This causes the greenhouse to heat up, much like the inside of a car parked in sunlight. By trapping the Sun's heat, a greenhouse keeps plants warm enough to live through a cold winter.

Some gases in the atmosphere, called **greenhouse gases**, behave much like the glass panes in a greenhouse. Sunlight passes through the blanket of greenhouse gases on its way to Earth. When sunlight reaches Earth's surface, the land, water, and living things absorb a small amount of the Sun's heat energy. This energy is used for maintaining plant and animal life. But most of the Sun's heat energy bounces off of Earth's surface and is radiated from Earth back into the atmosphere.

greenhouse effect: certain gases and other pollutants trapped in the atmosphere can prevent heat from the Sun from leaving Earth.

greenhouse gases: gases that trap heat from the Sun in Earth's atmosphere.

heat and light

heat and light

heat

heat

heat

A greenhouse keeps plants warm by trapping the Sun's heat.

The blanket of greenhouse gases traps some of the Sun's heat in the atmosphere close to Earth. Much like in a greenhouse, when the Sun's heat is trapped in the atmosphere, it continues to warm Earth. The greenhouse effect is important to maintaining Earth's climates.

Without the greenhouse effect, Earth would not be warm enough for humans or other organisms to live.

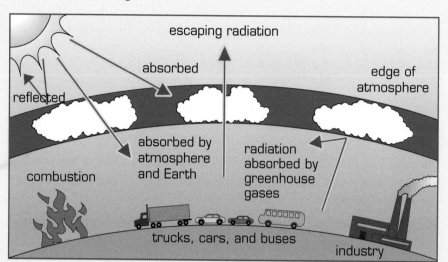

Greenhouse gases in the atmosphere behave much like the glass panes in a greenhouse.

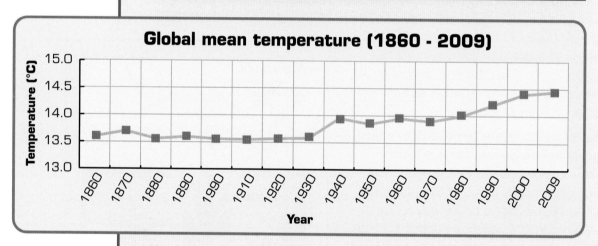

However, the more heat that is trapped by greenhouse gases, the more Earth heats up. If human activities enhance Earth's natural greenhouse effect too much, any extra warming can cause problems for humans, plants, and animals. Some scientists are worried that this has been happening. Earth's temperatures have been rising. Many scientists believe that the major reason for the rise in temperatures is that the atmosphere contains a greater concentration of greenhouse gases.

Some scientists call this rise in temperature **global warming**. When Earth is warmed, climates are affected all over the world. Every place becomes warmer. That is why most scientists call the rise in temperature **global climate change**.

global warming: a rise in Earth's temperature due to heat from the Sun being trapped in the atmosphere.

global climate change: a change in Earth's climate due to global warming.

The table below shows some greenhouse gases and their minimum contribution and maximum contribution to the total greenhouse effect. You are already familiar with some of them.

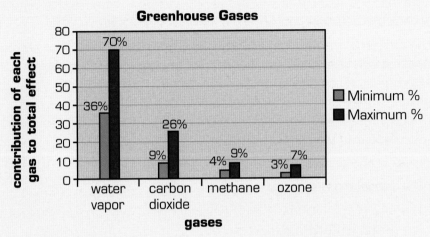

You will find many familiar gases in this list of greenhouse gases.

Stop and Think

1. What do you think will happen as Earth becomes warmer? List three effects on humans, plants, and animals.

2. Look at the chart of greenhouse gases. Where do you think greenhouse gases come from?

How Does CO_2 Add to the Greenhouse Effect?

You have read about how greenhouse gases in the atmosphere can cause temperatures around the world to rise. To fully understand the greenhouse effect, scientists would have to conduct experiments on Earth's climate. However, it is impossible to carry out these types of experiments. Instead, scientists investigate climate change by using computer-climate models. Remember that a model represents a scientist's best understanding of how something works. Scientists use climate models to "test" their ideas about the effects of increased CO_2 on Earth's temperature. They also use those models to predict how that might affect long-term temperature changes on Earth.

You will use a climate model in a computer program called NetLogo to carry out the same kinds of investigations scientists have done using climate models. Using NetLogo, you will observe how radiation from the Sun heats Earth and how greenhouse gases affect that process.

Using NetLogo To Model the Greenhouse Effect

When you open NetLogo and load the climate model, you will see a setup screen.

On the left, you will find the *Model Set-up Window*. You use this window to select the beginning parameters for your simulation.

In the center at the very top is a *speed* slider button. This slider button speeds up or slows down the simulation. To begin, this slider button should be set in the center on "normal speed." As you run the model to simulate climate change, you may want to speed it up or slow it down. To slow down the simulation, you can slide this button to the left. To speed it up, you slide it to the right.

The rest of the screen has three main sections:

- The *model input settings* are on the top left.

- The *plot graph window* is on the bottom left. This window displays a line graph of Earth's temperature.

- The *graphics window* is on the right.

The *model input settings* are where you set your parameters for the simulation. This area has three parts:

- *Parameter settings* are on the top left. The *sun-brightness* slider button controls the amount of solar radiation coming from the Sun. A value of 1.0 corresponds to the Sun. The *albedo* slider button controls how much of the Sun's energy hitting Earth is absorbed. It is affected by the amount of land and water. Earth's albedo is about 0.6.

- *Add/Remove* buttons are on the bottom left. Each click of the *add* CO_2 button adds 25 units of CO_2 to the atmosphere. Each unit of CO_2 represents 100,000 metric tons of CO_2. Each click of *remove* CO_2 button removes 25 units, or 25 times 100,000 metric tons, of CO_2 from the atmosphere.

- *Temperature/CO_2 amount* measurements are in boxes on the right. *Temperature* shows the current temperature in °F on Earth's surface. CO_2 *amount* shows the current number of CO_2 units in the atmosphere. The *Global temperature* graph on the bottom left shows the global temperature in °F on Earth's surface

One other button at the top right of the *model input settings*, *watch a ray*, allows you to watch the path of a single **solar ray**, or heat energy from the Sun. Click once to watch the ray and click again to go back to the normal setting.

solar ray: heat energy from the Sun.

How Do Greenhouse Gases Keep Earth Warm Enough for People to Live Comfortably?

You will begin by running the simulation with the amount of CO_2 currently emitted into the atmosphere. This will give you a chance to see how the blanket of greenhouse gases keeps Earth warm. Remember, without the blanket of greenhouse gases, Earth would be too cold for organisms to easily live.

Procedure

1. First, open the program on your computer. Your teacher will tell you which model to open. You should see a startup screen.

2. Set the parameters for the NetLogo simulation. Set the *sun-brightness* slider button at 1.0. Set the *albedo* slider button at 0.6. Then press the *setup* button. You will see a screen like the one shown below. The pink and green areas are Earth. The blue is Earth's atmosphere.

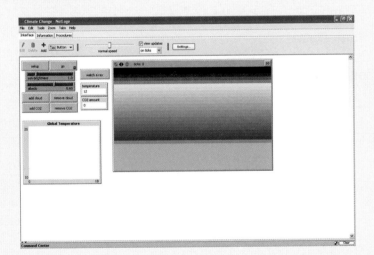

3. Click on the *add CO_2* button until you have added 300 units of CO_2. Three hundred units represents 30 million tons of CO_2. This is the current global amount of CO_2 added annually to the atmosphere.

4. Press the *go* button. The yellow arrowheads streaming downward represent solar rays. If the solar rays are absorbed by Earth, the heat is represented by a red dot. Sometimes the red dots will transform into infrared radiation and leave Earth. Infrared radiation is represented by a red arrowhead leaving Earth.

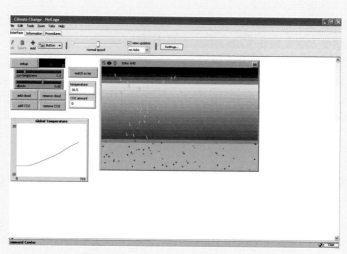

5. Move the *speed* slider button all the way to the right.

6. On your *Climate Change* page, record your observations of what happens. You will have to run the simulation for a few minutes until Earth's temperature becomes stable.

Analyze Your Data

1. What happens when a solar ray hits Earth? Describe its path. If it escapes Earth, what happens to it then?

2. At what temperature did infrared radiation begin to leave Earth? What happened to the temperature at this point?

3. As Earth heated up, did more or less heat leave Earth as infrared radiation? Why do you think this happened? What would happen to the temperature of Earth if the amount of infrared radiation leaving Earth did not change?

4. At what temperature did the temperature of Earth stop rising? How do you think people and animals would survive on Earth at this temperature?

What Happens When the Concentration of Greenhouse Gases in the Atmosphere Increases?

Predict

You have already read about what happens when the concentration of greenhouse gases in the atmosphere increases. You will soon be running the simulation

---

Climate Change

4.MTL.1

Name: _____ Date: _____

Observation: What happened when you ran the simulation with 30 million tons of CO_2? At what temperature did Earth's temperature become stable?

Prediction: What will happen to Earth's temperature if you add more CO_2?

Observation: What happened when you ran the simulation with 42.5 million tons of CO_2? At what temperature did Earth's temperature become stable?

Observation: What happened when you removed 10 million tons of CO_2? At what temperature did Earth's temperature become stable?

Prediction: What will happen if Earth's atmosphere contains no CO_2?

Observation: What happened when you removed all the CO_2 from the atmosphere? At what temperature did Earth's temperature become stable?

On a separate piece of paper, record what else you want to find out and the other simulations you ran. Record your data and questions in a table with three columns: question you asked; how you set up the parameters in the model to answer the question; and your observations.

© It's About Time

again, this time with more CO_2 in the atmosphere. You will run the simulation with the amount of CO_2 that scientists predict will be emitted into the atmosphere by 2030. Before running the simulation, predict what will happen to Earth's temperature as you add CO_2 to the atmosphere. Record your prediction on your *Climate Change* page so you can come back to it later.

Procedure

1. Click on the *add CO₂* button until the CO_2 amount equals 425. This represents 42.5 million metric tons of CO_2. Slide the *speed* slider button all the way to the right to speed up the simulation.

2. Observe what happens, and record your observations on your *Climate Change* page. You will have to run the simulation for a few minutes until Earth's temperature becomes stable.

3. Record your observations.

4. Now remove 100 units of CO_2 from the atmosphere.

5. Observe what happens, and record your observations on your *Climate Change* page. You will have to run the simulation for a few minutes until Earth's temperature becomes stable.

Analyze Your Data

1. With 425 units of CO_2 molecules in the atmosphere, what happened when infrared radiation left Earth? Describe the path of one ray.

2. What happened to the temperature? At what temperature did the temperature become stable?

3. What happened when you removed 100 units of CO_2 from the atmosphere? Describe why that happened.

4. How do your results compare with your predictions?

What Happens if There Is no Greenhouse Gas Blanket?

Predict

You have now seen how greenhouse gases keep Earth warm, and you have seen how more greenhouse gases make Earth warmer. What do you think would happen if there were no greenhouse gas blanket? Make a prediction. Be as specific as you can about what the temperature would be. Record your prediction on your *Climate Change* page.

Procedure

1. Use the *remove CO₂* button to remove all of the CO_2 from the atmosphere.

2. Run the simulation with the *speed* slider button all the way to the right.

3. Describe the paths of the rays. How are they different than what you observed earlier?

4. Observe what happens to the temperature on Earth, and record your observations on your *Climate Change* page. You will have to run the simulation for a few minutes before the temperature becomes stable.

Analyze Your Data

1. At what temperature did Earth stop heating up?

2. What was happening to keep the temperature from increasing any more?

Other Explorations

Procedure

1. Effects of Clouds: Run the simulation again. This time, add clouds to the model. Record your results. You might want to see what happens with several different amounts of CO_2 or clouds in the atmosphere. For each simulation you run, record your results.

2. What else do you want to find out? Record your questions, how you set up the model to answer each question, and your results in a table on a piece of paper.

Reflect

Answer the following questions in your group. Be prepared to share your answers with the class.

1. Each time you ran the simulation, you noticed that Earth's temperature eventually became stable. Why do you think that happened?

2. Why do you think is it important that the temperature of Earth become stable at a certain point? What would happen if the temperature did not become stable?

3. You have seen what happens to the heat that reaches Earth from the Sun when there are different amounts of CO_2 in the atmosphere. Make a claim about the effects of more CO_2 on Earth's temperatures. What evidence do you have for your claim?

4. List three ways you know of that people contribute CO_2 to the atmosphere.

5. How do you think you could you reduce the amount of CO_2 going into the atmosphere?

6. Do you think it is important to manage the amount of CO_2 in the atmosphere? Why or why not?

Learning Set 4

Back to the Big Question

How Can You Improve Air Quality in Your Community?

You now know a lot about how acid rain affects the environment. However, you still may not know how acid rain affects your community. It is very difficult to examine the air for the molecules that make acid rain. If you live near a large lake, you could analyze the water for acidity. However, you may not have lake water available. You can, however, investigate the effects of acid rain in an indirect way—by investigating the soil to see how well it can neutralize or buffer acid that falls to the ground. Remember that acids fall to the ground in dry deposition and wet deposition. You observed in the lake bottom investigation that some materials buffer acids better than other materials. The type of soil in your community and how well that soil buffers acid can tell you how much acid rain affects your community.

How Does Soil Type Affect the Acids in Acid Rain?

You investigated how the geology of a lake can affect the acidity of the water. Now you will investigate how soil type can affect acidity.

Part 1: Measuring Soil pH

In the first part of the investigation, you will measure the pH of the soil in your community from three different locations.

Procedure

1. Select three different 1 m² soil locations, such as a garden, wooded area, park, or meadow. Label your sites: *Location 1*, *Location 2*, and *Location 3*.

2. At each location, observe the plants living on these soils, especially those that are in the greatest numbers. Record as much description as you can about the area, the soil, and the number and type of plants on your *Soil pH* page. You may not recognize the exact type of plant, so record them as weed, grass, tree, and flowering plant.

Materials

- pH paper
- distilled water
- 454 g (16 oz) of soil from each of 3 different locations
- measuring cups and spoons
- trowel
- self-sealing plastic bags
- white vinegar
- large funnel
- 3 coffee filters
- plastic cup
- baking soda
- safety glasses
- *Soil pH* page

Remember that vinegar is an acid. Use caution when pouring vinegar. Do not taste. Be sure to wear your safety glasses.

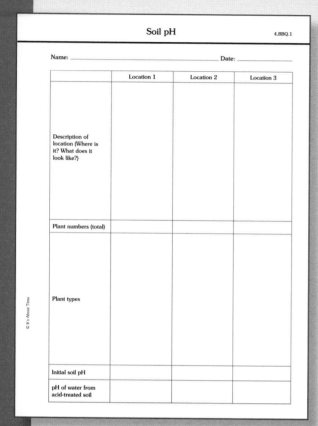

3. Using the trowel at each location, dig down about 5 cm (2 in.) and scoop out about 454 g (16 oz) of soil. Seal the soil in separate plastic bags labeled with the location. Be sure to clean your trowel after collecting soil at each location.

4. Work with one soil sample at a time. Mix one tablespoon of soil with one tablespoon of distilled water and stir thoroughly. Measure the pH of this mud solution with universal pH paper. Record the pH of each sample on your *Soil pH* page.

Analyze Your Data

1. What were the differences in pH among your three sites?

2. What were the differences among the number and type of plants at the three sites?

3. How many of your soil samples were acidic? What were the characteristics of the plants that grew on the acidic soil?

4. How many of your soil samples were basic? What were the characteristics of the plants that grew on the basic soil?

Part 2: The Effect of Soil on pH

In the second part of the investigation, you will treat soil samples from your three different locations with a solution of vinegar. You will use pH paper to observe how different types of soil neutralize acid.

Procedure

1. Pour 1 tsp of vinegar into 473 mL (2 cups) of distilled water. Stir well and check the pH with pH paper. The pH of the vinegar/water mixture should be about 4.

   • If your solution is below pH 4, add a sprinkle of baking soda, stir well, and recheck the pH.

   • If it is above 4, add a drop or two of vinegar and recheck the pH.

2. Put one coffee filter into the funnel and fill the filter with soil from *Location 1*. Do not pack down the soil.

3. Hold the filter over a paper cup and slowly pour the vinegar/water solution over the soil until some water collects in the paper cup. You need only a small amount of water. Dispose of the coffee filter and soil sample as directed by your teacher.

4. Check the pH of the collected water using a new strip of pH paper. Record the pH on your *Soil pH* page.

5. Repeat the procedure with the soil from *Location 2* and *Location 3*. Use a new coffee filter and a clean funnel for each sample. Record your results on your *Soil pH* page.

Analyze Your Data

1. In which soil(s) did the pH of the collected water stay the same as the original mixture?

2. In which soil(s) did the pH of the collected water increase?

3. In which soil(s) did the pH of the collected water decrease?

Reflect

Discuss your results in your group and answer the following questions. Be prepared to share your answers in class.

1. Why do you think some soil(s) did a better job at neutralizing the acidity of the water? Neutralizing the water means bringing its pH closer to 7.

2. What could you add to the soil to increase its buffering capacity?

3. Which soil location do you think is closest to the soil in the Adirondacks? Use evidence from your readings and investigations to develop your answer.

Communicate

Discuss in class your group's answers to the *Reflect* questions. Then read about buffering capacity on the next pages and discuss the following questions:

• What do you think happens to the acid that the soil cannot neutralize?

• How big of a problem do you think acid rain is in your community? Present evidence to justify your answer.

Buffering Capacity of Soil

You read earlier that rain is normally slightly acidic from the CO_2 in it. When rain falls to the ground, the chemicals that make the rain acidic go into the soil. When the rain contains only a small amount of acid, trees have the ability to absorb the acid from the soil and neutralize it. The ability to neutralize acid is known as the buffering capacity.

Some types of trees are better at neutralizing the acids in the soil than other trees are. But when an area gets a lot of acid rain containing strong acids, such as sulfuric acid and nitric acid, the trees cannot neutralize all the acid and are damaged. Some trees found in the Adirondacks, such as maple sugar and red spruce, are very sensitive to high levels of the acids in acid rain. As a result, these trees grow more slowly when there is acid rain, or even die.

The acids in rain can be neutralized in other ways. Soil that has a lot of limestone (calcium carbonate) is able to neutralize many acids. Areas of the country that have this type of soil are the Midwest, the Great Plains, and most of the western states. Areas such as the Adirondacks have mostly thin, non-calcium bedrock soils made from granite. These soils contain very little limestone and are not good at neutralizing acid.

Some trees, such as these red spruces, are damaged by acid rain.

Limestone soils (above) neutralize acid better than granite soils (right).

When rain enters lakes and other bodies of water, the water can neutralize the acids. **Hard water** contains high levels of calcium and magnesium salts. It can neutralize a lot of acid. However, **soft water** lacks calcium salts and magnesium. It cannot neutralize acids as well as hard water. The type of water depends on the type of soils. Non-calcium bedrock soil, such as is found in the Adirondacks, gives rise to soft water with little buffering capacity.

hard water: water that contains compounds with calcium and magnesium.

soft water: water that contains compounds with sodium and potassium but little calcium and magnesium.

Soft water, such as the lake water in the Adirondacks, cannot neutralize acids as well as hard water.

For a long time, scientists believed that all the chemicals in acid rain were taken up by trees or ran off into water that neutralized them fairly quickly. However, recent studies show that the chemicals build up in certain kinds of soils, such as those found in the Adirondacks. They remain there for a long time—years or even decades. Because the Adirondacks have the type of soil that stores up the chemicals deposited by acid rain, acid rain from 30 years ago or more can still be affecting the Adirondacks today.

The material in soil contains many of the elements that trees need for growth and survival. These elements include sulfur, nitrogen, calcium, magnesium, sodium, and potassium. When acid rain falls on soil, calcium and other elements in the soil are replaced by the acid. In this way, the pH of the soil is lowered, but the pH of any rain runoff is increased. The elements essential to life are washed away with the rain runoff. Once these elements are removed from the soil, they are no longer available to the roots of the trees. This leaching of minerals from the soil is very harmful to plants. At the same time, aluminum is also leached from the soil and is washed into bodies of water. The concentration of this element can rise in ponds, lakes, and streams to levels that are toxic to fish.

Communicate

Much of what you may have read or heard about acid rain is about its effect on lakes, ponds, and streams, and the organisms that live in those surface waters. Keeping that in mind, discuss the following question in class: Is acid rain an air-quality problem or a water-quality problem? Why?

Acid rain is really a people problem. Some acid rain is caused naturally, through the emissions of volcanoes. But the majority of acid rain is caused by the activities of humans. As a class, make a list of what people can do to help with the acid-rain problem. Sort the list into things you can do now and what you can do in the future. Discuss which items you can do alone and which items you can do by joining with others. Also discuss the good points and bad points of each item on the list.

Update the *Project Board*

You now have ideas on how one type of pollution, acid rain, may affect your community. Add what you have learned about your community to the *What are we learning?* column. Record your evidence in the *What is our evidence?* column. This information about your community will help you in answering the *Big Question*. Add your new information about your community to the *What does it mean for the challenge or question?* column.

How can you improve air quality in your community?				
What do we think we know?	What do we need to investigate?	What are we learning?	What is our evidence?	What does it mean for the challenge or question?

Learning Set 5

How Can Air Quality Be Improved?

You may feel that air pollution is such a big problem that you and your community cannot do anything about it. However, poor air quality is a problem that people can solve. As an individual, you can take steps to reduce your own contribution to worsening air quality. You can walk or ride your bicycle rather than ride in a car, and you can conserve the resources you use at home. For example, you can turn off the lights when you are not using them.

Entire cities, states, and regions can also make decisions that improve air quality. For example, cities can increase public transportation and use vehicles that are more efficient and less polluting. They can pass local laws to limit emissions. They can also provide incentives for companies to limit emissions in the area.

As a nation, the United States has begun to pay attention to the problem of poor air quality. The government has been passing laws regulating emissions from power plants and other sources of pollution, especially those that produce pollution that moves across state lines. Looking for other, less-polluting sources of power is also an option for improving air quality.

In this *Learning Set*, you will read about and investigate ways to improve air quality. Data from Los Angeles will give you a chance to determine if improvements have been made there. Then, you will investigate methods for preventing pollutants from entering the air. This will help you develop a recommendation for improving air quality in your community.

If you have traveled across the Southwest, you may have seen large fields of solar panels and wondered what they were used for.

5.1 Understand the Question

Think About How Air Quality Can Be Improved

You now have a good idea about how pollutants contribute to poor air quality. And you have a good idea of what air pollutants might be in the air and how they might get there. That is enough for you to figure out what air-pollution problems you might have in your community. However, to answer the *Big Question, How can you improve the air quality in your community?*, you need to know how air quality can be improved. In this section, you will read about many different methods for removing pollution from air and how to prevent some pollution from getting into the air in the first place. You will also read about laws enacted to make sure that power plants, factories, and vehicles put out less-polluting emissions. But first, you will think about what you already know about how to reduce pollution. You may not realize it, but you probably already have a lot of ideas about how to reduce pollution.

Get Started

With your group, answer these questions. See if you can figure out ways to reduce air pollution just by thinking about what you know about cleaning.

1. Think about a cluttered desk or a mess in your bedroom. What can you can do to reduce the clutter or mess?

2. Now think about air. Air is a mixture of substances. Some are substances we need to live. Others are pollutants and mess up the air. What do you think can be done to clean up the messy air?

3. Think some more about how pollutants are formed. Pollutants are formed by chemical reactions. What ideas does that give you about how to reduce pollution in the air?

Communicate

Share Your Ideas

Share with the class your ideas about reducing pollutants. Make a class list of ways of reducing pollutants.

Reflect

Work with your group to answer these questions. Be prepared to share your answers with the class.

1. Suppose you wanted to reduce the pollutants in your community. What else would you need to know about reducing pollution to make recommendations about doing that?

2. Suppose you knew the different ways to reduce the pollutants in your community. What else would you have to know to be able to choose the pollution-control methods that are most appropriate for your community?

Keep track of the questions you need answered to make good recommendations about reducing air pollution in your community. You will add them to the *What do we need to investigate?* column of the *Project Board* later. Or you can add them right now.

Efforts to Reduce Air Pollution

Many people in many different professions are working to reduce air pollution. Some scientists and engineers have been working on ways of reducing the amount and kinds of air pollutants. They have been investigating what levels of different pollutants are safe to breathe. Some other scientists are studying the effects of pollutants on the environment.

Still other scientists have been investigating how air pollutants contribute to depletion of the beneficial ozone layer, the accumulation of carbon dioxide in the atmosphere, and global warming. These people all contribute to what is known about the effects of air pollution, how to reduce air pollution, and how much people need to reduce air pollution in order to live healthier lives.

This scientist is setting up an air-quality monitoring station.

AIR QUALITY

Economists, politicians, and public-policy experts also investigate how to reduce air pollution. Economists calculate how much it will cost to put pollution-control measures into effect. Public-policy experts weigh the costs and benefits of the different ways of controlling pollution and make recommendations about which pollution-control methods are most needed and most cost-effective. Based on all of this, politicians enact legislation (laws) and government agencies write regulations (rules) that tell manufacturers what they have to do to manage air pollutants.

The first federal (United States government) air-pollution legislation was the Air Pollution Control Act in 1955. This was about the time that people were beginning to recognize that the air was getting dirty and causing health problems. This act simply provided funding to study the problem of air pollution. In 1962, the United States Congress passed the first Clean Air Act. This act was the first law designed to actually reduce air pollution.

Several versions of the law followed this first law. The Clean Air Act of 1970 was a very important version of this law because it changed the government's role. Instead of just studying the problem of air pollution, the government began to write laws to limit pollution at its sources.

To enforce those important laws, in 1971, the government created the Environmental Protection Agency (EPA) to make sure states followed the laws. The EPA is a very important government department because it oversees the study and control of air pollution.

There are two major ways of reducing air pollution. One way is by removing pollutants from emissions before they get into the air we breathe. This would mean getting rid of the pollutants emitted by internal-combustion engines and power plants before they escape into the air through the exhaust pipe of the car or the smokestack of the power plant. The other way is by preventing pollutants from forming in the first place—somehow keeping cars and power plants from producing so many pollutants at the source.

The limits by the EPA are based on research by scientists who study the effects of pollutants on health and the environment. The allowable levels of pollutants are very low. However, as low as they are, the amounts of pollutants you breathe everyday does not mean that you are completely safe, because some of the pollutants are very toxic, even in very small amounts.

Reflect

In 1955, the federal government recognized there was a problem with air quality and passed the Air Pollution Control Act. But it was not until 1970 that any legislation to enforce air-quality standards was passed. Air-pollution legislation continues to improve, but there are still groups of people who work to slow down the improvement of air quality.

1. Why do you think we need laws to control air pollution?

2. Why do you think anyone or any company might not support efforts to improve air quality?

3. What kinds of companies do you think would want to limit air-quality legislation?

4. How would you know if air-pollution controls were working?

5. What else do you need to know about improving air quality to know how to improve the air quality in your community?

Update the *Project Board*

In this *Learning Set*, you will be exploring ways of reducing pollution, legislation that has been enacted to improve air quality, and the improvements in air quality that have resulted from implementing pollution-control methods. Add to the *What do we think we know?* column of the *Project Board* what you think you know about reducing pollution. Add to the *What do we need to investigate?* column what you need to learn more about to make recommendations about how to reduce air pollution in your community.

What's the Point?

Improving air quality involves not only removing pollutants from the air but also preventing pollutants from entering the air in the first place.

People in many different professions have been contributing to efforts to improve air quality. Scientists and engineers investigate ways of removing pollution from emissions before it gets into the air. Other scientists investigate the effects of pollution and how much pollution in the air is safe. Economists, public-policy experts, and politicians examine the costs and benefits of different methods of reducing pollution and propose laws to regulate generation of pollutants.

One result of all these efforts is the passing of laws designed to improve air quality and protect people. The first federal law that worked to reduce air pollution at its source was the Clean Air Act of 1970. The Environmental Protection Agency was then created in 1971 to oversee implementation and enforcement of these laws. Most people refer to pollution-control laws as the Clean Air Acts. These acts set standards of maximum allowable levels of pollutants. Thanks to these and related laws, air pollution has been reduced in many places.

To make recommendations about reducing air pollution in your community, you will have to know more about how to remove pollutants from the air and how to prevent them from getting into the air in the first place.

Laws, such as the Clean Air Acts, are passed in state or federal legislatures.

5.2 Explore

How Can Chemical Reactions Be Used to Improve Air Quality?

One way to reduce the pollutants in the air is by keeping them from getting into the air in the first place. Some pollutants are solid particles, and these can be removed with filters. But other pollutants are gases. You cannot catch a gas in a filter. However, you know that the pollutants that are emitted by cars and smokestacks are unstable molecules created as the products of chemical reactions. Engineers and scientists have found ways to set up chemical reactions that transform some pollutants into other substances before they reach the environment. This is how some pollutants are removed from smokestacks of power plants and factories. And this is how pollutants are removed from internal combustion engines in cars.

Using Chemicals to Clean Pollutants from Smokestacks of Power Plants and Factories

Many pollutants are removed from the smokestacks of power plants and factories by using chemical processes. Typically, an assembly called a "scrubber" is used to transform the gases coming out of a plant into other substances. A scrubber sprays water or some other liquid at the combustion products produced by a power plant or factory. Sometimes a base, usually lime, is added to the water. Some of the gases in the polluted air, such as the sulfur dioxide and sulfur trioxide, dissolve in the spray. This makes the spray more acidic. However, the lime in the spray is a base. The dissolved acid and the lime in the water neutralize each other and produce a solid precipitate. The products of this reaction are then collected and disposed of or used for manufacturing. For example, one product, calcium sulfate dihydrate, is collected and used to make wallboard.

Other scrubbers work a little differently. Water is sprayed at the combustion products from the power plant or factory, and the water becomes acidic and falls to the floor of the smokestack. The acidic water is drained out and treated with a base, often lime. The products of this process are exactly the same as the products of the first process. In both processes, many of the gaseous pollutants produced by the power plant or factory are transformed into non-polluting substances.

Stop and Think

1. Sketch what happens in a smokestack when a lime-water spray is used. Show the inputs to the smokestack, the chemical reaction and where it happens, and what happens to the products of the chemical reaction.

2. Sketch what happens in a smokestack when a plain-water spray is used. Show the inputs to the smokestack, the chemical reactions, their products, where the chemical reactions happen, and what happens to the products of the chemical reactions.

Cleaning Up the Products of Internal-Combustion Engines

Removing pollutants from polluted air before they get into the air you breathe is not easy. Many chemical reactions are involved in the formation of pollutants. Reversing them requires many more chemical reactions. The chemical reactions that remove acid-forming pollutants from smokestacks of power plants and factories happen relatively quickly. A factory or power plant can be built to contain these pollutants until they are transformed into non-polluting substances.

Removing pollutants from the products of a car or truck's internal-combustion engine, however, is a lot more difficult. Think about a car's exhaust system. Pollutants can be caught before they enter the air only if the chemical reaction that transforms them into another substance happens before they have time to escape from a car's exhaust pipe. (Exhaust is the name for the gases produced through internal combustion.) But a car's exhaust pipe is very short, a car produces a lot of exhaust, and there is little space under a car to contain the pollutants until they are transformed. Only chemical reactions that occur very quickly will remove pollutants from a car or truck's exhaust before they enter the air you breathe.

Unfortunately, the reactions that turn the pollutants from an internal-combustion engine into harmless substances are very slow. It would take days, if not longer, for those chemical reactions to complete. A way to speed up those reactions is needed.

How Can Chemical Reactions Be Sped Up?

To investigate how the speed of a reaction can be changed, you will consider the reaction in which hydrogen peroxide (H_2O_2) breaks apart into water and oxygen. As the reaction takes place, oxygen bubbles are released and rise to the top of the solution.

Hydrogen peroxide yields water plus oxygen.

$$2H_2O_2 \xrightarrow{\text{slow}} 2H_2O + O_2$$

This reaction usually happens very slowly because a lot of energy is required to break hydrogen peroxide into its parts.

Procedure

As you perform the investigation, watch for the bubbles of oxygen gas that show a reaction is occurring.

1. Use the wax pencil to label the test tubes "A" and "B."

2. Use the graduated cylinder to measure 5 mL of hydrogen peroxide, and pour it into test tube A. Repeat for test tube B.

3. Observe the test tubes for 1 min. Watch for bubbles of oxygen gas. Bubbles are your evidence that a chemical reaction is happening. Record your observations on your *Speeding up Chemical Reactions* page.

4. Using the scoop, add a small amount of the manganese dioxide to test tube "B." Use only enough of the manganese dioxide to cover the tip of the scoop.

5. Observe the test tubes again for 1 min. Look for evidence that a chemical reaction is occurring. Record your observations on your *Speeding up Chemical Reactions* page.

Analyze Your Data

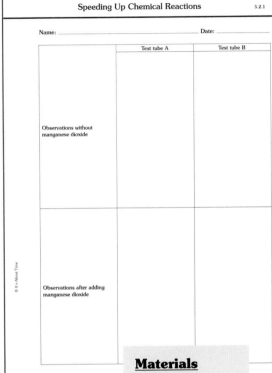

1. What chemical reaction was occurring when you first added the hydrogen peroxide to the test tubes?

2. What evidence do you have that the manganese dioxide increased the speed of the reaction?

3. Manganese dioxide is an example of a *catalyst.* Describe what you think a catalyst does.

Speeding Up Chemical Reactions		5.2.1
Name: _____		Date: _____
	Test tube A	Test tube B
Observations without manganese dioxide		
Observations after adding manganese dioxide		

Materials
- **2 test tubes**
- **10 mL of 3% hydrogen peroxide (H_2O_2)**
- **small metal scoop**
- **0.01 g of manganese dioxide (MnO_2)**
- **test tube rack**
- **10-mL graduated cylinder**
- **wax pencil**
- **safety glasses**
- **stopwatch**
- ***Speeding Up Chemical Reactions* page**

How Do Catalysts Work?

In your investigation, you saw that the manganese dioxide sped up the breakdown of hydrogen dioxide into water and oxygen. But how? The answer has to do with energy. Energy is the ability to do work or cause change. A certain amount of energy is required for any chemical reaction to occur. The amount of energy is known as a reaction's *activation energy*. It is shown by the peaks in the graph below. Certain substances, known as **catalysts**, can lower the activation energy needed for a reaction. This means that more particles of the reactants will have enough energy to take part in the chemical reaction.

catalyst: a substance that increases the rate of a chemical reaction by lowering the amount of energy needed for the reaction. The amount of the catalyst is the same before and after the reaction.

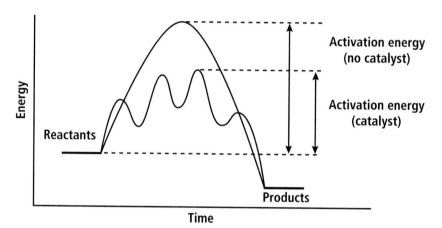

Catalysts lower the activation energy needed for a reaction.

A catalyst lowers the activation energy needed for a reaction, but is not used up during the chemical reaction. The amount of catalyst is the same at the end of a reaction as it was at the beginning.

Test tube A: $2H_2O_2 \xrightarrow{\text{slow}} 2H_2O + O_2$

Test tube B: $2H_2O_2 + MnO_2 \xrightarrow{\text{fast}} 2H_2O + O_2 + MnO_2$ (unchanged)

How Are Catalysts Used to Remove Pollutant Gases From Air?

Catalysts are used in many laboratory and industrial reactions to make reactions proceed faster. As in the example you explored, a catalyst is usually a metal. Scientists have found that the metals platinum, palladium, and rhodium can speed up the reactions that transform nitrogen oxides into nitrogen gas. They have found that platinum and palladium can also be used to transform carbon monoxide and VOC's into carbon dioxide and water. Some of the chemical chemical equations involving platinum (Pt) are shown below.

Nitrogen monoxide plus platinum yields nitrogen plus oxygen plus platinum.

$$2NO + Pt \rightarrow N_2 + O_2 + Pt$$

Carbon monoxide plus oxygen plus platinum yields carbon dioxide plus platinum.

$$2CO + O_2 + Pt \rightarrow 2CO_2 + Pt$$

VOC's plus oxygen plus platinum yield carbon dioxide plus water plus platinum.

$$VOC's + O_2 + Pt \rightarrow CO_2 + H_2O + Pt$$

To reduce emissions from cars and trucks, these catalysts do their work in **catalytic converters**. Catalytic converters remove carbon monoxide, nitrogen oxides, and VOC's produced by an internal-combustion engine. By law, every car now must have a catalytic converter to reduce pollutants released into the air.

In a car, the exhaust from the internal-combustion engine is piped into the catalytic converter, which transforms the pollutants into less harmful substances before the exhaust is released from the car's exhaust pipe.

catalytic converter: a piece of equipment in the exhaust line of a car that reduces the amount of pollutants released into the air.

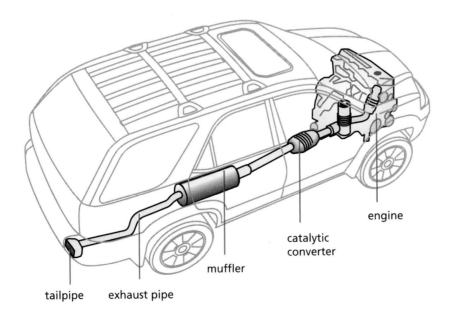

As gases from combustion go from the car engine to the exhaust, they pass through a catalytic converter.

engine

catalytic converter

muffler

tailpipe   exhaust pipe

AIR QUALITY

ceramic: a glass-like material that will not shatter or melt at high temperatures.

A modern catalytic converter uses two separate steps to reduce pollution. The first step removes nitrogen oxides by changing them back into nitrogen gas. To make this reaction proceed, **ceramic** pellets are coated with small amounts of platinum, palladium, and rhodium. When the exhaust from the internal combustion engine enters the catalytic converter, the catalysts cause the reactions that transform nitrogen oxides into nitrogen and oxygen to occur.

$$2NO \xrightarrow{\text{catalyst}} N_2 + O_2 \quad \text{and} \quad 2NO_2 \xrightarrow{\text{catalyst}} N_2 + 2O_2$$

The chemical reactions above are written using a kind of shorthand. Instead of showing the catalyst on both sides of a chemical equation, scientists use the word "catalyst" or list the catalyst used over the chemical reaction arrow. This notation specifies that a catalyst is used to speed up the reaction.

A catalytic converter contains ceramic pellets coated with small amounts of metals. These metals act as a catalysts and cause reactions that convert nitrogen oxides to nitrogen and oxygen.

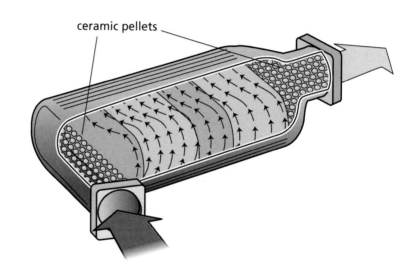

ceramic pellets

In the second step, carbon monoxide and VOC's are removed from the exhaust by transforming them into CO_2 and H_2O. A platinum or palladium catalyst is used. As the exhaust passes over the catalysts, carbon monoxide and VOC's mix with oxygen in the exhaust to form carbon dioxide and water.

$$2CO + O_2 \xrightarrow{\text{catalyst}} 2CO_2 \quad \text{and} \quad VOC's + O_2 \xrightarrow{\text{catalyst}} CO_2 + H_2O$$

In order for this second step to work, there must be oxygen left in the exhaust after the first set of reactions. To make sure a vehicle's catalytic converter can do its job completely, cars and trucks include an oxygen sensor. This sensor tells the car's computer if there is enough oxygen in the exhaust to transform all of the CO and VOC's into CO_2 and H_2O. If there is not enough oxygen, the computer lets more air into the engine.

The sensor also makes sure that there is not too much oxygen, because this would lead to the formation of more nitrogen oxides. If there is too much oxygen, the computer reduces the amount of air going into the engine.

Reflect

1. Check the equations of each reaction in a catalytic converter to see if they are balanced. Count each atom on the reactant side of the equation and match that number to the atoms for the same element on the product side of the equation. What did you find?

2. Although the technology for catalytic converters was available long ago, converters began to be added to cars only in 1975. Why do you think automobile manufacturers might not have wanted to put catalytic converters in cars?

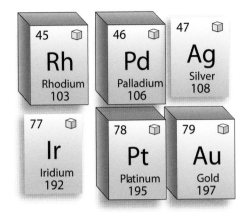

Rhodium, palladium, platinum, and gold are some of the metals on the periodic table that can be used as catalysts.

Other Ways Catalysts Are Used to Reduce Pollution

In addition to the catalytic converters in cars, catalysts are also used to clean up the air from industrial pollution. For example, a bakery was found to be emitting too high a concentration of VOC's in the form of ethanol. The ethanol was formed during the fermentation of sugar by yeast. To remove the ethanol, a scrubber with a catalyst was used to change the ethanol to carbon dioxide and water.

Ethanol plus oxygen plus catalyst yields carbon dioxide plus water plus catalyst.

$$CH_3CH_2OH + 3O_2 \xrightarrow{\text{catalyst}} 2CO_2 + 3H_2O$$

Commercial bakeries can produce high levels of ethanol, an air pollutant. Scrubbers with a catalyst can change the ethanol to carbon dioxide and water.

What's the Point?

Increasing the rate of chemical reactions is one way of treating pollutants before they get into the air you breathe. Smokestacks of some power plants and factories have scrubbers that use water and a basic compound to trap some polluting gases as solutions or solids. Sometimes the solids that form are even usable.

However, chemically removing the pollutants from car or truck exhaust is more difficult because the necessary chemical reactions could take days to complete. To speed up the chemical reactions that transform exhaust gases into non-polluting substances, cars and trucks use catalytic converters.

Catalytic converters in vehicles can reduce nitrogen oxides, VOC's, and carbon monoxide emissions. Catalytic converters use a solid chemical to speed up chemical reactions that transform pollutants into gases that are not harmful. A catalyst can be used over and over again because it is not used up in a reaction.

Before 1975, cars did not have catalytic converters. These cars released more pollutants into the air.

5.3 Investigate

How Can Pollutants be Physically Separated Out of Air?

You now know how to use chemical reactions to remove some of the gaseous pollutants from air. But how can the particulate matter and some of the other gases in polluted air be removed? Earlier, you probably suggested several ways to do this. You will now have a chance to try out your ideas.

You will be given a mixture that contains water, salt, sand, iron filings, and foam packing material. You will use the mixture to model air. The gases in air form a homogeneous mixture. The gaseous part of air has the same composition throughout. The particulate matter in air mixes with the gases to form a heterogeneous mixture. There can be more soot or dust in some parts of a sample of air than in other parts.

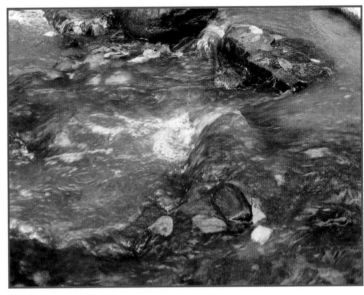

The contents of this stream are a heterogeneous mixture.

The mixture you will use is a lot like air. The salt water is a homogeneous mixture, like the gases in air. The particles of sand, iron filings, and foam packing material in the salt water make the whole mixture a heterogeneous mixture.

Separate a Mixture Into Its Parts

You will be given some tools, and you will develop a procedure for separating out the sand, iron filings, foam packing material, and salt from the water. You know some things about the properties of each of these substances that will help you develop your procedure.

Materials

- sand
- iron filings
- foam packing material
- salt
- water
- hand lens
- magnet
- coffee filters
- funnel
- stirring rod
- plastic cups
- hot plate
- aluminum pan
- tweezers
- plastic spoon
- safety glasses
- *Separating a Mixture* page

Some separation techniques

iron filings and sand

allowing parts to float or settle

attracting one of the substances to a magnet

picking apart the bits and pieces

salt and pepper

off ⊙ on

dissolving one substance but not the other

evaporating one part

filtration (using a variety of filters)

Mixtures can be separated by using many different procedures.

Separating a Mixture   5.3.1

Name: _____   Date: _____

Components of your mixture	Properties of each component in your mixture

Procedure for separating your mixture:

© It's About Time

Plan your Procedure

One person in your group should collect samples of salt, sand, iron filings, and foam packing material.

1. Examine the materials. For each, what properties does it have that you could use to separate it from the rest of a mixture if all of the materials were mixed into water? On your *Separating a Mixture* page, list each of the materials and your observations of the properties of each. Remember that the salt will be dissolved in the water.

2. Examine the equipment that is available to you, and devise a procedure for separating out each of the four materials in your mixture to obtain a pure sample of each. Record the procedure on your *Separating a Mixture* page.

3. Have your teacher approve your procedure, and then send one person in your group to get a sample of the mixture you need to separate.

Run Your Procedure

With the approval of your teacher, carry out your procedure. Be sure to follow the steps carefully. Record your results.

Communicate

Share Your Results

Share with the class what your group did to separate out each of the materials in your mixture. As you share, notice the similarities and differences in the ways each group separated out each of the materials.

As a class, make a list of separation methods the class used, how to make each method work, and when you think each of those methods is useful.

Reflect

1. Do you think each of your separated components is pure? How can you tell?

2. If you could rewrite the procedure, what would you change?

3. Which steps of your procedure do you think would be most useful for removing particulate matter from air? Why?

static electricity: an electrical charge on an object.

Using Electricity to Remove Particulate Matter (Soot) From Air

You used magnetism, filters, mechanical separation, and heat to separate out the materials in your heterogeneous mixture. Each of these procedures is a physical procedure. Each uses some physical process to remove a material from a mixture. All of the procedures you used, plus others, are used to physically separate particulate matter from air.

One common way to physically remove particulate matter from the air is by using **static electricity**. You are familiar with static electricity. You may have used static electricity to stick a balloon to the wall. When you rub the balloon, it gives the balloon an electrical charge. The charge on the balloon and the charge on the wall are opposite, so they attract each other, and the balloon sticks to the wall. You explored with static electricity using transparent tape in *Learning Set 2*.

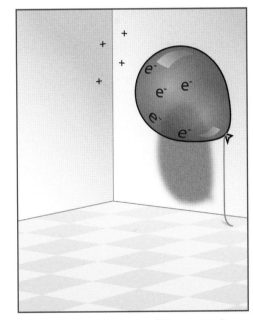

A balloon sticks to a wall because the negative charges on the surface of the balloon are attracted to the positive charges on the surface of the wall.

electrostatic precipitator: a device that uses a static electrical charge to remove solid particles from the air.

This same idea is used in **electrostatic precipitators** to remove particulate matter from smokestacks before it enters the air. Static electricity is used to give the solid particles a charge. Then the particles collect on a surface that has an opposite charge.

Demonstration

To help you understand how static electricity can be used to keep particulate matter from getting into the air, you will observe the operation of an electrostatic precipitator. As you watch the video, look for what happens to the particulate matter as the electrostatic precipitator works.

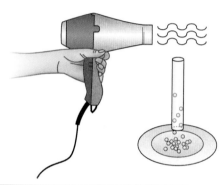

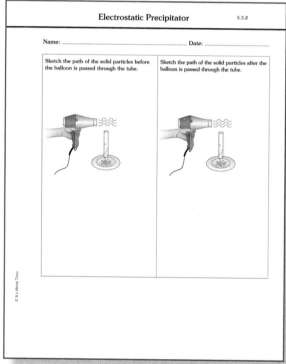

Reflect

1. Sketch the path of the solid particles on an *Electrostatic Precipitator* page.

2. How do you think the electrostatic precipitator works? How does it remove the solid particles?

3. What kind of air pollutants did the electrostatic precipitator remove from the air? How are these particles similar to and different from the particles in the smokestack of a power plant?

4. If you were to install an electrostatic precipitator on a coal-burning furnace, at what step in the process would you install the precipitator to clean the pollutants out of the air? Look back at your tour of the coal-burning power plant to support your answer.

Using Mechanical Filters to Remove Pollutants From the Air

Perhaps you have played with sand by letting it flow through an object, such as a sieve. Or maybe you have let flour flow through a sifter. Sieves and sifters have small holes in them. Only particles small enough to fit through the holes can pass through. Larger particles or chunks of material cannot pass through and remain behind.

A sieve catches large particles and allows only small particles to pass through.

Mechanical filters are another way to remove particulate matter from polluted air. They work much like sieves and sifters. They are usually made of cloth with very small holes. The cloth is usually charged, as in the electrostatic precipitator. The cloth attracts particles just as an electrostatic precipitator does. Large particles are caught by the cloth and cannot go through the small holes. Small particles that could get through the holes of the cloth are caught and held by the electrostatic charge on the cloth. Fabric filters are used in factories and also in homes. For example, vacuum cleaners have fabric filters. So do some furnaces.

Fabric filters can be used in vacuum cleaners or in furnaces.

AIR QUALITY

Filters are also used in vehicles. For example, diesel oil is a type of fuel that is used in many trucks and buses. Diesel engines are among the most polluting sources of power because of their high emissions of particulate matter and harmful gases. Often, you can even see the large pieces of particulate matter from the exhaust of a diesel engine being released into the air. One advance in clean technology for diesel

Vehicles with diesel engines are one of the most polluting sources of power.

engines is the diesel particulate filter. This device uses a catalyst to remove gas pollutants, such as VOC's and CO. In addition, a filter bag fits over the exhaust stream and removes particulate matter.

Using Water to Remove Pollutants From the Air

wet scrubber: a device that cleans gases from the smokestacks of power plants and factories.

You already read about how water can be used to chemically separate out gases from the air. Liquids can also be used to remove small particulate matter from the air.

You already know that a **wet scrubber** is one of the most common pollution-control devices used by industry. It operates on a very simple principle: polluted air is brought into contact with a liquid, such as water.

Pollutants react with the liquid and are removed from the air. Very small particulate matter is also captured by liquid droplets and can be removed with the liquid.

Usually, a wet scrubber works in three or more phases. In the first phase, the polluted air is passed through a liquid that can

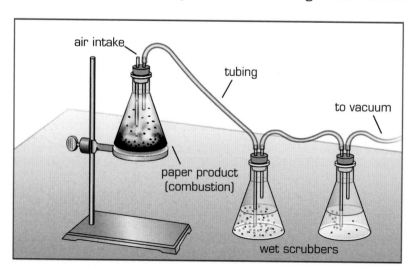

air intake

tubing

to vacuum

paper product (combustion)

wet scrubbers

dissolve most of the gaseous pollutants and neutralize them. In the next phase, the air is passed through another liquid that can remove the particles and dissolve the rest of the gases. In the third phase, the liquids are treated to remove the pollutants and particulate matter and pumped back into the wet scrubber to be used again.

You might be surprised that a wet scrubber does not actually do any scrubbing. The liquid does its work just by being there. What is important is that the liquid and the polluted air must come into contact with one another. The liquid in a wet scrubber can be sprayed into the air, or the polluted air might be forced into the liquid.

Stop and Think

1. What happens to pollutant gases in the wet scrubber? Why does this happen?

2. What do you think happens to particulate matter in a wet scrubber? Why does this happen?

3. If you were to install a wet scrubber on a coal-burning furnace, at what step in the process would you install the scrubber to clean the pollutants out of the air?

Reflect

You have read about many different types of pollution control—chemical methods, electrostatic methods, mechanical methods, and wet scrubbing methods.

1. Which kinds of pollutants does each method reduce?

2. Why do you think so many different kinds of pollution-control methods are needed?

3. If you wanted to get the air as clean as possible, how would you do it?

4. Why do you think car manufacturers and power plant operators might not always want to clean the air as much as they are required to by government regulations?

5. Why do you think it might take so long to pass laws that require industries to remove pollutants before they enter the air?

How Clean Does the Air Need To Be to be Safe?

The table below contains the 2008 standards for ambient air quality in the United States. The term *ambient* describes anything that surrounds you, such as air. The standards are meant to be applied to the air in your community as you walk and breathe the air. They are the maximum allowable amounts for each pollutant. Of course, any concentrations less than these are better. These are not standards for emissions directly out of the tailpipe of a car or the smokestack of a power plant. Those values would be much higher. Because the composition of pollutants in air changes from hour to hour and from day to day, the values in the table are often given as averages.

µg: micrograms, 0.000001 g, one millionth of a gram.

micron: 0.000001 m, one millionth of a meter. You could line up 10,000 of PM-10 particles in a 1 cm line. These particles are very small but very large compared to molecules. For example, about 2500 oxygen molecules would need to be lined up to make a line 1 micron long.

National Ambient Air Quality Standards (NAAQS)	
Pollutant	**Standard Value**
Particulate Matter (PM-10, PM-2.5)*	50 µg/m³ (about 30 ppb)
Carbon Monoxide, CO	9 ppm (8 hour average)
Ozone, O_3	0.12 ppm (1 hour average)
Nitrogen Dioxide, NO_2	0.053 ppm (yearly average)
Sulfur Dioxide, SO_2	0.03 ppm (yearly average)
Mercury, Hg	1 ppm in fish (to be eaten)

*Particulate Matter is measured by size. PM-10 is particulate matter that is **10 microns** in size; PM-2.5 is particulate matter that is 2.5 microns in size. PM-2.5 is smaller and more dangerous because it penetrates more deeply into the lungs.

These seem like very small numbers and although each of these pollutants is a poison, you might think that, because there is so little of each, their effects are harmless.

However, the amount that is harmless depends on how much air you take into your lungs. An adult human takes about 24,000 breaths each day, and each breath contains about 0.5 liters of air. The table below shows how much of each pollutant is safe for a healthy adult human to breathe in a day.

Maximum Allowed Pollutant Inhaled per Day in Grams	
PM-10 (soot)	0.00060 g
Carbon monoxide, CO	0.135 g
Ozone, O_3	0.0031 g
Sulfur dioxide, SO_2	0.000103 g
Nitrogen dioxide, NO_2	0.0013 g
Mercury, Hg 1 100-g serving of fish per week	0.00010 g

As you can see, the amount of each pollutant is still very small. However, this chart shows how very toxic each pollutant is. If all the pollutants were present in the air at these levels all day, every day, you would be a very sick person. But usually, you are not in the places all day that have the large amounts of these pollutants. For example, the concentration of carbon monoxide, nitrogen dioxide, and ozone is higher close to a busy street than it is in the classroom where you are sitting now.

Stop and Think

1. Which substance in the table is the most dangerous, on a per gram basis? How did you decide that?

2. Which substance in the table is the least dangerous, on a per gram basis? How did you decide that?

3. These numbers show the amounts of pollutants that are safe for a healthy adult to breathe in a day. How do you think these amounts of pollutants would affect a baby, an elderly person, or a sick person?

4. If you lived in a large city, which substance would be the hardest to avoid? Which would be easiest to avoid? Why?

5. Which substances do you think would be most important to remove from the air? Why?

What's the Point?

Advances in technology can clean the pollutants from emissions or keep pollutants from being made. Some of the ways to improve the quality of the air are by using physical means, such as electrostatic filters or mechanical filters, or chemical means, such as wet scrubbers, to separate pollution from the air. If you wanted to make air really clean, you might use chemical means of cleaning it and then filter it several different ways. But cleaning air is expensive, and some ways of cleaning air are more cost-effective than other ways. Some manufacturers and power-plant and factory owners do not want to improve air quality because of the high cost of installing air-control devices.

The EPA has set standards for how much of each pollutant is allowed in the air. These standards are based on what scientists say is safe for a healthy adult to breathe. But these amounts could still be harmful for babies, small children, elderly people, and those who are sick.

Many industrial plants use electrostatic precipitators, such as the one shown here.

5.4 Read

What Are Some Other Ways to Improve Air Quality?

Advances in technology can improve air quality in many different ways. Catalytic converters keep dangerous pollutants from leaving the tailpipes of vehicles. Electrostatic precipitators and wet scrubbers keep pollutants from leaving the smokestacks of power plants and factories. Filters can keep particulate matter from getting into the air. However, there is one other important way technology can be used to improve air quality—by keeping pollutants from being produced in the first place.

Improving Fuels Means Fewer Pollutants

One important way to improve the quality of air that comes out of cars and smokestacks is to improve the quality of the fuel used. Burning coal, for example, creates many pollutants. Improving the fuel—the coal—that is used in these plants can help eliminate some of the pollutants. One type of coal preparation, known as coal washing, removes some of the polluting substances from coal before it is burned. In this process, crushed coal is mixed with a liquid that causes some of the pollutants, such as sulfur, to separate and settle out.

Some coal deposits contain low-sulfur coal. The coal from these mines requires less coal washing.

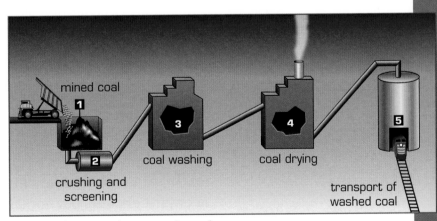

Once coal is mined, it goes through many steps in the coal-washing process.

Changing to Different Fuels Can Mean Fewer Pollutants

One effective way to reduce pollution is to switch to cleaner-burning fuels. Natural gas, for example, is cleaner than coal and oil. Natural gas is widely used in homes and industry. Many cities use natural gas in their city buses and taxis instead of gasoline. When natural gas burns, it still produces harmful emissions, but in smaller amounts than when coal and oil are burned.

Scientists are also looking for other fuels to use in power plants instead of coal. Nuclear fuel is cleaner than coal when it is used, but it creates nuclear waste that has to be stored or disposed of. Nuclear waste is very toxic for a long period of time. Because scientists do not yet know a good way of disposing of nuclear waste, even many people who want cleaner air do not want power plants to use nuclear fuel.

biofuel: a fuel made from biomass materials.

biomass: material that comes from living things.

Biofuels are fuels made from **biomass** materials, such as wood, waste paper, grasses, vegetable oil, and corn. Overall, these fuels are carbon-neutral and renewable. However, using land for growing biofuels means that the same land is not available for growing crops. As a result, developing this type of fuel would result in a decrease in the amount of food produced for people.

Biofuels made from biomass materials are a renewable source of energy.

Hydrogen is another possible fuel. At this time, however, scientists do not have a cost-effective technology that can be used to produce and store hydrogen.

Another way to control pollution is to use electricity instead of burning fuels. For example, electric cars use no gasoline. Instead, these cars get their energy from an electrical power source. An electric car is plugged into an electrical outlet when it is not being used to charge the battery with electricity.

Hydrogen fuel cells are a possible source of non-polluting fuel.

You might wonder how electric cars can reduce pollution. After all, you know that electrical power plants create a lot of air pollution. There are two ways electric cars can be useful in reducing pollution. First, when a car or bus uses electricity instead of gasoline, the cars and buses themselves do not pollute. Because the cars and buses are not putting pollutants into the air, the air is cleaner. Second, because the pollution caused by electric cars is emitted from a few large power plants rather than hundreds, thousands, or even tens of thousands of cars, it is easier to reduce pollution as new technologies for controlling pollution are developed. A single new pollution-control mechanism put on a power plant will reduce the pollution from every car and device that uses electricity from that power plant. But when pollution-control technologies are developed for cars, it can take 10 or more years for people to sell their existing cars and buy new ones that use the new technology.

Using Fuel More Efficiently Can Mean Fewer Pollutants

The cheapest, most effective, and quickest way to reduce pollution in all forms is by increased efficiency. Increasing efficiency means getting more done with the same amount of fuel. Scientists and engineers are working to design appliances that use less electricity. Today's refrigerators, air conditioners, and other appliances use much less electricity than those manufactured 10 years ago. Often this is because manufacturers have discovered how to insulate the devices better to keep the heat in or out. Refrigerators are more efficient now because scientists have found better ways to keep out the heat. Ovens are more efficient because scientists have found ways to keep in the heat. Even not opening the refrigerator or oven door more than necessary can reduce air pollution.

Insulation is very important to reducing pollutants. When houses and other buildings are built with insulation that keeps in the warm air in during the winter and out during the summer, this reduces power needs. Any time power needs are reduced, so is air pollution.

An insulated thermos bottle (left) keeps in heat. An insulated cooler (right) keeps out heat.

Cars with increased gas mileage also can reduce pollution. When a car needs less fuel to run, less air pollution is produced. New technologies for cars include hybrid cars that use a combination of fuel and battery power, reducing the amount of fuel burned, and thus, the emissions.

Smaller cars with better gas mileage can reduce air pollution.

Scientists and engineers have also found ways to increase the efficiency of light bulbs. Fluorescent light bulbs use much less electricity than incandescent light bulbs. Manufacturers have designed new types of fluorescent light bulbs, called compact fluorescents, that can be used instead of the incandescent bulbs people have been using since light bulbs were invented. Compact fluorescent light bulbs use only one-quarter of the electricity of conventional bulbs, last ten times as long, and reduce the amount of CO_2 emitted by 1300 lbs over the lifetime of one bulb! These bulbs are more expensive to buy, but because they last longer, they are actually cheaper to use. As more people switch to compound fluorescent light bulbs, pollution will be reduced.

A compact fluorescent light bulb (left) uses less energy than a conventional incandescent light bulb (right).

Changing to Alternative Energy Sources May Mean Even Fewer Pollutants

One other way to reduce pollutants is to get energy from sources other than fuels. Some power plants use no fuel at all but instead use the energy from the water falling long distances down waterfalls or dams (hydropower). This is one way to reduce pollution, but water is not always available. Other sources of energy that can be used instead of fuel are solar power (energy from the Sun), wind energy, energy from ocean waves, and geothermal energy (Earth's heat).

All these energy sources are being used in small ways around the world, but they are not widely used yet. However, some day in the future, people will have to discover how to use these energy sources instead of the fuels used most widely today. That is because the fuels used most widely today—oil, coal, and natural gas—are **nonrenewable** resources. This means that we have only limited amounts of them. When they are used up, they are gone forever. It will be important to find ways to use many different **renewable** sources of energy—nuclear energy, hydropower, solar power, wind energy, geothermal energy, or others—to continue producing electricity for homes and industries, as well as for cars, trains, ships, airplanes, and other vehicles.

nonrenewable: an energy source, such as oil or natural gas, or a natural resource, such as a metallic ore, that is not replaceable after it has been used.

renewable: a resource, such as solar energy or firewood, that can not be used up, or can be replaced by new growth.

A nuclear power plant (above) uses fuel that is less polluting. The power from a hydroelectric dam (right) uses a renewable energy source.

Using No Fuel Will Improve Air Quality and Conserve Resources

The best way to improve the air and conserve natural resources is to use no fuel at all. This solution is one that everyone can do. People are beginning to walk or ride bicycles instead of riding short distances in cars. Public transportation, such as buses, subways, and trains carry many people. Although many of these vehicles burn fuel, the amount of fuel used is much less than if everyone traveled in their own cars. And many public transportation vehicles are now electric or use natural gas.

Stop and Think

1. Of the methods for reducing air pollution you read about, which ones can you or your family do? Which ones can you not do? Justify your answers with evidence from the reading.

2. How could you encourage manufacturers to produce non-polluting products for you to use? How could you encourage them to pollute less when they manufacture products?

3. How could you work to make sure power plants and other industries reduce the pollutants they put into the air?

4. Power companies often offer free "Energy Audits" for homeowners, during which they measure the amount of heat lost from a house. They also sometimes give away compact fluorescent light bulbs. Why do you think they would they do this?

Update the *Project Board*

Update the *What are we learning?* column of the *Project Board* with what you have learned about reducing pollutants in the air. Remember to include what you know about chemical ways of reducing pollutants, ways of removing particulate matter from the air, and ways of generating fewer pollutants. Do not forget to record your evidence in the *What is our evidence?* column. You may have ideas about other ways to reduce air pollution. Record these ideas in the *What do we think we know?* column. You may still have questions about how to reduce air pollution. Record these questions in the *What do we need to investigate?* column.

How can you improve air quality in your community?

What do we think we know?	What do we need to investigate?	What are we learning?	What is our evidence?	What does it mean for the challenge or question?

What's the Point?

Air pollution can be reduced in many ways. One of those ways is by using cleaner fuels. Air quality can also be improved by using alternate energy sources, such as nuclear power, wind power, solar power, geothermal power, and hydroelectric power. More efficient use of energy or using no energy at all also reduces pollution.

A turbine engine that burns natural gas is cleaner than a turbine engine that burns liquid or solid fuel.

5.5 Explore

How Has Reducing the Pollution From Cars Improved Air Quality in Los Angeles?

You know that states, cities, and the entire country have enacted laws that require power plants, car manufacturers, and others to reduce the pollutants emitted into the air. You know some of the methods used to reduce the pollutants that are emitted. They can be removed from emissions by chemical or physical methods. Air quality can be improved by building more efficient buildings and vehicles. But does all of this really make the air cleaner? There is a way to find out.

As states and cities require new ways to clean up the air, they collect data on the types and amounts of pollutants found in the air. This data, collected over many months and years, provides information for future decision making. The government of California has been collecting this data. By analyzing data from Los Angeles, you will be able to determine the impact the Clean Air Acts and other laws have had on the air quality in Los Angeles.

A street in Los Angeles on July 27, 1943.

California Air Quality Timeline

The Los Angeles Times ran a headline on July 27, 1943, that read: *"City Hunting for Source of Gas Attack."* If you were walking in the city on that day, you would have been able to see only three blocks ahead of you. Citizens suffered from a variety of symptoms—vomiting, nausea, burning eyes, and difficulty in breathing. City officials thought a chemical plant was the cause of the problem, but when they closed down the plant, the air-quality problems continued. They could not determine why the air was so bad.

California Air Quality Timeline

Smokestack emissions are monitored.

| | 1940s | Los Angeles has the first bad episode of smog, which produces respiratory illnesses in the residents. The city calls it a "gas attack" and closes down a rubber plant that is thought to be the source of the problem. Los Angeles admits that the city has a serious air-quality problem and passes the Air Pollution Control Act. The Los Angeles County Air Pollution Control District is created to measure the visible smoke emissions from smokestacks. |

The first baghouse collects smoke and fumes from a factory. A baghouse is a series of huge fabric filters that smoke goes through. Standards are set for California air quality, including O_3 (0.5 ppm), SO_2 (3.0 ppm), NO_x (3.0 ppm), and CO (100 ppm). Scientists determine that smog forms from NO_x and hydrocarbons in the presence of UV radiation from the Sun.

1950s

The first baghouses are used to collect particulate matter.

The first automobile emissions control device is required.

1960s

The first automobile emissions control device is required. This device reduces VOC's by recycling engine gases back through the engine to be burned more fully. Scientists set the maximum 1-hr O_3 concentration at 0.1 ppm. New, lower standards are set for PM (60 µg/m³), SO_2 (0.5 ppm), NO_x (0.25 ppm), and CO (20 ppm).

Backyard burning is banned in some areas to help reduce PM in the air. Catalytic converters to reduce pollutants in automobile exhaust become widely available. This device reduces CO, NO_x, and VOC emissions from cars. The 1-hr O_3 concentration standard is reduced to 0.09 ppm.

1970s

Backyard burning is banned.

Cars and trucks must be checked yearly for emissions.

1980s

California Smog Check Program goes into effect. Cars and trucks must be checked yearly to make sure their emissions are within the allowed standards.

Cleaner diesel fuel is required. This fuel reduces PM and NO_x emissions. Cleaner Burning Gasoline becomes available. This new gasoline reduces O_3 and VOC's. Its use is like taking 3.5 million cars off California highways. Rules are set for lawn mowers, leaf blowers, weed trimmers, and other small engines. It changes the amount of air to fuel in combustion inside these engines and reduces VOC's.

1990s

Rules are put into effect for small engines, such as leaf blowers.

School bus idling is restricted.

2000s

New rules reduce school bus idling to "only when necessary for safety" and reduce CO, PM, and NO_x. New rules reduce "unnecessary" diesel truck idling. Diesel vehicles must install exhaust filters to reduce PM and fuel-efficient tires that cause trucks to burn less fuel. Diesel ships and trucks must use diesel fuel with 95 percent lower sulfur content to eliminate 15 tons of sulfur in diesel exhaust daily. Auto manufacturers must label their cars to show smog and greenhouse gas emissions.

On September 13, 1955, it seemed like there was another gas attack. The city experienced an all-time high in smog and ozone for over three hours. Again, people could see only a small distance in front of them, and they were having difficulty breathing. Although these major attacks of air pollution were only happening every 12 years, people had noticed the air getting steadily dirtier and dirtier. More smog developed every year and lasted longer, and more people had breathing problems. Soot coated buildings and windows. Between the major attacks of air pollution, the air quality was getting worse.

Clearly, something had to be done to improve the air quality in Los Angeles. California passed laws, and then the United States government passed laws. As industries began to follow these laws, the air quality improved. Read the timeline of air-quality legislation changes over the last 65 years on the previous page. As you read, make a list of the laws on a piece of paper. For each new law, record what you think the impact of the change would be and why.

Stop and Think

1. Look at the California Air Quality timeline and choose either the 1970s, 1980s, or 1990s. What air-quality changes happened in that decade? Describe why the change would make a difference in air quality in Los Angeles. How would a change like this also make a difference in the air quality in your community?

2. In 2002, the rules for bus idling were changed. Idling means to leave a vehicle running when it is parked. Why would this be a good rule for lowering air pollutants? How might this rule change the air quality in your community?

3. The most recent change on the timeline is in 2007, when auto manufacturers were required to label cars to show emissions. How could this rule help to lower air pollutants?

4. Which of the changes listed on the timeline for California would be the most important for improving the air quality in your community? Why?

5. Which of the changes on the timeline would be the least important for your community? Why?

6. Can you think of any sources of air pollution in your community that are not listed? What are they?

How Much Has the Air Pollution in Los Angeles Been Reduced?

You made a chart of the ways you expected the air quality to change with each of the new rules and regulations. These kinds of changes take place slowly. Using data about the air quality in Los Angeles, you will be able to see how much the state of California has been able to reduce air pollution. The graphs below contain data collected for ozone, nitrogen oxides (NO_x), and VOC's.

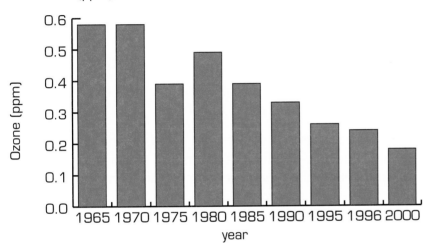

Ozone (ppm), maximum recorded 1-hour average in Los Angeles

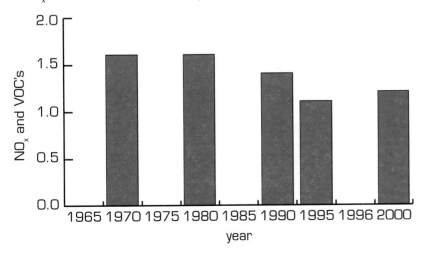

NO_x and VOC's (million tons/year) from all vehicles in Los Angeles

AIR QUALITY

Procedure

1. In 1970, the highest one-hour average for ozone was 0.58 ppm. In what year was this average cut in half? How many years did it take to get to this level?

2. How do the levels of NO_x and VOC's compare with the decrease in ozone? Do the levels change faster, slower, or at the same rate? By what percentage do NO_x and VOC's decrease in the year that ozone decreases to one-half of its original value?

Stop and Think

1. Which of the three variables, NO_x, VOC's, and sunlight, would the state of California have no control over?

2. As the population increases, the distance traveled on California roads increases each year. What effect would you expect this to have on NO_x and VOC levels? Higher, lower, or no effect?

3. The formation of "bad" ozone requires NO_x, VOC's, and sunlight. Temperature also affects smog formation. In Los Angeles, ozone tends to be highest in the summer, when the temperature is higher. Also, ozone levels are usually higher in the afternoon, when the temperature is higher than in the morning. Why do you think it took so long to reduce the ozone in the air in Los Angeles?

4. Why do you think the levels of NO_x and VOC's change at a different rate than ozone? Think about how NO_x and VOC's are produced and why they form.

5. The data provides evidence that improvements have been made in the air quality in California. Why do you think these improvements are or are not significant?

How Much Has the Reduction of Pollutants Improved the Air Quality?

Smog has been, and still is, a serious problem in Los Angeles. In cities with smog problems, the government issues Smog Alerts so people know just how bad the smog is. Smog Alerts are usually issued when the ozone level reaches about 0.20 ppm. At this level, children, older citizens, and citizens with lung disease and asthma are cautioned to remain indoors.

Teens, adults, and generally healthy people are warned to minimize athletic activities, such as running, jogging, and taking part in sports events. Those activities cause people to breathe more quickly. The more breaths you take, the more air you bring into your lungs. If you engage in athletic activities on a day when the smog is particularly bad, you will bring a lot of extra dirty air into your lungs.

Examining how often Smog Alerts are issued can tell you about the quality of the air. The chart below shows how many Smog Alerts were issued each year in Los Angeles between 1977 and 1999. If you compare the trends in this data to the timeline of regulations and to pollution data, you will be able to see how the regulations have affected Los Angeles smog. The questions below will help you analyze the data.

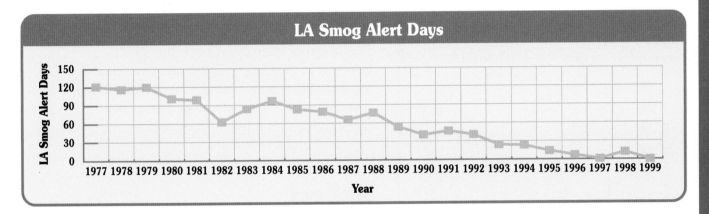

Analyze Your Data

1. In data, a trend is a change in data over time. What is the trend of this data set?

2. Which year in the data seems the most significant to you? Why?

3. Compare the Smog Alert days data with the timeline. In which years do changes in the laws seem to impact the number of Smog Alert days following that year? Find at least two examples of changes in the laws seeming to make a difference in the Smog Alert days.

4. Choose one of these examples and look back at the amount of ozone, NO_x, and VOC's for the same year. Describe any changes in these levels for the same time period. Why do you think there were, or were not, changes?

Reflect

1. How would you describe the changes in air quality in Los Angeles? If you lived in Los Angeles, what would you be able to do now that you would not have been able to do in the early 1970s?

2. Would you say the air-quality regulations in Los Angeles have been a success? Why or why not? What else do you think could be done?

Has the Rest of California Experienced the Same Changes as Los Angeles?

Los Angeles has done a good job in monitoring and controlling pollution. The ozone and smog problems have been tremendously improved. However, California as a whole has made less progress on nitrogen oxide and VOC levels. Why is this the case?

One of the problems has been the steady increase in population during this time. As the population grows, so do the Vehicle Miles Traveled, VMT. And, with each mile traveled, more pollution is emitted from tailpipes.

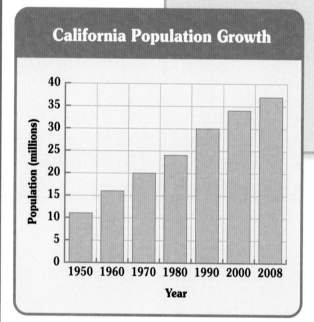

California Population Growth

Reflect

1. If the population of California had not increased since 1950, how would the air quality of Los Angeles and other cities have been affected? Why?

2. Which of the steps taken by California to decrease air pollution do you think are the most important to consider as the state's population increases? Why?

What's the Point?

Los Angeles has had some of the worst air in the country, but California leads the nation in fighting for improved air quality. Laws have been passed that have been effective in controlling the increase in pollution. Over the past 40 years, California has reduced ozone, NO_x, and VOC's. The state has also reduced the number of Smog Alert days in Los Angeles. Through legislation, California has been able to reduce air pollution. However, Los Angeles remains a city with very poor air quality. Much more needs to be done.

5.6 Read

How Has Reducing the Pollution From Power Plants Improved Air Quality in the Adirondacks?

The air-quality problems in the Adirondacks are somewhat different from those in Los Angeles. Whereas most of the sources of pollution in Los Angeles are within the city itself, the sources of pollution that affect the Adirondacks are a long distance away. You now know that air pollution does not stop at city limits. It moves across county lines, state lines, and even international borders. Air pollution can travel across lakes, mountains, rivers, oceans, and continents. Because scientists understand that air pollution has no boundaries, they realize that the solutions must be national or even international if they are to make a real impact on air quality.

Antarctica is not near any sources of pollution, yet scientists have found evidence of air pollution trapped in the ice.

The chemicals that produce acid rain in the Northeastern United States come mostly from coal-burning power plants in the Midwest. The acid rain from these chemicals affects the entire Eastern United States. But some areas, such as the Adirondacks, are harmed more than other areas because of location, geography, geology, biology, and climate.

acre: a measure of land area, approximately 61 m (200 ft) by 61 m.

There are few low-cost, local solutions to the effects of acid rain. In some areas where there are small ponds (usually 10 **acres** or less), basic materials such as limestone can be added to increase the buffering capacity of the water. But this works in only a very few cases. And it does not stop the source of the acid rain.

The acid in small ponds can be neutralized by adding basic material, such as limestone.

To decrease the amount of acid rain in the environment, people must keep the chemicals that produce acid rain from being released into the air. These pollutants must be stopped at their source.

The Adirondack Council is one New York State group that has monitored and pushed for laws to reduce acid rain. Their studies led to national legislation to regulate the pollutants that can be emitted in the Midwest power plants. When those plants do not follow the laws, New York sues the companies that own the power plants.

Stop and Think

1. Why is it better to stop pollution at its source than to deal with it once it is in the environment? Give two reasons.

2. Why do you think it always takes longer to solve a problem than to prevent it in the first place?

Federal Legislation Aimed at Reducing Emissions That Cause Acid Rain

Once the magnitude of the acid-rain problem in the Adirondacks was recognized and the sources were determined, state and national legislation was enacted. Some of the key laws are listed below.

1962

Clean Air Act:
First legislation to study air pollution.

1970

Clean Air Act (Revised):
Wrote laws to limit pollution at its source.

1980

National Acid Precipitation Assessment Program:
Helped legislators understand the acid-rain problem. The results of research were used to amend the Clean Air Act.

1990

Clean Air Act Amendments:
Set controls on coal-fired power plants and instructed the Environmental Protection Agency to create the nation's first acid rain control program.

1997

National Ambient Air Quality Standards:
Established regional standards for fine particulate matter, volatile organic compounds, nitrogen oxides, carbon monoxide, sulfur dioxide, and lead.

Clean Air Act Title IV Acid Deposition Control Program:
Set national emission caps (limits) on power plants, put in place over a period of years. Even with these controls, scientists think that ecosystem recovery may not occur for another 25 years or more.

2003

Clean Air Mercury Rule:
Would have permanently capped and reduced mercury emissions from power plants. However, this program was struck down by the courts due to the toxic nature of mercury. They wanted a stronger rule.

Clear Skies Act:
Would cut SO_2 emissions by 73%, NO_x emissions by 67%, and mercury emissions by 69% by 2018. Limits for each pollutant would be established. Sources could trade these limits among themselves to achieve the required reductions at the lowest cost. This legislation, proposed by President Bush, has not yet been passed. Many environmental groups oppose this legislation. They feel it would weaken the Clean Air Act.

2005

Clean Air Interstate Rule:
Focuses on 29 eastern states having SO_2 and NO_x emissions that contribute significantly to fine particle and ozone pollution problems in downwind states. Sources can buy and sell pollution credits in a cap-and-trade program.

Stop and Think

1. What parts of the federal legislation do you think would be most effective in improving the air quality in your community?

2. The Clear Skies Act of 2003 has not been passed by Congress. Why do you think the legislature or Congress would not pass a law that says it will improve air quality?

3. If you could propose a law to improve air quality, what kind of law would you propose? How would it affect your community? How would it affect the rest of the country?

What Are the Results for the Adirondacks?

Some of the best approaches for reducing the effects of acid rain and mercury deposition are the use of electrostatic precipitators, scrubbers, and the burning of low-sulfur coal. Consumers are being urged to buy more efficient cars, more efficient appliances and light bulbs, and to better insulate their houses.

Studies show that since the Clean Air Act went into effect, most lakes in the Adirondacks are improving. However, because of the acids stored in soils and an increase in NO_x, full recovery of Adirondack lakes to the point where they can again begin to neutralize acid will take 25–100 years. Studies show that sulfur levels (sulfuric acid) had decreased by 92 percent in many Adirondack lakes by the year 2000. At the same time, nitrogen (nitric acid) rose in 48 percent of the tested lakes.

Reflect

The efforts to prevent acid rain in the Adirondacks and many other parts of the country fall into three categories: legislation, technology, and alternative fuels. Which pollution-reducing steps in legislation, technology, and alternative-fuel use do you think would do the most to improve air quality in your community? Why?

What's the Point?

Environmental groups and the government are working very hard to improve the quality of the air that moves into the Adirondacks from the Midwest. The coal-burning power plants in the Midwest are being forced to reduce their release of SO_2, NO_x, and mercury. Progress has been made, especially in SO_2 emission. Because mercury is not used up in any way, it will be a long time before it disappears. Nitrogen oxides are bound more firmly to molecules in the Adirondack soils, and they leave the soil very slowly. It may take another 100 years to fully neutralize the soil and lakes.

There are some direct methods of reducing acid rain and mercury deposition in the Adirondacks. They include having Midwest power plants use equipment that reduces the amount of pollution released into the air. Other methods include changes in the products people use. By making different choices, people can decrease their energy consumption and therefore produce less pollution. A united front among government policies, industrial practices, and consumer choices can have a major impact on air quality in the Adirondacks.

Improving air quality is important for the health of the planet.

More to Learn

Are All Air Pollutants Found Outdoors?

Poor air quality affects large numbers of people in cities. It also affects the environment of large areas of the world where there are few people, such as the Adirondacks. However, air pollution is not only outdoors. Air pollution can also be indoors. Indoor pollution can exist in many forms.

The most deadly indoor pollution is carbon monoxide (CO), which causes poisoning. Carbon monoxide forms when a source of combustion, such as a furnace, does not get enough oxygen from air to form carbon dioxide (CO_2). Every apartment and house should have carbon monoxide detectors that sound an alarm when CO levels rise to dangerous levels.

Another indoor pollutant is radon gas. This gas is found only in certain geological areas where the rock beneath the ground contains radioactive elements. Radon can seep into the basements of houses. Long exposure to radon gas can cause lung cancer. Radon can be detected with radon detectors, and basements can be sealed to prevent the gas from seeping in.

A carbon monoxide detector sounds an alarm when it senses a dangerous level of carbon monoxide in the air.

Volatile organic compounds (VOC's) are present in many households. The best clue to these pollutants is your sense of smell. VOC's smell very strong. Paint, nail polish remover, and many cleaning supplies have VOC's. Also, flooring, such as carpeting or finished floors, can have VOC's that can be breathed in. If you must use a product indoors that has VOC's, the best solution is to open the windows or doors.

Particulate matter is also an indoor pollutant. You know that some indoor particulate matter is produced from combustion. This matter may come from heating vents. Other particulate matter may come from carpets, fabric, chalk, or dust. To find out how much particulate matter is in the air in your school, you may want to repeat the investigation you did in *Section 2.7*, this time collecting particulate matter from locations inside your school where you want to investigate the amount of particulate matter in the air.

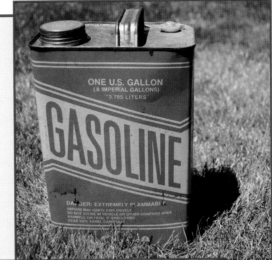

Some sources of VOC's are paint thinner (top left), gasoline (top right), oil paint (bottom left), and fingernail polish (bottom right).

Laws to Improve Indoor Air Quality

The Clean Air Act and many other laws have been passed to improve outdoor air pollution, but few laws exist to improve indoor air quality. Many of the symptoms caused by indoor air pollution are not easy to detect and may occur at very low levels of pollutants that are difficult to measure. This makes it hard to determine what pollutants to regulate and at what level. Federal indoor-air standards protect workers in factories and other industries, but these standards may not be appropriate for homes, offices, or schools.

Some states have passed laws to regulate indoor air quality, but the laws vary from state to state. Some of these laws educate residents about the dangers of indoor pollutants. Others notify parents before pesticides (chemicals that kill insects and other pests) are used in schools, require sellers of property to tell buyers about dangers, such as radon, and require schools to improve their indoor air quality. Many states have also passed laws to ban or restrict smoking in public places.

Reflect

1. Suppose you collected particulate matter in your classroom. If you collected particulate matter in another place inside your school, how do you think the particulate matter would be similar to and different from what you collected in your classroom? What things would make it similar? What things would make it different? Why?

2. If you wanted to improve the air quality inside your school, what would you need to know about the air quality in the school?

3. How would methods for improving air quality inside your school differ from methods you could use to improve outdoor air quality?

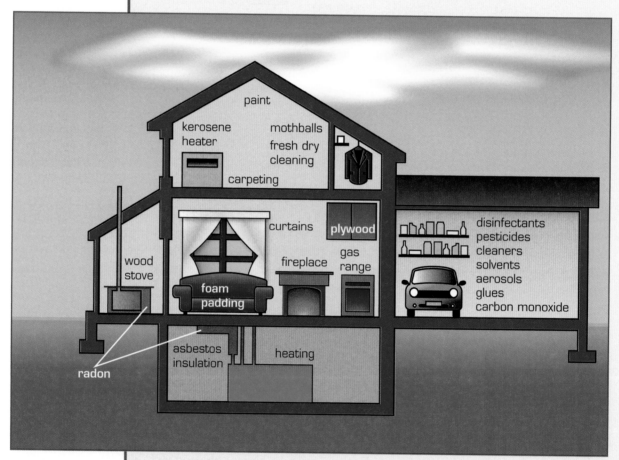

A typical home can have many sources of indoor pollution.

Answer the Big Question

How can you improve air quality in your community?

You began this Unit by reading a parable about a small country named Malaire. The people of Malaire were not careful about how they used technology, and they ended up ruining the quality of air in their country. To answer the *Big Question* for this Unit, *How can you improve air quality in your community?* you investigated the properties of air and learned about some of the chemical reactions that cause poor air quality. You also learned about different ways of removing pollutants from the air or preventing them from getting into the air. You read two case studies involving regions with poor air quality—Los Angeles and the Adirondack Mountains. You know how the air became polluted in those places and what has been done to reduce the pollution. The chart on the next two pages summarizes sources and affected areas of the environment from poor air quality, and ways of removing pollutants from the air.

In an "air walk" around your community, you identified local sources that improve or worsen air. You may also have conducted some additional investigation of sources of air pollution in your community. Some of the sources that worsen air quality in your community may be the same as the sources in Los Angeles or in the Adirondack Mountains. Some are probably different.

Your community may look like this one.

You are now ready to complete this Unit and make recommendations about how to improve air quality in your community. Knowing what the problems were in Los Angeles and the Adirondack Mountains and how those problems were addressed will help you make your recommendations.

Pollution Pathways

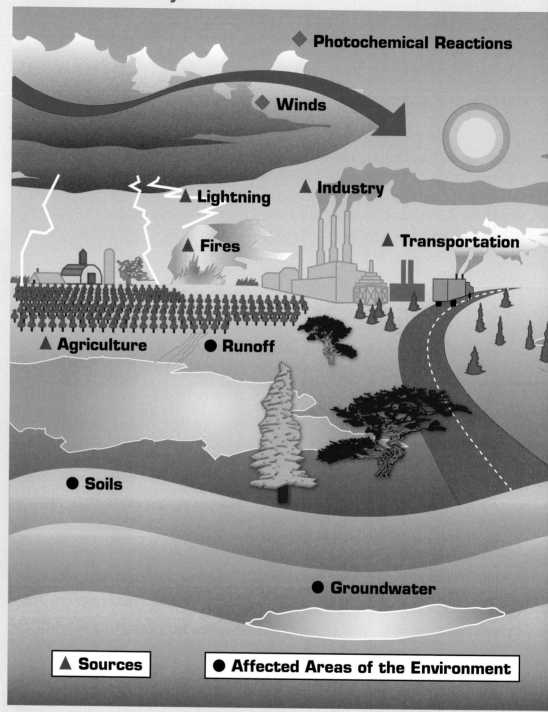

Photochemical Reactions

Winds

Lightning

Industry

Fires

Transportation

Agriculture

Runoff

Soils

Groundwater

▲ **Sources**

● **Affected Areas of the Environment**

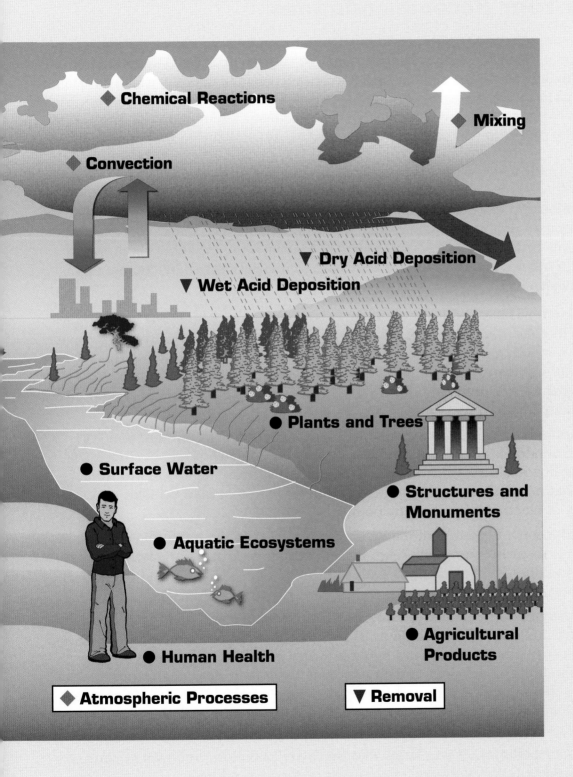

◆ **Chemical Reactions**

◆ **Mixing**

◆ **Convection**

▼ **Dry Acid Deposition**

▼ **Wet Acid Deposition**

● **Plants and Trees**

● **Surface Water**

● **Structures and Monuments**

● **Aquatic Ecosystems**

● **Agricultural Products**

● **Human Health**

◆ **Atmospheric Processes**

▼ **Removal**

Plan Your Recommendations

Your recommendations will suggest ways people can improve the air quality in your community. The changes you suggest might be very small or very large, but they should make some impact on air quality. You will begin by deciding which air-quality problems in your community you want to improve. You may choose to address sources of poor air quality or effects of poor air quality. Each group will focus on two air-quality problems and propose recommendations for reducing those problems.

As you decide which air-quality problems to address, you should consider the results of your investigations, the readings you have completed, and the information you have collected about your community. With your group, review the air walks you took in your community and what you learned about your community during this Unit. Compare your community to what you now know about the air quality in other communities. You may want to review some of the factors that affect air quality.

- Climate: Think about the weather in your community and how it might be like the weather in Los Angeles or the weather in the Adirondacks. Determine how the weather might affect the air in your community. If the weather in your community is very hot and dry, like in Los Angeles, you might want to think about how to reduce the effects of the weather on air quality in your community.

- Population: Does your community have a high population? Are you surrounded by thousands and thousands of people with lots of cars, trucks, and buses? Are trains or airports nearby? If so, you might want to think about how to reduce the pollution from large numbers of vehicles and the use of electricity by so many people.

- Geography: Is your community on the ocean or in the mountains? Is it in a flat area or in rolling hills? Are there mountains to trap the air and cause inversions? If so, you might want to think about reducing the effects of thermal inversions.

- Types of nearby industry: Emissions from factories and other industrial sites can cause the same kinds of pollution problems that are caused by power plants. In what ways might industry impact the air quality in your community? Does your community have large factories? High smokestacks? Are there metal smelting or mining activities nearby? If so, you might want to think about how to reduce the pollution from industrial plants and power plants.

- Indoor pollution: If you know that there are pollution problems in your school or home, you may choose one of those to address.

List on paper your ideas about the pollution problems you want to address. This list may include many possible ideas. Discuss each idea with your group. Think about which recommendation ideas might be the most possible. For example, you may want to reduce the pollutants from nearby industrial plants, but you may not know what pollutants they emit and how they already work to reduce their pollution. It might be too hard to get the information you need to address some problems.

Work with your group to select two air-quality problems from your list. Use a separate *Recommendation Planning* page for each. Begin by recording the sources of the pollutants, which of the *Sickening Six* pollutants are causing problems, and the effects of the pollutants.

For each, think of ways of reducing the pollutants or their effects. Describe what you can do to improve this air-quality issue. Identify evidence and science knowledge that support your idea, and record those. If you find that your evidence or science knowledge contradicts your idea or that you do not have evidence or science knowledge to support your idea, work with your group to improve or change your idea. Any recommendations you make will have to be supported by science knowledge and evidence.

Then, for each idea, consider the potential positive results and the negative impacts of these changes. For example, you might want to ban buses because they emit pollutants, but this would cause other problems. People might drive cars instead, and more cars on the road would cause more pollution. Answer the questions below to help identify the possible effects of your proposed solutions.

- What pollutant or pollutants will your recommendation decrease in concentration in your community's air?
- What will be the change in health effects on people, animals, and/or plants?
- How will your change effect people's lives? If they have to stop doing something, what will they do instead? What will be the effects of those new things they do?
- How many people will this change affect? Everyone, or just particular people?
- Who or what agency will have to apply this change? At what cost? A lot or a little? Will anyone lose their job?

Recommendation Planning Page				ABQ.1
Name: _____			Date: _____	
Source of Poor Air Quality	How Pollutant(s) Are Made	Harm to Organisms or Structures	Ways to Minimize Pollutants	Solutions

© It's About Time

- Will the cost of food, electricity, fuel, or transportation increase or decrease for most people because of your recommended change?

If your suggested change has more negatives than positives, think of another way to address your air-quality issue. When you have identified two ways of addressing pollution problems that will have more positive effects than negative effects, move on to making your recommendations.

Recommend

Once you have given the problem your full consideration, use a *Create Your Explanation* page for each recommendation.

Your recommendation will be your claim. It should be a statement that includes all of these parts.

- Which air-quality problem are you addressing?

- What are the health, environmental, or structural effects of this air-quality problem?

- What ways can you suggest for minimizing the pollutants?

- What is your solution—something you can do to improve the air quality?

You might want to state your claim as something like this:

To address [*the problem you chose*], we suggest [*your solution*]. This would improve [*bad health, environmental, or structural effects caused by the pollution problem*]. It would minimize [*which pollutants*] by [*what methods*].

After you have stated your claim, you will need to record evidence and science knowledge that supports it. Your evidence can come from the investigations you conducted and your knowledge about Los Angeles or the Adirondacks. Your evidence should show how the solution or method you chose will reduce pollution. Or you might also include evidence showing how your solution or method will reduce the harmful effects of pollution. Your evidence could include both of these.

Create Your Explanation

1.3.2/2.BBQ.2/3.5.2
4.2.2/4.6.7/4.7.1/ABQ.2

Name: _____ Date: _____

Use this page to explain the lesson of your recent investigations.

Write a brief summary of the results from your investigation. You will use this summary to help you write your Explanation.

Claim – a statement of what you understand or a conclusion that you have reached from an investigation or a set of investigations.

Evidence – data collected during investigations and trends in that data.

Science knowledge – knowledge about how things work. You may have learned this through reading, talking to an expert, discussion, or other experiences.

Write your Explanation using the **Claim**, **Evidence**, and **Science knowledge**.

© It's About Time

The science knowledge you include should support your ideas about how your proposed solution will impact air quality. You may include anything you know about the different pollutants, what you know about chemical reactions that produce pollutants or prevent pollutants from getting into the air, what you know about separating out pollutants from air, and what you have read about health and environmental effects of pollutants.

If you find that the evidence you have available or the science you know does not support your idea as well as you thought, you will have to improve or change your idea.

When you have recorded good evidence and science knowledge that support your recommendation, you will develop an explanation to go with your claim. Your explanation should tie together your recommendation and your evidence and science knowledge in a way that will convince people that your recommendation is a good one. It should also tell people what is going on chemically that makes you sure your recommendation is a good one.

Communicate
Solution Showcase

You will share your solution recommendations with the class in a *Solution Showcase*. The goal of this *Solution Showcase* is to describe your two recommendations and all the supporting evidence for picking these solutions.

Make a poster that you can use to present to the class your recommendations for improving air quality. Your poster should be divided in two. The top should present one of your recommendations. The bottom should present the other one. For each recommendation, include the following:

- the air-quality problem you chose to address and why this is an important problem to address

- the pollutants involved in your problem and the effects of these pollutants

- your recommendation about how to reduce the problem and how to implement your solution

- the evidence and science knowledge that support your recommendation

- your explanation statement

As you participate in the *Solution Showcase*, you will be both audience and presenter. Be prepared to answer, and also ask other groups, the following questions:

- Which pollutants did you decide to focus on? Why were these the pollutants you chose to limit?

- Do you think your group made a convincing argument for your solutions? What could you have done to make a stronger argument?

- How did your solutions compare to others' solutions? Which solutions work together and which do not?

- Which solutions would be very difficult to put into effect? Which solutions are more simple to do?

As other groups are presenting, listen carefully to how these groups support their recommendations. Think about how their ideas are similar to or different from your group's ideas. Listen carefully to the evidence used by the other groups. Consider whether that same evidence could have been used to support your recommendations. Think, too, about how realistic each recommendation is.

If you do not understand how some solution solves an air-quality problem, or if you think some evidence or science knowledge is not complete enough, raise your hand and ask questions. Remember to be respectful.

Reflect

1. Which of the recommendations made by other groups do you think could make a difference in the air quality of your community?

2. What type of evidence did the group who made this recommendation use to support their ideas?

3. Which of the recommendations would be good to do but would have a high cost? What might you suggest to lower the cost of the change?

4. How can you tell others about the recommendations your class made? Who would be interested in hearing about these changes you would suggest?

5. What would you tell others about the recommendations your class made? Which ones would you want to make sure your representatives knew about?

You may want to pass on some of your recommendations to your local or national representatives. Who knows? You may have come up with some ideas that others have not thought of yet. Or you may be able to convince your representatives that some recommendation they have already been thinking about is worth pursuing.

English & Spanish Glossary

A

µg Micrograms, one millionth of a gram, 0.000001 gram.

µg Microgramos, una millonésima de un gramo, 0.000001 gram.

acid rain Any of several ways that acid falls out of the atmosphere.

lluvia ácida Una de varias maneras en que el ácido cae de la atmósfera.

acid A solution that tastes sour, has more hydrogen ions than pure water, and has a pH of less than 7.

ácido Una solución que tiene sabor amargo, tiene más iones de hidrógeno que el agua pura, y tiene un pH menor de 7.

acidic Solutions that have more hydrogen ions than pure water.

ácido Soluciones que tienen más iones de hidrógeno que agua pura.

acidity The concentration of hydrogen ions in a solution.

acidez La concentración de iones de hidrógeno en una solución.

acre A measure of land area, approximately 61 m (200 ft) by 61 m.

acre Una medida de área de terreno, aproximadamente 61 m (200 pies) por 61 m.

air pollution The introduction of chemicals, particles, or organisms to air that are harmful to living things and structures.

contaminación del aire La introducción de químicos, partículas, u organismos a aire que es dañina para los seres vivientes y las estructuras.

air quality The condition of air in terms of the amount of pollutants it contains.

calidad del aire La condición del aire en términos de la cantidad de contaminantes que contiene.

atom The basic building block of matter.

átomo El elemento fundamental de la materia.

atomic mass The average number of total protons and neutrons in an atom's nucleus.

masa atómica La cantidad promedio del total de protones y neutrones en el núcleo de un átomo.

atomic number The number of protons in an atom's nucleus.

número atómico La cantidad de protones en el núcleo de un átomo.

atomic theory The idea that all matter is formed from atoms and that atoms have a unique structure.

teoría atómica La idea que toda la materia está formada de átomos y que los átomos tienen una estructura única.

B

bacteria Small organisms, some of which live underground on the roots of specific plants. Some bacteria can convert nitrogen into a form that plants can use.

bacteria Organismos pequeños, algunos de los cuales viven bajo tierra en las raíces de determinadas plantas. Algunas bacterias pueden convertir el nitrógeno en una forma que las plantas pueden usar.

balance An instrument used by scientists to measure mass.

balanza Un instrumento usado por los científicos para medir masa.

base A solution with a bitter taste, a slippery feel, and a pH more than 7.

base Una solución con un sabor amargo, una sensación resbaladiza, y un pH mayor de 7.

biofuel A fuel made from biomass materials.

biocumbustible Un combustible derivado de materiales de la biomasa.

biomass Material that comes from living things.

biomasa Materiales que provienen de cosas vivientes.

boiling point The temperature at which a liquid changes to a gas.

punto de ebullición La temperatura en la cual un líquido cambia a gas.

buffering capacity The ability to neutralize acid.

capacidad de amortiguamiento La habilidad de neutralizar ácido.

C

catalyst A substance that helps a slow chemical reaction to occur more quickly by lowering the amount of energy needed for the reaction. A catalyst does not change during the reaction.

catalizador Una sustancia que ayuda a que una reacción química lenta ocurra más rápidamente reduciendo la cantidad de energía necesaria para la reacción. Un catalizador no cambia durante la reacción.

catalytic converter A piece of equipment in the exhaust line of a car that reduces the amount of pollutants released into the air.

convertidor catalítico Una pieza de equipo en la línea de escape de un automóvil que reduce la cantidad de contaminantes liberados al aire.

ceramic A glass-like material that can take high temperatures.

cerámica Un material parecido al vidrio que puede aguantar altas temperaturas.

chemical bond An attraction between atoms that share electrons.

enlace químico Una atracción entre átomos que comparten electrones.

chemical change A change in the composition, or chemical makeup, of a sample of matter. A chemical change is also known as a chemical reaction.

cambio químico Un cambio en la composición o estructura química, de una muestra de materia. El cambio químico se conoce también como una reacción química.

chemical equation A statement that expresses what is happening in a chemical reaction in a brief, abbreviated way.

ecuación química Un declaración que expresa lo que está sucediendo en una reacción química en una manera breve y abreviada.

chemical family Group of elements found in a column of the periodic table. These elements exhibit similar properties.

familia o serie química Grupo de elementos que se encuentran en una columna de la tabla periódica. Estos elementos exhiben propiedades similares.

chemical reaction A change in the composition, or chemical makeup, of a sample of matter. A chemical reaction is also known as a chemical change.

reacción química Un cambio en la composición o estructura química de una muestra de materia. Una reacción química se conoce también como un cambio químico.

chemical symbol A one- or two-letter shorthand notation for describing a chemical element.

símbolo químico Una anotación gráfica de una o dos letras para describir un elemento químico.

Clean Air Act The law that defines the Environmental Protection Agency's responsibilities for protecting and improving the nation's air quality.

Ley de aire puro La ley que define las responsabilidades de la Agencia de Protección Ambiental (EPA, por sus siglas en inglés), para proteger y mejorar la calidad del aire de la nación.

climate The normal weather conditions of a region, throughout the year, averaged over a series of years.

clima Las condiciones normales del tiempo de una región, a través del año, promediadas sobre una serie de años.

coefficient A number in front of each chemical formula that shows how many molecules of that compound are used or produced in a chemical reaction.

coeficiente Una número al frente de cada fórmula química que muestra cuántas moléculas de ese compuesto son usadas o producidas en una reacción química.

combustion The process of burning. The reaction of a fuel with oxygen that produces light and heat.

combustión El proceso de quemazón. La reacción de un combustible con oxígeno que produce luz y calor.

compound A pure substance made up of two or more different elements.

compuesto Una sustancia pura compuesta de dos o más elementos diferentes.

concentrate To increase the concentration of a substance in a mixture; a stronger solution.

concentrado Aumentar la concentración de una sustancia en una mezcla; una solución más fuerte.

concentration The amount of solute in a solvent.

concentración La cantidad de soluto en un solvente.

condensation The process in which a gas cools to form a liquid.

condensación El proceso en el cual el gas se enfría para formar un líquido.

convection The transfer of heat in a fluid through a current made up of warm, rising fluid and cool, sinking fluid.

convección La transferencia de calor en un fluido a través de una corriente compuesta de fluido caliente ascendente y fluido frío descendente.

D

dense Having a high mass per unit volume.

denso Tener una masa alta por unidad de volumen.

density The relationship between the mass and volume of a substance. Density is calculated by dividing the mass by the volume.

densidad La relación entre la masa y el volumen de una sustancia. La densidad se calcula dividiendo la masa por el volumen.

dilute To decrease the concentration of a substance in a mixture; a weaker solution.

diluir Disminuir la concentración de una sustancia en una mezcla; una solución más débil.

double bond A bond where 2 atoms share 4 electrons.

enlace Doble una unión donde 2 átomos comparten 4 electrones.

E

electron A subatomic particle of an atom found outside the nucleus. It has a negative charge.

electrón Una partícula subatómica de un átomo que se encuentra fuera del núcleo. Tiene una carga negativa.

electrostatic precipitator A device that uses a static electrical charge to remove solid particles from the air.

precipitador electroestático Un dispositivo que usa carga eléctrica estática para remover partículas sólidas del aire.

element The simplest type of substance made of identical atoms.

elemento El tipo de sustancia más simple compuesta de átomos idénticos.

Environmental Protection Agency (EPA) The government agency that protects, restores, and improves the environment to guarantee public health and environmental quality.

Agencia de Protección Ambiental (APA) La agencia de gobierno que protege, restaura y mejora el medio ambiente para garantizar la salud pública y la calidad ambiental.

evaporation A change from a liquid to a gas at a temperature that is lower than the boiling point.

evaporación Un cambio de líquido a gas a una temperatura que es más baja que el punto de ebullición.

exosphere The highest level of the atmosphere; from the edge of the thermosphere, gradually becoming outer space.

exosfera El nivel más alto de la atmósfera; desde el borde de la termosfera, gradualmente convirtiéndose en el espacio sideral.

extensive property Property of matter that depends on the amount of matter present in a sample, for example, the mass of the matter.

propiedad extensiva La propiedad de la materia que depende de la cantidad de materia presente en una muestra, por ejemplo, la masa de la materia.

F

food chain The flow of energy stored in food from one organism to another.

cadena alimenticia (o alimentaria) El flujo de energía almacenada en los alimentos de un organismo a otro.

fossil fuel A nonrenewable resource formed from the remains of living things over millions of years.

combustible fósil Un recurso no renovable formado de remanentes de organismos vivientes a través de millones de años.

freezing point The temperature at which a liquid turns into a solid.

punto de congelación La temperatura en la cuál un líquido se vuelve un sólido.

freezing The process in which a liquid cools to form a solid.

congelación El proceso en el cual un líquido se enfría para formar un sólido.

fuel Any substance that reacts with oxygen to produce light and heat.

combustible Cualquier sustancia que reacciona con oxígeno par producir luz y calor.

G

gas Matter that has no definite shape or volume. A gas takes the shape and volume of its container. The particles are far apart and move rapidly and randomly.

gas Materia que no tiene una forma o volumen definido. Un gas toma la forma y volumen de su recipiente. Las partículas están alejadas y se mueven rápidamente y al azar.

global climate change A change in Earth's climate due to global warming.

cambio climático global Un cambio en el clima terrestre debido al calentamiento global.

global warming A rise in Earth's temperature due to heat from the Sun being trapped in the atmosphere.

calentamiento global Un aumento en la temperatura de la Tierra debido al calor del sol atrapado en la atmósfera.

greenhouse effect Certain gases and other pollutants trapped in the atmosphere can prevent heat from the Sun from leaving Earth.

efecto invernadero Ciertos gases y otros contaminantes atrapados en la atmósfera pueden impedir que el calor del sol abandone la Tierra.

greenhouse gases Gases that trap heat from the Sun in Earth's atmosphere.

gases de invernadero Los gases que atrapan el calor del sol en la atmósfera de la Tierra.

ground ozone Ozone found in the troposphere; also known as bad ozone.

ozono en el suelo Ozono que se encuentra en la troposfera; también conocido como ozono malo.

groundwater Water found in the soil and beneath the surface of Earth.

agua subterránea El agua que se encuentra en el terreno y debajo de la superficie de la Tierra.

H

hard water Water that contains compounds with calcium and magnesium.

agua dura El agua que contiene compuestos con calcio y magnesio.

heating The transfer of thermal energy from a warmer substance to a cooler one.

calentamiento La transferencia de energía térmica de una sustancia caliente a una fría.

heterogeneous A mixture that varies in composition from one part to another.

heterogénea Una mezcla que varía en composición de una parte a otra.

homogeneous Any mixture that has a uniform composition of substances.

homogénea Cualquier mezcla que tiene una composición uniforme de sustancias.

humidity Water vapor in air.

humedad Vapor de agua en el aire.

hydrocarbon A compound that contains only hydrogen and carbon atoms.

hidrocarburo Un compuesto que contiene solamente átomos de hidrógeno y carbono.

hydroxide ion One oxygen atom, one hydrogen atom, and an extra electron.

ión de hidróxido Un átomo de oxígeno, un átomo de hidrógeno y un electrón adicional.

I

indicator A tool that can be observed to determine the condition of something.

indicador Una herramienta que puede ser observada para determinar la condición de algo.

intensive property Property of matter that does not depend on the amount of matter present in a sample, for example, the density of the matter.

propiedad intensiva La propiedad de la materia que no depende de la cantidad de materia presente en una muestra, por ejemplo, la densidad de la materia.

ion An atom that has more protons than electrons and has an overall positive charge, or fewer protons than electrons, and has an overall negative charge.

ión Un átomo que tiene más protones que electrones y tiene una carga total positiva, o menos protones que electrones, y tiene una carga total negativa.

ionic bond A bond between a positive and a negative ion, where the negative ion gives up an electron to the positive ion.

enlace iónico Una unión entre un ión positivo y uno negativo, donde el ión negativo le cede un electrón al ión positivo.

L

law of conservation of matter Matter is neither created nor destroyed.

Ley de conservación de la materia La materia no es ni creada ni destruida.

leaching The removal of nutrients in the soil by acids.

lixiviación La remoción de nutrientes en el terreno por los ácidos.

lichen Two distinct organisms, a fungus and an alga, living as one.

liquen Dos organismos distintos, un hongo y un alga, viviendo como uno.

liquid Matter that has a definite volume but not a definite shape. A liquid takes the shape of its container. The particles remain close together and slide past each other in a fluid motion.

líquido la materia Que tiene un volumen definido pero no una forma definida. Un líquido toma la forma de su recipiente. Las partículas permanecen juntas y se deslizan una a la otra en un movimiento de fluido variable.

M

macroscopic A word used to describe an observation that can be seen by the unaided eye.

macroscópico Una palabra usada para describir una observación que puede ser vista por el ojo simple.

mass The amount of "stuff" something contains.

masa La cantidad de "cosas" que algo contiene.

matter Anything that has volume (takes up space) and has mass.

materia Cualquier cosa que tiene volumen (ocupa espacio) y tiene masa.

melting point The temperature at which a solid changes to a liquid.

punto de fusión La temperatura a la cual un sólido cambia a líquido.

mesosphere The atmosphere from about 48 km–85 km (30–53 mi) above Earth's surface.

mesosfera La atmósfera desde alrededor de 48 Km.–85 Km. (30–53 mi) sobre la superficie de la Tierra.

metal A substance, usually a solid that is hard, shiny, can conduct electricity, and can be made into a wire. Metals are found on the left side and center of the Periodic Table of the Elements.

metal Una sustancia, generalmente un sólido duro, brillante, que puede conducir electricidad, y que se puede convertir en un cable o alambre. Los metales se encuentran en el lado izquierdo y el centro de la Tabla Periódica de Elementos.

micron One millionth of a meter, 0.000001 m. One centimeter would measure 10,000 of PM-10 particles. These particles are very small but are very large compared to molecules. For example, a micron would measure about 2500 oxygen molecules.

micrón Una millonésima de un metro, 0.000001 m. Un centímetro medirá 10,000 partículas PM-10. Estas partículas son muy pequeñas pero son muy grandes comparadas con las moléculas. Por ejemplo, un micrón medirá alrededor de 2500 moléculas de oxígeno.

microscopic A word to describe an observation that cannot be seen with the unaided eye.

microscópico Una palabra para describir una observación que no puede ser vista por el ojo simple.

mixture Two or more substances combined such that each substance may retain its own identity.

mezcla Dos o más sustancias combinadas de forma tal que cada sustancia puede retener su propia identidad.

molecular formula A shorthand method of representing the types of atoms and the numbers of atoms in a molecule.

fórmula molecular Un método corto de representar los tipos de átomos y la cantidad de átomos en una molécula.

molecule A combination of two or more atoms.

molécula Una combinación de dos o más átomos.

N

neutral A solution with a pH of 7. pH 7 has an equal number of hydrogen ions and hydroxide ions.

neutral Una solución con un pH de 7. El pH 7 tiene una cantidad igual de iones de hidrógeno e iones de hidróxido.

neutralize Increase the pH of an acid; one way is by combining the acid with a base.

neutralizar Aumentar el pH de un ácido; una manera es combinando el ácido con una base.

neutron A subatomic particle of an atom found in the nucleus. It is electrically neutral.

neutrón Una partícula subatómica de un átomo encontrada en el núcleo. Es neutral eléctricamente.

noble gases A family of elements with full electron energy levels. These elements do not undergo chemical reactions and are found in column 18 in the periodic table.

gases nobles Una familia de elementos con niveles de energía de electrón completos. Estos elementos no sufren reacciones químicas y se encuentran en la columna 18 de la tabla periódica.

nonmetal An element that is a gas or a soft, brittle solid. It does not conduct electricity.

no metálico Un elemento que es un gas o un sólido blando y frágil. No conduce electricidad.

nonrenewable An energy source, such as oil or natural gas, or a natural resource, such as a metallic ore, that is not replaceable after it has been used.

no renovable Una fuente de energía, tales como el petróleo o gas natural, o una fuente natural, tal como un mineral metálico, que no se puede reemplazar después que ha sido utilizado.

nucleus The center part of an atom.

núcleo La parte central de un átomo.

O

ozone A molecule made up of three oxygen atoms.

ozono Una molécula compuesta de tres átomos de oxígeno.

P

part per billion (ppb) Comparison of the number of particles of one substance to one billion particles of another substance. One out of a billion.

parte por billón (ppb) Comparación de la cantidad de partículas de una sustancia a un billón de partículas de otra sustancia. Una de un billón.

part per million (ppm) Comparison of the number of particles of one substance to one million particles of another substance. One out of a million.

parte por millón (ppm) Comparación de la cantidad de partículas de una sustancia a un millón de partículas de otra sustancia. Una de un millón.

particle Atoms and molecules that make up substances.

partícula Átomos y moléculas que componen sustancias.

particulate matter (PM) Solid particles that become airborne and can be inhaled by people.

materia particulada (MP) Partículas sólidas que son transportadas por el aire y pueden ser inhaladas por las personas.

percent Out of one hundred.

por Ciento de cien.

period A word to describe something that repeats in a regular pattern.

período Una palabra para describir algo que se repite en un patrón regular.

Periodic Table of the Elements A table listing all the known elements and their properties.

Tabla Periódica de los Elementos Una tabla con un listado de todos los elementos conocidos y sus propiedades.

pH paper A universal indicator that determines how acidic a solution is.

papel pH Un indicador universal que determina cuán ácida es una solución.

pH scale A measure of the concentration of hydrogen ions in a substance.

escala pH Una medida de la concentración de iones de hidrógeno y una sustancia.

photochemical A chemical reaction that requires sunlight energy.

fotoquímica Una reacción química que requiere la energía de la luz solar.

photosynthesis The process through which green plants use the energy of sunlight to make food and oxygen.

fotosíntesis El proceso a través el cual las plantas verdes usan la energía de la luz solar para fabricar alimento y oxígeno.

physical change A change in the form or appearance of matter, but not in its composition.

cambio físico Un cambio en la forma y apariencia de la materia, pero no es su composición.

plasma A state of matter that forms from gases at very high temperatures.

plasma Una estado de la materia que se forma de gases a temperaturas muy altas.

pollutant A substance that can make air, soil, or water harmful to organisms and structures.

contaminante Una sustancia que puede hacer que el aire, la tierra o el agua sean dañinos a los organismos y las estructuras.

polluted Containing substances that can cause harm to plants, animals, and structures; unclean or impure.

contaminado Que contiene sustancias que pueden causar daño a las plantas, animales y estructuras; sucio o impuro.

precipitation Water that falls to Earth's surface.

precipitación Agua que cae a la superficie de la Tierra.

primary pollutant Pollutant formed directly from natural activities and human activities.

contaminante primario Contaminante formado directamente de actividades naturales y actividades humanas.

product A substance that is formed by a chemical reaction.

producto Una sustancia formada por una reacción química.

proton A subatomic particle of an atom found in the nucleus. It has a positive charge.

protón Una partícula subatómica de un átomo encontrada en un núcleo. Tiene una carga positiva.

pure substance A type of matter composed of a single type of particle and always has distinct, predictable properties.

sustancia pura Un tipo de materia compuesta de un tipo sencillo de partícula y siempre tiene propiedades distintas y predecibles.

R

ratio One number divided by another.

proporción/razón Un número dividido por otro.

reactant A substance that enters into a chemical reaction.

reactiva Una sustancia que entra a una reacción química.

renewable A resource, such as solar energy or firewood, that can not be used up, or can be replaced by new growth.
renovable Un recurso, tal como la energía solar o la leña, que no se puede acabar, o puede ser reemplazada por un nuevo crecimiento.

representative Typical or similar to, when referring to sampling.
representativo Típico o similar a, cuando se refiere a una muestra.

rust A chemical reaction that occurs when certain metals react with oxygen and water and produce a reddish brown or green film as the metal breaks down.
óxido Reacción química que ocurre cuando ciertos metales reaccionan con oxígeno y agua y producen una capa color rojizo-marrón o verde cuando el metal se estropea o descompone.

S

salt A substance formed when an acid and a base combine.
sal Una sustancia formada cuando un ácido y una base se combinan.

sample A small part of something or one of the many things in a set.
muestra Una parte pequeña de algo o una de muchas cosas en un conjunto.

sampling To choose a part to examine.
muestreo Escoger una pieza para examinarla.

saturated The condition in a solution when no more solute can dissolve in the solvent at the given conditions.
saturado La condición en una solución cuando no se puede disolver más soluto en un solvente en unas condiciones dadas.

secondary pollutant Pollutant formed from primary pollutants.
contaminante secundario Contaminante formado de contaminantes primarios.

single bond A bond where 2 atoms share 2 electrons.
enlace sencillo Una unión donde 2 átomos comparten 2 electrones.

smog An air pollutant formed from nitrogen oxides and VOC's and activated by sunlight energy.
niebla Un contaminante del aire formado de óxidos de nitrógeno y VOC's (por sus siglas en inglés) y activado por la energía de la luz solar.

soft water Water that contains compounds with sodium and potassium but little calcium and magnesium.
agua blanda Agua que contiene compuestos con sodio y potasio pero poco calcio y magnesio.

solar ray Heat energy from the Sun.
rayo solar Energía térmica del sol.

solid Matter that has a definite shape and volume and an organized arrangement of particles that remain very close together and vibrate slowly.
sólido Materia que tiene una forma y volumen definido y una configuración organizada de partículas que se mantienen muy juntas y vibran lentamente.

solubility The ability of a solute to dissolve in a solvent.

solubilidad La habilidad de un soluto para disolverse en un solvente.

solute The component of a solution said to dissolve in the solvent.

soluto El componente de una solución que se dice que se disuelve en el solvente.

solution Another term for a homogeneous mixture.

solución Otro término para una mezcla homogénea.

solvent The component of a solution present in the greatest amount.

solvente El componente de una solución presente en una cantidad mayor.

soot Particulate matter that is a product of combustion.

hollín Materia particulada que es un producto de combustión.

spring runoff The water that comes from melting snow and runs into lakes and other bodies of water.

escorrentía de primavera El agua que resulta de nieve derretida y corre hacia los lagos y otros cuerpos de agua.

state Form, type, or kind.

estado Forma, tipo, o clase.

static electricity An electrical charge on an object.

electricidad estática Una carga eléctrica sobre un objeto.

stratosphere The atmosphere from about 10–48 km (6–30 mi) above Earth's surface.

estratosfera La atmósfera desde alrededor de 10–48 Km. (6–30 mi) sobre la superficie de la Tierra.

subatomic particles Particles that make up an atom.

partículas subatómicas Partículas que componen un átomo.

sublimation The process of a substance changing directly from a solid to a gas.

sublimación El proceso de una sustancia cambiando directamente de sólido a gas.

subscript A number written below the line. In formulas, it shows how many atoms of that type of element are in a molecule.

subíndice Un número escrito debajo de la línea. En fórmulas, muestra cuántos átomos de ese tipo de elemento hay en una molécula.

surface water Water found in ponds, lakes, streams, and oceans on the surface of Earth.

agua de superficie El agua encontrada en lagunas, lagos, riachuelos y océanos en la superficie de la Tierra.

T

temperature A measure of the average speed of the particles of matter. Temperature changes as the particles move faster (warmer) or slower (colder).

temperatura Una medida de la velocidad promedio de las partículas de la materia. La temperatura cambia mientras las partículas se mueven más rápido (caliente) o más despacio (frío).

theory A big idea in science, often developed over time, using evidence gained through observations and experimental data.

teoría Una gran idea en la ciencia, a menudo desarrollada con el tiempo, usando evidencia obtenida a través de observaciones y experimentos de datos.

thermal energy The energy of motion of the particles of matter in a substance.

energía térmica La energía de movimiento de las partículas de la materia en una sustancia.

thermal inversion A weather condition where an overlaying mass of heated air prevents the circulation of air beneath it, stopping convection.

inversión térmica Una condición del tiempo donde una masa cubierta de aire caliente impide la circulación del aire debajo de ella, deteniendo la convección.

thermosphere The atmosphere that extends from about 85 km to between 500 and 1000 km (53 mi to between 311 and 621 mi) above Earth's surface.

termosfera La atmósfera que se extiende desde alrededor de 85 Km. hasta entre 500 y 1000 Km. (53 mi hasta entre 311 y 621 mi) sobre la superficie de la Tierra.

triple bond A bond where 2 atoms share 6 electrons.

enlace triple Una unión donde dos átomos comparten 6 electrones.

troposphere Earth's atmosphere from the ground to about 10 km (6 mi) up.

troposfera La atmósfera terrestre desde el suelo hasta alrededor de 10 Km. (6 mi) arriba.

U

universal indicator A test used to measure the pH of anything.

indicador universal Una prueba usada para medir el pH de cualquier cosa.

unstable Can easily change.

inestable Que puede cambiar fácilmente.

UV light Ultraviolet rays; very short, high-energy rays from the Sun.

luz UV Rayos ultravioletas; rayos del sol de alta energía, muy cortos.

V

VOC (volatile organic compound) A pollutant that reacts with nitrogen oxides to make smog.

COV (compuesto orgánico volátil) Un contaminante que reacciona con óxidos de nitrógeno para producir neblina.

volume A measure of how much space something takes up.

volumen Una medida de cuánto espacio ocupa algo.

W

wet scrubber A device that cleans gases from the smokestacks of power plants and factories.

depurador húmedo Un dispositivo que limpia los gases de las chimeneas en las plantas eléctricas y las fábricas.

Index

triple bonds, defined, AQ 91

troposphere, defined, AQ 148

U

universal indicators, defined, AQ 210

unstable molecules

and combustion, AQ 135-AQ 136

defined, AQ 82

limitations of models, AQ 198

UV (ultraviolet) light

defined, AQ 145

in smog formation, AQ 145-AQ 147

V

VOCs (volatile organic compounds)

catalytic converters and,
AQ 262-AQ 266

defined, AQ 119, AQ 149

as indoor pollutants,
AQ 296-AQ 297

levels of, AQ 122

reductions in Los Angeles,
AQ 287-AQ 290

in smog formation, AQ 146-AQ 148

volume

See also density

defined, AQ 28

demonstrations of, AQ 23-AQ 28,
AQ 38-AQ 41

as property of air, AQ 28-AQ 30

W

water

See also groundwater; surface water

acid rain effects on, AQ 216-AQ 220

as air component, AQ 108-AQ 110

in catalytic converter process,
AQ 262-AQ 265

changes of state, AQ 51-AQ 54

and combustion, AQ 135-AQ 138

as energy source, AQ 281

molecular models of,
AQ 101-AQ 102

properties of, AQ 43

wet scrubbers, AQ 272-AQ 273

water vapor

as air component, AQ 103,
AQ 108-AQ 110

as greenhouse gas, AQ 241

weather, effects on pollution, AQ 132

wet scrubbers, defined, AQ 272

wind

effect on air quality, AQ 189-AQ 190,
AQ 196

as energy source, AQ 281

patterns in United States, AQ 172,
AQ 189

IT'S ABOUT TIME®
AUTHENTIC AND SUSTAINABLE STEM™

333 North Bedford Road, Mount Kisco, NY 10549
Phone (914) 273-2233 Fax (914) 206-6444
www.IAT.com

Staff Credits

Co-Presidents
Tom Laster and Laurie Kreindler

Director of Product Development
Barbara Zahm, Ph.D.

Managing Editor
Maureen Grassi

Project Development Editor
Ruta Demery

Project Manager
Sarah V. Gruber

Associate Editor, Student Edition
Gail Foreman

**Assistant Editor,
Teacher's Planning Guide**
Kelly Crowley

Safety and Content Reviewer
Gary Hickernell

Equipment Kit Developers
Dana Turner
Henry J. Garcia

Creative Director
John Nordland

Production/Studio Manager
Robert Schwalb

Layout
Sean Campbell
Louise Landry

Illustrators
Tomas Bunk
Dennis Falcon

**Technical Art/
Photo Research**
Sean Campbell
Doreen Flaherty
Fredy Fleck
Roberta Fox
Michael Hortens
Marie Killoran
Christine Labate
Louise Landry
Scott Petrower
MaryBeth Schulze
Jason Skinner
Nystrom, Cartography Department,
Herff Jones Education Division

Pre-press
Rich Ciotti

Photography Credits

Page 7	David McShane
Page 8 (right)	Jeff Turner
Page 30	Dean Bergmann
Pages 51, 62, 78, 81, 91, 99, 103, 155, 157, 162, 197, 210 (bottom), 211, 212	Jason Harris
Page 71	Warwick Hillier
Page 107	Anthony Bradshaw
Pages 148, 183, 202 (right)	NASA
Page 228	Johan Steen
All other photographs	istockphoto and other stock houses

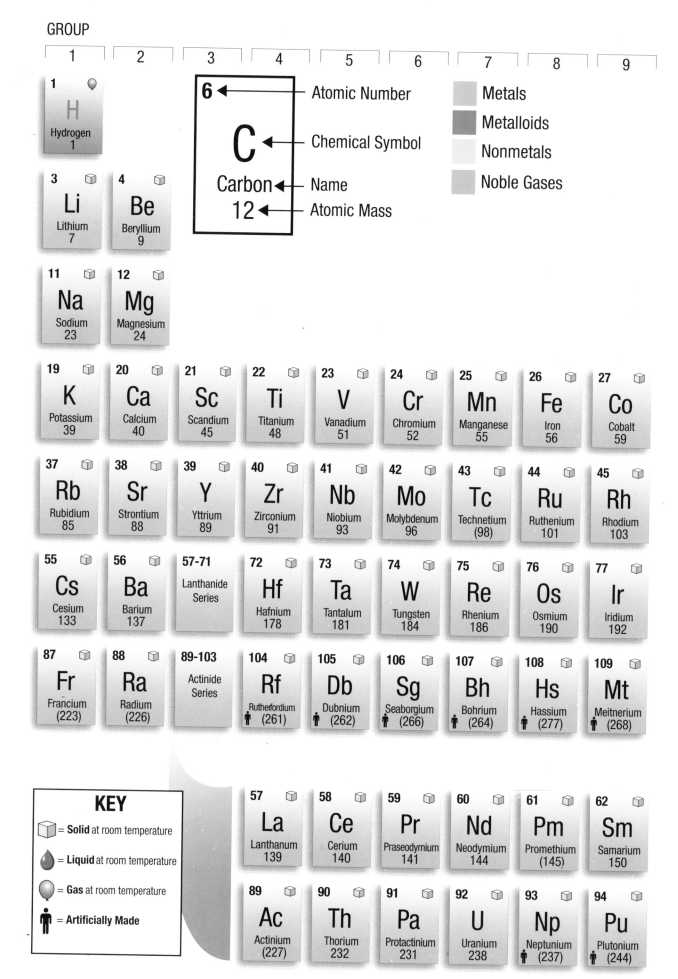

GROUP

| 1 | 2 | 3 | 4 | 5 | 6 | 7 | 8 | 9 |

1 H Hydrogen 1

Atomic Number 6
Chemical Symbol C
Name Carbon
Atomic Mass 12

Metals
Metalloids
Nonmetals
Noble Gases

3 Li Lithium 7
4 Be Beryllium 9

11 Na Sodium 23
12 Mg Magnesium 24

19 K Potassium 39
20 Ca Calcium 40
21 Sc Scandium 45
22 Ti Titanium 48
23 V Vanadium 51
24 Cr Chromium 52
25 Mn Manganese 55
26 Fe Iron 56
27 Co Cobalt 59

37 Rb Rubidium 85
38 Sr Strontium 88
39 Y Yttrium 89
40 Zr Zirconium 91
41 Nb Niobium 93
42 Mo Molybdenum 96
43 Tc Technetium (98)
44 Ru Ruthenium 101
45 Rh Rhodium 103

55 Cs Cesium 133
56 Ba Barium 137
57-71 Lanthanide Series
72 Hf Hafnium 178
73 Ta Tantalum 181
74 W Tungsten 184
75 Re Rhenium 186
76 Os Osmium 190
77 Ir Iridium 192

87 Fr Francium (223)
88 Ra Radium (226)
89-103 Actinide Series
104 Rf Rutherfordium (261)
105 Db Dubnium (262)
106 Sg Seaborgium (266)
107 Bh Bohrium (264)
108 Hs Hassium (277)
109 Mt Meitnerium (268)

KEY

= **Solid** at room temperature

= **Liquid** at room temperature

= **Gas** at room temperature

= **Artificially Made**

57 La Lanthanum 139
58 Ce Cerium 140
59 Pr Praseodymium 141
60 Nd Neodymium 144
61 Pm Promethium (145)
62 Sm Samarium 150

89 Ac Actinium (227)
90 Th Thorium 232
91 Pa Protactinium 231
92 U Uranium 238
93 Np Neptunium (237)
94 Pu Plutonium (244)